ASTRONOMICAL PROBLEMS

ASTRONOMICAL PROBLEMS

An Introductory Course in Astronomy

by

B. A. VORONTSOV-VEL'YAMINOV

Professor of Astronomy,
University of Moscow

Translated by

P. M. RABBITT, Ph.D.

Translation Edited by

ARTHUR BEER, M.A., Ph.D.

and

JOHN B. HUTCHINGS, B.Sc.

The Observatories,
University of Cambridge

THE QUEEN'S AWARD
TO INDUSTRY 1966

PERGAMON PRESS

OXFORD · LONDON · EDINBURGH · NEW YORK
TORONTO · SYDNEY · PARIS · BRAUNSCHWEIG

Pergamon Press Ltd., Headington Hill Hall, Oxford
4 & 5 Fitzroy Square, London W.1
Pergamon Press (Scotland) Ltd., 2 & 3 Teviot Place, Edinburgh 1
Pergamon Press Inc., Maxwell House, Fairview Park, Elmsford,
New York, 10523
Pergamon of Canada Ltd., 207 Queen's Quay West, Toronto 1
Pergamon Press (Aust.) Pty. Ltd., 19a Boundary Street, Rushcutters Bay,
N.S.W. 2011, Australia
Pergamon Press S.A.R.L., 24 rue des Écoles, Paris 5e
Vieweg & Sohn GmbH, Burgplatz 1, Braunschweig

First English edition 1969

This book is a translation of the Russian
Сборник задач и Упражнений по
Астрономий published by Izd. Tekhniko-
Teoreticheskoi Literatury, Moscow 1957,
with additional problems provided by the
author at proof stage.

Library of Congress Catalog Card No. 67–22828

Printed in Hungary
08 001972 2

CONTENTS

Preface to the Fourth Russian Edition   vii

Introduction. How to Solve Astronomical Problems   ix

    I   Interpolation (Problems 1–10)   1

    II   The Celestial Sphere (Problems 11–33)   7

    III   Systems of Celestial Coordinates (Problems 34–100)   12

    IV   Culmination, the Determination of Geographical Latitude, and the Coordinates of Celestial Bodies (Problems 101–169)   27

    V   Refraction (Problems 170–188)   36

    VI   The Apparent Motion of the Sun (Problems 189–217)   40

    VII   The Determination of Time and Longitude (Problems 218–302)   44

    VIII   The Calendar (Problems 303–324)   60

    IX   The Rising and Setting of a Heavenly Body (Problems 325–363)   64

    X   Precession (Problems 364–380)   71

    XI   Problems Solved with the Help of the Celestial Globe (Problems I–XIV)   75

    XII   Planetary Movement (Problems 381–466)   81

    XIII   Parallax and Aberration (Problems 467–506)   101

    XIV   The Earth (Problems 507–574)   110

    XV   The Movement and Phases of the Moon (Problems 575–619)   123

    XVI   Eclipses (Problems 620–654)   129

    XVII   Gravitation (Problems 655–733)   136

    XVIII   Astronomical Instruments and Methods (Problems 734–805)   149

XIX   The Moon (Problems 806–826)   161

XX   The Planets (Problems 827–874)   164

XXI   Comets (Problems 875–910)   171

XXII   Meteors and Meteorites (Problems 911–944)   178

XXIII   The Sun (Problems 945–991)   186

XXIV   The Movements and the Nature of the Stars
        (Problems 992–1084)   195

XXV   Double Stars (Problems 1085–1123)   213

XXVI   Variable Stars and Novae (Problems 1124–1154)   225

XXVII   The Structure of the Universe (Problems 1155–1176)   234

XXVIII Miscellaneous Problems (Problems 1177–1200)   239
        Problems of Artificial Celestial Bodies (Problems
        1201–1212)   245

Answers and Solutions   247

Appendix   295

Plates   315

PREFACE TO THE FOURTH
RUSSIAN EDITION

AN IMPORTANT part in the teaching of any technical subject, in higher educational establishments as well as schools, is experience in the solution of problems. As well as providing practice in the methods of computation, it enables the teacher to follow the students' progress both in comprehension and application of theory. The literature of astronomy is badly lacking in this respect, both in quantity and range of topics; and in fact the author is aware of the existence of only one textbook devoted to exercises in astronomy. This is "Astronomical Problems" (*Astronomicheskii zadachi*), a textbook for young people by Professor N. P. Kamenschikov, published in 1923.

This textbook is intended for use in universities, teachers' training colleges, and in school college preparatory or sixth forms. The syllabus covered by all three types of institution is much the same, the differences lying in the depth rather than the field of learning. For this reason the material in each chapter is divided into two sections. The first section is elementary. The second section is more difficult, set approximately at the level of the teachers' training colleges.

In each section the problems are grouped into sub-topics, and set in order of increasing difficulty. In every chapter the problems are preceded by a summary of the theory and the formulae to be exercised, under headings I and II, applying to sections I and II, respectively. Problems are presented, requiring both exact and approximate solutions, so that on occasion the same data may be repeated with varying degrees of accuracy.

We have presented two, and exceptionally three, examples of the most typical problems, so that the teacher may use one or more for demonstration, leaving a similar exercise for the student.

However, the author realizes that students become frustrated if presented with the same problem, under different formulations (e.g. Nos. 29 and 30), and the teacher is asked to note that this occurs in a number of places in the book.

In the preparation of this book, the author used the books referred to in the first Russian Edition of this work. As many of the problems are unoriginal, or "natural", the source of a problem is given only in those cases where the problem seemed unusual. Many of the problems and exercises were devised by the author, but only about 300 of these (marked with an asterisk*) appear to be unique in the literature. Ninety per cent of the problems borrowed by the author were originally published without answers.

The author is particularly grateful to Professor P. P. Parenago for checking the majority of the problems for the first edition, and to M. A. Borchov, who undertook the labour of checking and correcting the work as a whole.

B. Vorontsov–Vel'yaminov

INTRODUCTION

HOW TO SOLVE ASTRONOMICAL
PROBLEMS

IN ALL parts of the text, the problems under the heading "Section One" assume knowledge which is within the compass of the programmes of college preparatory or sixth forms. There are rather harder problems under the heading "Section Two" in each chapter, but the acquaintance with mathematics and physics which is necessary to solve them is rarely beyond the range of elementary trigonometry and physics.

The problems in the textbook may be divided into three categories. These are problems requiring careful thought, exercises in astronomy, and problems illustrating important astronomical methods or results.

For the solution of many problems of the first type, it is often helpful to use a celestial globe (Chapter XI), employing it where a plan is necessary. Plans, even if roughly drawn by hand, make spatial comprehension very much easier. In exercises of the second type, one must try to make the necessary measurements (on photographs or on maps) as carefully and accurately as possible. The nearer the results obtained are to the universally accepted data, the better will be the understanding of how problems are solved by the method of astronomical investigation, which is based on accuracy of measurement. The majority of the numerical problems may be solved to an accuracy of three significant figures, and for this reason we strongly recommend calculation with the help of a slide rule. The use of a slide rule or of tables of logarithms is essential in the solution of a great many problems. Problems on the calculation of various functions from very complex formulae demand a rigorous sequence of calculation, and provide schooling in accuracy of calculation in general. In this respect the best practice is provided by problems on the conversion of coord-inates, and the calculation of ephemerids.

From a study of the necessary formulae, and the sequence in which they are employed, one must decide on a scheme of calcula-tion. One should construct a table in columns, of quantities to be determined, either by reference to tables or by calculation. Sym-bols for these quantities should be inserted in the table, ordered according to the sequence of calculations, and then the numerical values for these symbols inserted, as the computation is made. The calculation in general, and adding in particular, is assisted by writing the figures in columns. Corrections are more easily made, and errors typical of beginners are more easily spotted in this way. An example of how such a system is built up and worked out is given on page 19.

An important point in dealing with approximate quantities is not to carry out the calculation to an accuracy greater than that of the data. For example, it is quite meaningless to use five-figure logarithms, if in the given conditions the numbers are correct to three significant figures. It is worth noting that angles given to an accuracy of $0 \cdot 1°$ usually correspond to three-figure logarithms; that angles given to an accuracy of $0' \cdot 1$ usually correspond to four-figure logarithms, and that angles given to an accuracy of $1'' \cdot 0$ are generally equivalent to five-figure logarithms.

The sign n (for negative) is inserted below and to the right of a logarithm if the number corresponding to that logarithm is negative. The logarithm of a product (or a quotient) is the sum (or difference) of the logarithms of the numbers involved. Thus, if an odd number of logarithms which have n as a suffix, is sum-med (or subtracted from each other), then the suffix n is attached to the result, because the product (or the quotient) will in this case be negative. If the number of logarithms with the suffix n, which are added or subtracted, is even, then it is not necessary to attach n to the result, as it will be positive.

A good general rule in working with logarithms is always to replace subtraction by addition, as this eliminates a large source of errors. The subtraction of log a is the same as the addition of log $1/a$, or the addition of the complement of log a. We may illustrate this by the following example:

$$\log (5/0\cdot3) = \log 5 - \log 0\cdot3 = 0\cdot699 - (0\cdot477 - 1).$$

That is, $\log (5/0\cdot3) = 0\cdot699 + 0\cdot523$. The number $0\cdot523$ is the complement of the logarithm $0\cdot477$. In a similar way, the complement of $7\cdot315$ is $2\cdot685$.

In a few problems, the necessary tabular data are not given, and students must find them for themselves in the tables given in the Appendix. Detailed solutions are provided for most of the typical problems.

In different problems, numerical data for the same quantities may differ slightly. There are three reasons for this. Where the problem does not require exactness of solution, the figures are rounded to make the calculation shorter. In other cases the differences in the data arise from the fact that, under one and the same term, slightly different quantities are implied. For example, by the word "year" we may mean the simple calendar year of 365 days, the leap year of 366 days, the mean duration of the calendar year—365·25 days, or the duration of the tropical year, 365·2422... days, which changes in the course of time, though very slowly. Lastly, astronomy is a continuously improving science, and the numerical values of quantities are constantly being redetermined, more and more precisely. For some quantities, different students have obtained different results, and different persons, in setting the problems, have placed greater reliance on one or other set of numerical data.

In the problems given in Section Two, the use of the differential calculus is necessary in exceptional cases only, and is limited to finding polynomial or logarithmic derivatives.

The solution of some of the problems requires the *Astronomical Ephemeris* for the given year. It is also useful to have a reference book of astronomical constants.

A final section of problems relating to Artificial Celestial Bodies was provided by the author for this translation at proof stage.

CHAPTER I

INTERPOLATION

BEFORE making use of the various tables, it is necessary to know how to find the value of a changing quantity (a function), which depends on the value of an independently varying quantity (an argument).

If two variables are connected by a mathematical equation (for example, $y = 2x$), then changes in the value of one quantity (x) will be related to changes in the value of the other (y). Quantities which change according to their own laws are called *Arguments*, and quantities dependent on such an argument are called *Functions*. In the example above x is the argument, and y is the function. The value of the argument $x = 1$ corresponds to the value of the function $y = 2$, the value of the argument $x = 3$ corresponds to the value of the function $y = 6$, and so on.

In tabulating a function, columns are made of both argument and function, in which the value of the function appears in the same row as the corresponding value of the argument. Values of the argument are usually spaced at equal intervals. For example, we may calculate values of the function $y = 2x$ corresponding to values of x increasing by 5 units, and draw up the table:

x	y	a
$x_1 = 0$	$y_1 = 0$	
$x_2 = 5$	$y_2 = 10$	$a_2 = 10$
$x_3 = 10$	$y_3 = 20$	$a_3 = 10$
$x_4 = 15$	$y_4 = 30$	$a_4 = 10$ and so on.

In most cases, one requires a value for a function corresponding to a value of the argument, intermediate to those contained in the table — for example, in the case above, for $x = 7$ or 8. This process is called interpolation, and is, for example, constantly used in finding the logarithm or antilogarithm of a given number. In astronomy, interpolation from the ephemeris is frequently necessary.

If a change in a function is in direct proportion to a change in the argument, as in our example, then the problem is very simply solved. In order to make sure that the function changes in proportion to the argument, we write down in a neighbouring column two successive differences between sequent values of the function.

These differences are denoted by a in the table, and should be constant. In our example they are equal to 10. To find the value of y corresponding to x lying between x_3 and x_4, we use the simple equation

$$y = y_3 + a_4 \frac{x - x_3}{x_4 - x_3}.$$

For instance, for y corresponding to $x = 12$, we have

$$y = 20 + 10 \times \frac{12 - 10}{15 - 10} = 20 + 10 \times \frac{2}{5} = 24.$$

In other words, the value of the function is equal to the tabular value corresponding to the nearest lesser value of the argument, plus the first difference (between the given value of the function and the next one), multiplied by the ratio of the increment to the argument to the tabular difference of the neighbouring arguments. If the first differences, a, are not constant then, calculating from each of the preceding ones, we can obtain the second differences b (Table 1). And if these are not constant, we may in this way calculate the third differences c, and the fourth differences d, until we reach a set of differences which seem constant, or are very small.

In Table 2 we give as an example a situation where even the sixth set of differences are not constant. However, after the fourth set of differences little change is evident and, consequently, in interpolation we can neglect the differences after four; that is, we need not take them into consideration.

TABLE 1

x	y	a	b	c	d
x_1	y_1				
		a_2			
x_2	y_2		b_3		
		a_3		c_4	
x_3	y_3		b_4		d_5
		a_4		c_5	
x_4	y_4		b_5		
		a_5			
x_5	y_5				

TABLE 2

x	y		a	b	c	d	e	f
1·0	+19°19′·6	+1159′·6						
2·0	16 2 ·2	962 ·2	−197′·4	−51′·4				
3·0	11 53 ·4	713 ·4	−248 ·8	−33 ·5	−17′·9			
4·0	7 11 ·1	431 ·1	−282 ·3	−15 ·9	−17 ·6	+0′·3	+1′·2	
5·0	+2 12 ·9	+132 ·9	−298 ·2	+ 0 ·2	−16 ·1	+1 ·5	+0 ·9	−0′·3
6·0	−2 45 ·1	−165 ·1	−298 ·0	+13 ·9	−13 ·7	+2 ·4	−0 ·4	−1 ·3
7·0	7 29 ·2	449 ·2	−284 ·1	+25 ·6	−11 ·7	+2 ·0		
8·0	−11 47 ·7	−707 ·7	−258 ·5					

Suppose that in this case we wish to calculate the value of y for $x = x_1 + \theta h$, where x is the nearest least tabulated value of the argument, h is the tabular difference between neighbouring arguments, and θ lies between 0 and 1. Then the theory of interpolation leads to the formula:

$$y = y_1 + 0\left\{a_2 + \frac{\theta-1}{2}\left[b_3 + \frac{\theta-2}{3}\left(c_4 + \frac{\theta-3}{4}d_5\right)\right]\right\},$$

where y_1 is the value of y corresponding to $x = x_1$. Differences higher than the fourth are very seldom employed, and this formula is sufficient. If we require only the second or the third set of differences, then the remainder are set at zero. For example, in interpolation with the third set of differences:

$$y = y_1 + \theta \left\{ a_2 + \frac{\theta-1}{2} \left[b_3 + \frac{\theta-2}{3} c_4 \right] \right\},$$

and with the second set of differences:

$$y = y_1 + \theta \left[a_2 + \frac{\theta-1}{2} b_3 \right].$$

As an example, let us calculate the value of y corresponding to $x = 1\cdot2$, from Table 2. In our example $h = 1\cdot0$, $\theta = 0\cdot2$, $y = 1159'\cdot6$. Interpolating with the fourth set of differences, we obtain

$$y = 1159\cdot6 + 0\cdot2 \left\{ -197\cdot4 + \frac{0\cdot2-1}{2} \left[-51\cdot4 + \right. \right.$$
$$\left. \left. \frac{0\cdot2-2}{3} \left(-17\cdot9 + \frac{0\cdot2-3}{4} 0\cdot3 \right) \right] \right\}$$

or

$y = 1159\cdot6 + 0\cdot2 \{ -197\cdot4 - 0\cdot4 [-51\cdot4 - 0\cdot6(-17\cdot9 - 0\cdot7 \times 0\cdot3)] \}$
$= 1159\cdot6 + 0\cdot2 \{ -197\cdot4 - 0\cdot4 [-51\cdot4 - 0\cdot6(-18\cdot1)] \}$
$= 1159\cdot6 + 0\cdot2 \{ -197\cdot4 - 0\cdot4 [-40\cdot54] \}$
$= 1159\cdot6 + 0\cdot2 \{ -181\cdot2 \} = 1123\cdot4$
$y = 1123'\cdot4$

Carrying out this calculation using only the second differences, which are far from being constant, we obtain

$$y = 1159\cdot6 + 0\cdot2 \left[-197\cdot4 + \frac{0\cdot2-1}{2} (-51\cdot4) \right] = 1124'\cdot2.$$

This is a less exact value, but it differs from the result of our previous calculation by only $0'\cdot8$. From this example it is obvious that the higher the order of the difference, the smaller is its effect on the result, and in any given case one must decide what order of differences is to be used in interpolation.

Some functions depend simultaneously on two arguments. Table III shows the variation of a function z with the values of two arguments x and y. Let us interpolate the value of z corresponding to the values $x = 1\frac{1}{3}$ and $y = 37$. This is done by finding z for

$x = 1\frac{1}{3}$ ($\theta = \frac{1}{3}$) for every column of the Table, by the methods described.

$y = 36$

x	y	a	b	c
1	210			
		+195		
2	405		−27	
		+168		−13
3	573		−40	
		+128		
4	701			

$y = 40$

x	y	a	b	c
1	199			
		+185		
2	384		−26	
		+159		−12
3	543		−38	
		+121		
4	664			

$y = 44$

x	y	a	b	c
1	187			
		+173		
2	360		−23	
		+150		−13
3	510		−36	
		+114		
4	624			

We can now tabulate these interpolated values of z against y.

y	z	a	b
36	277		
		−14	
40	263		−3
		−17	
44	246		

This yields the value of z for $y = 37$ as

$$z = 277 - \tfrac{1}{4}14 + \tfrac{3}{32}3 = 274.$$

It is sometimes necessary to find the value of a function for an argument which lies outside the limits of the Table. This is known as extrapolation. Extrapolation is made either forwards or backwards, according to whether the value of x is greater or less than the values of x tabulated. The formula for backwards extrapolation is

$$y = y_1 - a_2 \frac{x_1 - x}{x_2 - x_1},$$

so that, returning to the first of our examples, we obtain for $x = -5$,

$$y = 0 - 10 \frac{0 - (-5)}{5 - 0} = -10.$$

The formula for extrapolating forwards in this example is

$$y = y_4 + a_4 \frac{x - x_4}{x_4 - x_3}.$$

Thus, for $x = 27$ we find

$$y = 30 + 10\frac{27-15}{15-10} = 30+24 = 54.$$

Interpolation is made easier in many astronomical calendars by giving the change in a function in a given unit of time.

The examples below provide practice in interpolation. Many of the terms used may as yet be unfamiliar to the student, but for the purpose of the exercises this is unimportant. A good understanding of the processes of interpolation and extrapolation is important as the solution of many later problems depends upon them.

All tables designated by roman numerals may be found at the end of the book.

SECTION TWO PROBLEMS

1. From Table II interpolate the time correction for 6 hours Greenwich time on the 20th July, 1931.

2. Determine the Declination of the Sun at 18 hr Greenwich time on the 29th June, 1931,[†] from Table II.

3. Find the Right Ascension of the Sun at 18 hr Greenwich time on 6th July, 1931, from Table II.

4. Interpolate the Right Ascension of the Sun at the time 1 hr 32 min 44 sec Greenwich time on 13th July, 1931 (Table II).

5. Interpolate the Declination of the Sun at the time 17 hr 12 min 30·4 sec Greenwich time on 10th July, 1931[†] (Table II).

6. Find the time equation for the time $t = 4$ hr 50 min 19·1 sec Greenwich time on 2nd July, 1931 (Table II).

7. From Table IX determine the value of the annual precession in Right Ascension for $\alpha = 1\cdot8$ hr, $\delta = +63°$.

8. Find the annual precession for $\alpha = 5\cdot2$ hr, $\delta = +45°\cdot9$.

9. Find the annual precession for $\alpha = 17\cdot9$ hr, $\delta = +56°\cdot9$.

10. Find the annual precession for $\alpha = 19\cdot8$ hr, $\delta = -37°\cdot9$.

† Do not use the hour differences in the solution of Problems 2 and 5.

CHAPTER II

THE CELESTIAL SPHERE

I

FOR many purposes the stars in the sky may be represented by points on the surface of an imaginary sphere, of arbitrary radius, centred on the observer. "Distances" between points on the sphere are then expressed as angles.

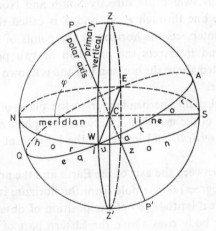

FIG. 1. The basic lines and points of the celestial sphere.

If we represent the Sun and the Moon in this way, they appear as discs on the surface of the sphere, of angular diameters about $\frac{1}{2}°$, as that is the angle they subtend at our eye, in the sky. As the length of arc of 1° is approximately 1/57 of the radius of the circle, we see that the distances to the Sun and Moon are approximately 114 times their diameters. A length of arc of 1″ (equal to sin 1″ as the angle is very small) is 1/206,265 of the radius.

The *zenith* is the point on the sphere directly above the head of the observer. If this is denoted by point Z, then the point Z', the other point of intersection with the sphere of the diameter through Z, is called the *nadir*. The plane perpendicular to ZZ' through the centre of the sphere, intersects the sphere in a great circle called the mathematical *horizon*.

The apparent diurnal movement of the celestial sphere is caused by the rotation of the Earth, and therefore proceeds about the axis of the Earth, which passes through the centre of the sphere, and intersects it at two points, P and P', say, the North and South *celestial poles*. The plane perpendicular to this axis intersects the sphere along the line known as the *celestial equator*. The plane passing through the celestial poles and the zenith is called the plane of the *meridian*. The horizon and the meridian intersect at points S and N, which are directly South and North from the observer. The line through P, Z, and S is called the *noon line*. The equator intersects the horizon at the points of East (E) and West (W), and intersects the meridian at two points, one of which is located above the horizon (A) and is known as the point of the equator.

The vertical plane, perpendicular to the plane of the horizon and the plane of the meridian, intersects the sphere along the line of the *prime vertical*, and intersects the horizon at the points E and W.

The angle between the axis of the Earth and the horizon, or the altitude (in degrees) of the pole from the horizon, is the same as the geographical latitude (ϕ) of the position of observation.

A heavenly body rises above the eastern part of the horizon, and sets below its western sector. The Pole Star (α Ursae Minoris) is situated at a distance of only 58′ from the North Pole. Depending on the position of the observer, some stars rise and set, while others are always located above the horizon. The equator divides the sky into northern and southern hemispheres. All stars intersect the northern or southern parts of the meridian 3 min 56 sec earlier each day. This obviously applies also to the times of rising and setting of stars. The diurnal paths of all bodies in the sky are parallel to the equator.

As the Earth rotates about the Sun, during the course of the year, the Sun apparently traces a great circle on the celestial sphere. This circle is known as the ecliptic, and intersects the equator (Fig. 2) at an angle $\varepsilon = 23°27'$, known as the obliquity of the ecliptic. As the celestial sphere rotates, the position of the ecliptic changes in relation to the horizon, in contrast to all the

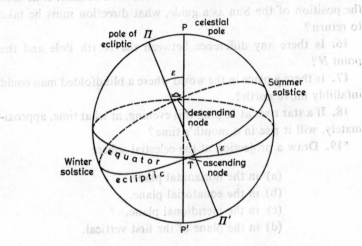

FIG. 2. The equator and the ecliptic.

other lines on the sphere which we have described. The ecliptic intersects the equator at two points known as the points of Vernal and Autumnal Equinox. The former (γ) is in the constellation of Pisces and the latter ($\simeq$) is in the constellation Virgo.

SECTION ONE PROBLEMS

*11. How far from the eye must a coin of diameter 1·7 cm be held, so that it just covers the disc of the Sun or the Moon?

12. The diameter of a spherical aerostat is 13 m. How far away is it if its angular diameter is half that of the Moon?

13. What sector of the sky is an observer looking at if he sees that all stars are rising?

14. In which sectors of the sky does the altitude of a body

  (a) continuously increase, and
  (b) continuously decline?

15. On an autumn morning a hunter goes into the woods in the direction of the Pole Star. He returns after sunrise. If he uses the position of the Sun as a guide, what direction must he take to return?

16. Is there any difference between the North Pole and the point N?

17. Is there a place in the world where a blindfolded man could infallibly move north?

18. If a star rises at 10 p.m. this evening, at what time, approximately, will it rise in a month's time?

*19. Draw a projection of the celestial sphere

  (a) in the horizontal plane,
  (b) in the equatorial plane,
  (c) in the meridional plane,
  (d) in the plane of the first vertical.

20. Show that the equator intersects the horizon at points which lie at $90°$ to the points N and S (i.e. at the points E and W).

21. Show that the horizon, equator, and first vertical all intersect at the same two points.

22. The latitude of Moscow is $\phi = 55°45'$. Determine the angular distance from the zenith to the celestial pole in Moscow.

23. If an observer is at a latitude of $35°$, what angle does the equator subtend with his horizon?

24. At what angle does the celestial equator intersect the horizon (at the points E and W) for an observer located at latitude $40°$? What will these angles be if the latitude of the observer is $10°$; $20°$; $50°$; $70°$; $-40°$?

25. Under what two conditions does the altitude of a heavenly body remain unaltered in the course of a day?

26. What important circles in the celestial sphere do not have corresponding circles on the earth?

27. How is the ecliptic situated relative to the horizon at the North Pole?

28. What are the greatest and least angles between the ecliptic and the horizon in Moscow ($\phi = 55°45'$)?

29. Under what conditions does the pole of the ecliptic coincide with the zenith of the observer?

30. At what place on earth may the ecliptic coincide with the horizon, and when will this occur?

31. What is the angle between the ecliptic and the horizon at the moment of setting of the point of the Vernal Equinox for an observer located at 18° geographical latitude?

32. What is the inclination of the ecliptic to the horizon at the moment of rising of the point of the Vernal Equinox, at a latitude of 55°? At the moment of setting of this point? The same for latitude $66\frac{1}{2}°$.

33. Determine the linear distance between two stars, situated at distances of r_1 and r_2 from us, and visible in the sky at an angular separation of θ.

27. How is the ecliptic situated relative to the horizon at the
North Pole?
28. What are the greatest and least angles between the ecliptic
observer located at 18° geographical latitude?
32. What is the inclination of the ecliptic to the horizon at the
... of ... at the ...

CHAPTER III

SYSTEMS OF CELESTIAL
COORDINATES

I

TO DEFINE the positions of points, or heavenly bodies, on the
celestial sphere, we must use a system of spherical coordinates.
There are four systems of coordinates in general use. In each of
these systems, the position of a point is determined by two coordinates, one of which is the angular separation of the point
from the plane of some basic circle (analogous to geographical
latitude), and the other, the angle in this basic circle from some
determinate point on it (analogous to geographical longitude).
The four systems are described below.

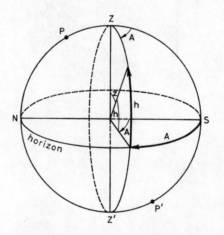

FIG. 3. The horizontal system of coordinates (h and A).

Horizontal Coordinates

These are denoted by *h* and *A* in Fig. 3 (*h*, the altitude, is measured from the horizon to the point along the great half circle of altitude). *A*, the azimuth, is measured from the south point *S*, along the horizon, in a direction running clockwise, to its intersection with the circle of altitude passing through the point itself. The zenith distance, *z*, is often used instead of the altitude *h*. *z* is the angular distance from the point to the zenith, and is equal to $90° - h$. *A* and *H* (or *z*) depend on the latitude and time of the observation.

Equatorial Coordinates

First system. These coordinates (α and δ) are shown in Fig. 4. δ, the Declination, is measured from the equator to the point along the great half circle drawn through it and the celestial poles (i.e. along the circle of Declination). In the northern hemisphere of the sky the Declination is positive, and in the southern, the Declination is negative. α, the Right Ascension, is measured from the point of the Vernal Equinox, γ, anticlockwise in the northern hemisphere, along the equator to its intersection with the circle of Declination passing through the point. It is usually expressed in units of time, putting 24 hr equal to 360°. On this scale, 1 hr

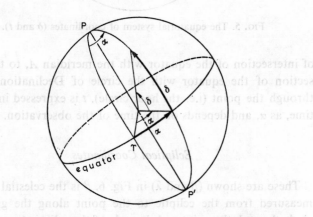

FIG. 4. The equatorial system of coordinates (δ and α).

is 15°; 1 min is 15′; 1 sec is 15″; 1° = 4 min. Tables IV and V at
the end of the book give the relation between these units and
degrees. In this system, the coordinates δ and α do not depend
either on the diurnal rotation of the celestial sphere, or on the
place of observation.

Equatorial Coordinates

Second system. These coordinates, δ and t, are shown in Fig. 5.
δ is the Declination as described above. t is the hour angle, measured in a clockwise direction (towards the west) from the point

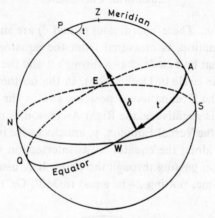

FIG. 5. The equatorial system of coordinates (δ and t).

of intersection of the equator with the meridian A, to the intersection of the equator with the circle of Declination passing
through the point (i.e. the hour circle). t is expressed in units of
time, as α, and depends on the time of the observation.

Ecliptical Coordinates

These are shown (β and λ) in Fig. 6. β is the celestial latitude,
measured from the ecliptic to the point along the great half
circle through the point and the pole of the ecliptic (i.e. the circle

of latitude). To the north of the ecliptic β is positive; to the south it is negative. λ is the celestial longitude, measured from the point of the Vernal Equinox, γ, anti-clockwise along the ecliptic to its intersection with the circle of latitude passing through the given point. λ and β, like α and δ, do not depend on the time or place of observation.

The first three systems of coordinates are shown in Fig. 7. On star maps and globes, the net of equatorial coordinates α and δ

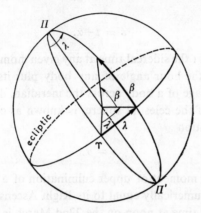

FIG. 6. The ecliptical system of coordinates (β and λ).

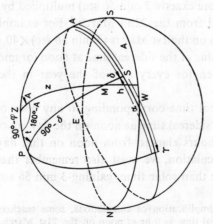

FIG. 7. A comparison of the two systems in both the equatorial and horizontal coordinates.

are frequently used, and the line of the ecliptic is drawn. In most reference books, the α and δ coordinates of celestial bodies are also given.

The sidereal time, s, is given by the value of the hour angle of the point of the Vernal Equinox. That is, when the sidereal time is s, the hour angle t of any body having a Right Ascension α is given by the formula

$$t = s - \alpha,$$

so that

$$s = t + \alpha.$$

This means that the sidereal time at any given moment is numerically equal to the hour angle of any body plus its Right Ascension. The passage of a body across the meridian, due to the diurnal rotation of the celestial sphere, is known as culmination. In upper culmination

$$s = \alpha.$$

That is, at the moment of upper culmination of a body, the sidereal time is numerically equal to its Right Ascension.

The sidereal time at noon on the 22nd March is approximately 0 hr. At midday of any day of the year the sidereal time is equal to 4 min (more exactly 3 min 56 sec) multiplied by the number of days elapsed from the 22nd March.[†] For example, the sidereal time at noon on the 1st May is (3 min 56 sec)$\times$40 = 2 hr 37 min. The exact value of the sidereal time at noon (or midnight), Greenwich, is given for every day of the year in the astronomical calendar.

The sidereal time corresponding to any hour of solar time is equal to the sidereal time at noon on the day concerned, plus the number of hours elapsed from noon on that day. For a more accurate calculation, we must also remember that sidereal time passes faster than solar time, gaining 3 min 56 sec in 24 hr. For

---

[†] For the simplification of calculations, some teachers may prefer to take the sidereal time as 0 hr at noon on the 21st March, or the length of each month to be 30 days. In these cases, answers should be calculated to the nearest $\frac{1}{4}$ hr only.

example, at 6·0 o'clock in the evening on the 1st May, the sidereal time is equal to 2 hr 37 min + 6 hr + (3 min 56 sec) × $\frac{6}{24}$ = 8 hr 37 min 59 sec.

II

The solution of many astronomical problems requires three basic formulae for an obtuse angled spherical triangle with sides a, b and c (expressed in degrees) and angles A, B and C. These formulae,

$$\cos a = \cos b \cos c + \sin B \sin c \cos A, \tag{1}$$

$$\sin a \cos B = \cos b \sin c - \sin b \cos c \cos A, \tag{2}$$

$$\sin a \sin B = \sin b \sin A, \tag{3}$$

enable us to find the remaining side and angles of the triangle, given the other two sides and the angle between them.

Using these three formulae, we can carry out a transformation between celestial coordinates. We draw a plan of the celestial sphere, as in Fig. 7, for a place of latitude ϕ, and horizontal (z and A) and equatorial (δ and t) coordinates for a point M. Applying the three formulae to the triangle PZM, we obtain formulae determining z and A for a given t and δ:

$$\cos z = \sin \phi \sin \delta + \cos \phi \cos \delta \cos t, \tag{4}$$

$$\sin z \cos A = -\sin \delta \cos \phi + \cos \delta \sin \phi \cos t, \tag{5}$$

$$\sin z \sin A = \cos \delta \sin t. \tag{6}$$

If α and δ are given, we can obtain $t = s - \alpha$ if we know the sidereal time.

For convenience in calculation we modify these formulae as follows. We set

$$m \sin M = \sin \delta, \tag{7}$$

$$m \cos M = \cos \delta \cos t, \tag{8}$$

where M is an auxiliary angle, to be determined, and $0 < m < 1$.

Then we have
$$\cos z = m \cos (\phi - M), \tag{9}$$

$$\sin z \cos A = m \sin (\phi - M), \tag{10}$$

$$\sin z \sin A = \cos \delta \sin t. \tag{11}$$

As the function is more accurately obtained from the tangent than from the sine or cosine, we obtain from (7) and (8)

$$\tan M = \tan \delta \sec t \tag{12}$$

whence we obtain M. The quadrant in which the angle M lies is determined from equation (7). As $m > 0$, the sign of sin M is the same as the sign of sin δ. If, for example, tan M is positive, and sin M is negative, M lies in the third quadrant. We can find m from

$$m = \sin \delta \operatorname{cosec} M. \tag{13}$$

$\phi - M$ is now known and A is calculated from the formula

$$\tan A = \frac{\cos \delta \sin t}{m \sin (\phi - M)}. \tag{14}$$

The quadrant of A is determined by the sign of sin A, which is the same as that of sin t, as sin z and cos δ are always positive. Having found A, z is determined from the formula

$$\tan z = \tan (\phi - M) \sec A. \tag{15}$$

The quadrant in which z lies is found from (9), where we can see that the sign of cos z is the same as the sign of cos $(\phi - M)$, since $m > 0$.

Thus the final calculation is performed using equations (12)–(15).

The formulae for the transformation of z and A into δ and t, and δ and α into λ and β, and λ and β into α and δ are deduced in a closely analogous way.

In this type of calculation it is desirable to lay out a scheme of calculation in advance, setting out in a column the designations of numbers which are to be determined by reference to tables, or by calculation. For brevity in the example given, we do not write the sign *log* before trigonometrical functions. The sign n before a logarithm indicates that the number itself is negative. The letter ∂ indicates that a logarithm is complemented. Exercise 84, for instance, is conveniently solved in the following scheme:

t hr 2 hr 22 min 36 sec	$\cos \delta$ 9·62897
$t°$ 35° 39′ 00″	$\sin t$ 9·76554
$\tan \delta$ 0·32765	∂m 0·01378
$\partial \cos t$ 0·09013	$\sin(\phi - M)$ 0·79878$_n$
$\tan M$ 0·41778	$\tan A$ 0·20707$_n$
M 69°5′·2	A 121°49′·9
$\phi - M$ −9°8′·7	$\tan(\phi - M)$ 9·20677$_n$
$\sin \delta$ 9·95662	$\partial \cos A$ 0·27784$_n$
$\partial \sin M$ 0·02960	$\tan z$ 9·48461
m 9·98622	z 16°58′·4

SECTION ONE PROBLEMS

34. At what point in the heavens is the Declination equal to −90°?

35. The Pole Star is 58′ away from the North celestial Pole. What is its Declination?

36. What are the azimuths of the points of north, south, east and west?

37. What is the Declination of the point of the zenith at a geographical latitude of 42°?

38. What are the horizontal coordinates of the celestial pole with a geographical latitude of +23°27′?

39. What are the hour angle and the azimuth of the zenith?

40. What is the hour angle of the point of west? Of the point of east?

41. What is the Right Ascension (α) and the Declination (δ) of the point of the Vernal Equinox?

42. For what points on the celestial sphere are both the Right Ascension and the Declination equal to zero? What are the astronomical latitudes and longitudes of these points?

43. What is the astronomical latitude and longitude of the North celestial Pole?

44. Determine the Right Ascension and the Declination of the North Pole of the ecliptic.

45. What is the longitude and latitude of the North Pole of the ecliptic?

46. Determine the zenithal distance of the Sun when the length of the shadow cast by an object is the same as its height.

47. The Declination of a body is $+30°$, and its Right Ascension is 7 hr. In what constellation is it situated? (consult a star map).

48. Find the following stars on a star map using their coordinates. (It is best to use a map on which the names of the stars are not given; as, for example, Professor Michaelov's larger atlas.)

α		δ	mag.
3 hr	21·0 min	$+ 8°47'$	3·80
9 hr	26·0 min	$+63°22'$	3·75
15 hr	13·2 min	$- 9° 8'$	2·74
18 hr	4·0 min	$+ 9°33'$	3·73
22 hr	26·5 min	$+58° 3'$	variable
0 hr	37·3 min	$+40°43'$	variable

The last column gives the brightness of the star, in stellar magnitudes. Find from a catalogue or star map the exact α and δ and the stellar magnitude of the stars:

σ Ceti; β Cygni; ε Lyrae; γ Canis Majoris; φ Saggitarius; χ Ursae Majoris; and α Ursae Minoris.

49. Why is it convenient to measure azimuths in the direction south–west–north–east?

50. Why is Right Ascension reckoned from the west to the east, and not in the opposite direction?

51. The Right Ascensions of three stars are $284°15'17''$, $17°57'1''$, $191°13'59''$. Express them in hours, minutes and seconds of time.

52. Express the Right Ascensions of stars which are 3 hr 17 min 9 sec, 19 hr 2 min 39 sec, and 21 hr 0 min 3 sec, in terms of angular measure.

53. Express in angular measure the angle between the curves of Declination of two stars, one of which culminated at 5 hr 12 min and the other at 5 hr 32 min sidereal time.

54. The azimuth of a body is $45°$, and its height is $60°$. In what part of the sky should one look for this star?

55. A heavenly body has an hour angle of $t = 18$ hr. In what section of the celestial sphere is it visible?

56. What is the hour angle of a star 6 hr after its upper culmination?

57. What is the hour angle of the star Deneb at 23 hr 17 min sidereal time, if its Right Ascension is 20 hr 38 min?

58. Under what conditions will a star whose Right Ascension is α be found to the east of the meridian at a given moment of sidereal time?

59. The sidereal time is 21 hr 14 min. The Right Ascension of a star is 14 hr 30 min. Find the hour angle of the star.

60. The hour angle of a star is measured as 14 hr 22 min. Its Right Ascension is 14 hr 30 min. Find the sidereal time at the moment of its observation.

61. What is the sidereal time if a star with a Right Ascension of 21 hr 9 min 23 sec has an hour angle of $98°11'15''$ to the east?

62. Where is Sirius ($\alpha = 6$ hr 41 min) located in the sky on the 21st March an hour after sunset, if the observer is situated on lat. $40°$? Whereabouts is Sirius on the 23rd September an hour after sunrise (for middle latitudes of the northern hemisphere)?

63. What would be the position in the sky of a star of Right Ascension 7 hr and Declination $40°$, 1 hr after sunset on the 21st March, for an observer located on lat. $40°$?

64. The two brightest stars in the northern hemisphere of the sky are Vega ($\alpha = 18$ hr 34 min) and Capella ($\alpha = 5$ hr 10 min). In what sector of the sky (in the western or the eastern) and at what hour angle will they appear, at the moment of upper culmination of the point of the Vernal Equinox? At the moment of the lower culmination of the same point?

65. What is the interval of sidereal time between the lowest culmination of Capella and the upper culmination of Vega? (See the data in the preceding problem.)

66. What is the hour angle of Capella at the moment of the highest culmination of Vega? What is it at the moment of its lowest culmination? (See Problem 64.)

67. What is the Declination of stars which are visible on the horizon on any place on Earth?

68. Under what conditions does the azimuth of a star remain constant from its rising to its culmination?

69. Under what conditions is the azimuth of any star equal to $270° - \lambda$ where λ is the astronomical longitude of the star?

70. Find the geometrical position of the points on a sphere for which the astronomical longitude equals the Right Ascension.

71. Find the geometrical position of the point on a sphere for which the astronomical latitude is the same as the Declination.

72. Find those points on a sphere whose latitudes are equal to the Declination, and whose longitudes are equal to the Right Ascension.

73. The mid-line of the Milky Way describes a great circle which intersects the equator at an angle of 62°. The Right Ascension of one of these points of intersection is 18 hr 40 min. Determine the equatorial coordinates of the north pole of the Milky Way.

74. Which stars never intersect the prime vertical?

SECTION TWO PROBLEMS

75. In a spherical triangle we are given the side $a = 57°22'11''$, the side $b = 72°12'19''$ and the angle $C = 94°1'49''$. Calculate the side c and the angles A and B.

*76. Deduce a formula to express the angular distance l between two points on a sphere, the coordinates of which are given in an equatorial system.

*77. Using the formula found in Problem 76, determine the angle of separation (along a great circle) of the stars α and β Ursae Majoris, whose coordinates are:

$$\alpha_1 = 10 \text{ hr } 59 \text{ min}, \quad \delta_1 = +62°10', \quad \alpha_2 = 10 \text{ hr } 57 \text{ min},$$
$$\delta_2 = +56°47'.$$

78. The beginning and the end of a meteor trail in the sky are at 90° and 136°19'0'' from the North celestial Pole, respectively, and the angle between the curves of Declination passing through these points is 62°20'42''. Determine the length of the meteor trail in degrees, and the angles at which it intersects the two circles of Declination referred to.

79. Deduce the formula for the transformation of the horizontal coordinates A and z into equatorial coordinates t and δ, for a place of latitude ϕ. Transform them to their logarithmic form.

80. Deduce three formulae transforming the equatorial coordinates α and δ into the ecliptical coordinates λ and β. Apply the formulae to the coordinates of the Sun.

Hint. Draw up a plan and designate the obliquity of the equator to the ecliptic by ε.

81. Deduce the formula converting the ecliptical coordinates λ and β to the equatorial coordinates α and δ, denoting the obliquity of the ecliptic by ε. How would the deduction of the formulae be simplified if we applied them to the Sun, which moves along the ecliptic?

82. Convert to their logarithmic form the formulae for the transformation of the equatorial coordinates α and δ to the ecliptical β and λ.

83. Deduce three general formulae for the conversion of the spherical coordinates x and y into x' and y', if the first are determined by reference to a great circle on the sphere s, and the second are determined by reference to a great circle s', at an angle i to s. One of the points of intersection of s' with s has the coordinates $\theta, 0$, in the first system, and the coordinates $\theta', 0$, in the second system.

84. Find the zenith distance and azimuth of α Draconis ($\alpha = 14$ hr 1 min 57 sec, $\delta = 64°48'\cdot8$) in Leningrad ($\phi = 59°56'\cdot5$) at 16 hr 24 min 33 sec sidereal time.

Hint. See the scheme of calculation given on p. 19.

85. Find the zenith distance and the azimuth of α Leo ($\alpha = 10$ hr 4·7 min, $\delta = +12°18'$) in Moscow ($\phi = 55°46'$) for the moment of sidereal time $s = 5$ hr 23·8 min.

86. Calculate the zenith distance and the azimuth of Arcturus at Saratov ($\phi = 51°32'0''$) at 13 hr 34 min 54 sec sidereal time ($\alpha = 14$ hr 11 min 58 sec, $\delta = +19°36'6''$).

87. Calculate α and δ for a star with coordinates $z = 49°15'10''$ and $A = 298°28'50''$, observed from Moscow at the sidereal time

$s = 11$ hr 11 min 36 sec. (Make use of the formulae obtained in Problem 79.)

88. A comet has the equatorial coordinates $\alpha = 81°48'\cdot7$, $\delta = +68°28'$. What are its ecliptical coordinates λ and β ($\varepsilon = 23°27'26''$)? (Use the formulae obtained in Problem 82.)

89. Find the latitude β and the longitude λ of the star α Orion, having the coordinates $\alpha = 5$ hr 49 min, $\delta = +7°23'$. (Use the formula obtained in Problem 82.)

90. On the 9th May the Right Ascension of the Sun was 45°30'. If the inclination of the ecliptic to the equator is 23°27' determine the Declination of the Sun. (Make use of the answer to Problem 81.)

91. The longitude of the Sun is $71°11'\cdot7$. Calculate its equatorial coordinates, if $\varepsilon = 23°27'\cdot2$. (Make use of the answer to Problem 81.)

92. The longitude of the Sun is $43'\cdot6$. Find its Declination and Right Ascension. Repeat for the moment when the longitude of the Sun is $143\cdot6°$ (on the 15th August). Carry out an approximate check on the accuracy of the calculation, comparing it with the data given in the astronomical ephemeris.

*93. Determine the longitude of the Sun on the 2nd January and on the 5th July, if on these days δ and α for the Sun given by the astronomical calendar are: $-23\cdot0°$, 18 hr 49 min and $+22\cdot8°$, 6 hr 55 min.

Hint. Use the answer to Problem 82. Check the accuracy of your calculation of the longitude of the Sun, using its mean diurnal movement along the ecliptic.

94. A point of observation lies at $\phi = 52°30'$ northern latitude; 3 hr 40 min after its upper culmination the Sun is situated at a height of $h = 33°8'$. What are the azimuth A and the Declination δ of the Sun?

95. How long after its upper culmination is the Sun situated at an altitude of $h = 35°$ on the 13th June in Kiev ($\phi = 50°27'$ lat. N.), if the Declination of the Sun is $\delta = +23°12'$?

96. When observing planets it is important to know the directions of their axes relative to the circle of Declination passing through the centre of their visible discs. However, it is easier for the observer to trace the circle of altitude, as it passes through the disc of the planet, and to record it on a diagram. Then, to mark the axes of the planet on the diagram, the angle between the circles of Declination and of altitude passing through the centre of the planet, must be known. Deduce the formula determining this angle p, if the coordinates of a planet α and δ and the moment of observation (sidereal time) are known. Find three formulae determining this angle, and the zenithal interval z of the planet. Reduce them to their logarithmic form, using the auxiliary terms m and M.

*97. To find whether a star situated close to the ecliptic is visible from a place of latitude ϕ, we must know the angle between the ecliptic and the horizon. Determine this angle as a function of sidereal time s, and deduce the conditions of its maximum and minimum.

*98. x, y, and z are the heliocentric equatorial coordinates of a body, with the x-axis directed towards the point of the Vernal Equinox, and the y-axis in the plane of the equator. X, Y, and Z are the rectangular coordinates of the body with their origin in the centre of the Sun, the x-axis in the direction of the point of Vernal Equinox, and the y-axis in the plane of the ecliptic (heliocentric rectangular ecliptical coordinates). Prove that $x=X$, $y = Y \cos \varepsilon - Z \sin \varepsilon$, $z = Y \sin \varepsilon + Z \cos \varepsilon$, where ε is the obliquity of the ecliptic.

*99. A heavenly body is situated at a distance ϱ from the Earth and has the equatorial geocentric (relative to the Earth) coordinates α and δ. The equatorial geocentric coordinates of the Sun are X_0, Y_0, and Z_0 (where the X_0-axis is directed towards the point of the Vernal Equinox, and the Y_0-axis lies in the plane of the equator). Let x, y and z be the heliocentric rectangular coordinates of the body (see the preceding problem). Prove that for the determination of ϱ, α, and δ the following formulae are adequate:

$$\varrho \cos \alpha \cos \delta = x + X_0,$$
$$\varrho \sin \alpha \cos \delta = y + Y_0,$$
$$\varrho \sin \delta = z + Z_0.$$

*100. Let R be the distance of the Earth from the Sun, and L its heliocentric longitude. Let a heavenly body at a distance ϱ from the Earth have the geocentric ecliptic coordinates β and λ. Prove that

$$\varrho \cos \beta \cos \lambda = x - R \cos L,$$
$$\varrho \cos \beta \sin \lambda = y - R \sin L,$$
$$\varrho \sin \beta = z,$$

where x, y, and z are the ecliptical rectangular heliocentric coordinates of the body.

CHAPTER IV

CULMINATION, THE DETERMINATION OF GEOGRAPHICAL LATITUDE AND THE COORDINATES OF CELESTIAL BODIES

I

AT THE upper culmination of a body, it reaches its highest point above the horizon. Its hour angle $t = 0$ and the sidereal time s at that moment is equal to the Right Ascension of the body.

At its lowest culmination a star is at its furthest point from the zenith. Its hour angle $t = 12$ hr and the sidereal time at that moment is $s = \alpha + 12$ hr.

Figure 8 represents the projection of the celestial sphere on the

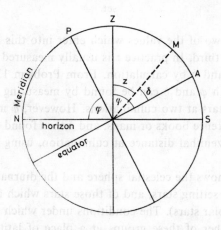

FIG. 8. The celestial sphere in projection upon the plane of the meridian.

27

plane of the meridian, at the moment of highest culmination of a body. The Declination δ, the zenithal distance z, and the latitude ϕ of the place of observation are connected by the formula

$$z = \pm(\phi - \delta).$$

The sign $+$ applies if the star culminates to the south of the zenith, and the sign $-$ applies if the star culminates between the zenith and the North celestial Pole.

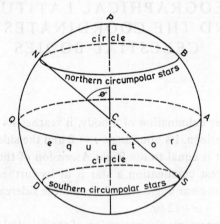

FIG. 9. The circles of stars which never rise and stars which never set.

Knowing two of the values which enter into this formula, we may find the third. In practice z is usually measured by observation, and ϕ and δ by calculation. From Problem 135 it can be seen that both ϕ and δ can be found by measuring the zenithal distance of stars at two culminations. However, ϕ may often be found in reference books or maps, and δ then found by measurement of the zenithal distance at culmination, using the formula above.

Figure 9 shows the celestial sphere and the diurnal paths both of rising and setting stars, and of those stars which never rise or set (circumpolar stars). The conditions under which stars belong to one or other of these groups at a place of latitude ϕ, may easily be found from Figs. 8 or 9.

SECTION ONE PROBLEMS

101. What is the value for the azimuth of a star at the moment of its highest culmination from a place at latitude ϕ? Is this the same for all stars?

102. For what star is the azimuth in your town never equal to zero?

103. At what Declination is a star's azimuth equal to $0°$ at the moment of upper culmination, and when is it equal to $180°$?

104. Moscow, and the capital of Abyssinia, Addis Ababa, lie almost on the same meridian. The latitude of Moscow is $+56°$, and of Addis Ababa, $+9°$. What is the difference between the altitudes of the star Sirius, observed at its upper culmination in the two cities?

*105. Compare the azimuths and altitudes of the same star at lower culmination for observers situated at latitudes ϕ and $\phi+30°$.

106. Show that the altitude of a star at its lower culmination is expressed by the formula

$$h = \phi+\delta-90°.$$

107. What is the zenith distance of Vega ($\delta = +38°42'$) at its moment of upper culmination at Moscow ($\phi = 55°45'$)?

108. At what zenith distance does the star Capella ($\delta = +45°54'$) pass through upper culmination in Leningrad ($\phi = 59°57'$), and in Tashkent ($\phi = 41°18'$).

109. A star is located at $15°$ from the North celestial Pole. Will it always be visible above the horizon at Leningrad ($\phi = 59°57'$)?

110. Is it possible for the same star to pass through the celestial meridian at the town Orel ($\phi = 52°58'$) both at the point N and at the point S? Is this phenomenon possible at other places on Earth?

111. The polar distance of a star $= 20°15'$. What is its zenith distance at its lower culmination at Vologda ($\phi = 59°13'$)?

112. A star has a north polar distance of $48°$. Is it always above the horizon at Odessa ($\phi = 46°29'$)?; Moscow ($\phi = 55°45'$)?; Kiev ($\phi = 50°27'$)?; and Tbilisi ($\phi = 41°43'$)?

113. The declination of Fomalhaut (α Piscis Australis) is $-30°5'$. Is it visible in Archangelsk ($\phi = 64°34'$)?

114. From what geographical positions is the constellation Southern Cross visible if it lies between the limits of southern Declination $-55°$ and $-64°$? Indicate on a terrestrial globe or map which countries these places include.

115. Somebody believes that an acquaintance of his living in Saratova, ($\phi = 51°32'$) saw the star Capella by day from the bottom of a very deep well. Is this possible from geometrical considerations? (It is known that in general stars are not visible from wells by day.)

116. A star describes an arc of $180°$ above the horizon from its rising to setting, and at the time of its upper culmination stands at $55°$ from the zenith. What is the inclination of the celestial equator to the horizon at this place?

117. What is the Declination of a star observed in Archangelsk ($\phi = 64°32'$), at its lower culmination to have an altitude of $10°$?

118. In Odessa ($\phi = 46°29'$) the higher culmination of Sirius is observed at a zenith distance of $63°5'$. What is its Declination?

119. What is the Declination of a star, culminating in the point of N at a place with latitude ϕ?

120. What is the Declination of a star culminating at the zenith of a place whose latitude is ϕ?

121. For what values of the Declination δ of a star will it never set, at latitude ϕ? For what values will it never rise?

122. What is the Declination of a star passing through its highest culmination at the zenith in the towns of Moscow, Kiev, and Tbilisi? (For their latitudes see Problem 112.)

123. What is the greatest southern Declination of stars visible in Leningrad ($\phi = 59°57'$) and in Tashkent ($\phi = 41°18'$)?

*124. On a certain midday in Moscow ($\phi = 55°45'$) the altitude of the Sun was $57°17'$. Using an astronomical ephemeris find the day of the year on which this measurement was made.

*125. The instruments of the Soviet drifting scientific Research Station *North Pole* used for observation of the stars were able to determine its position on the Earth's surface to an accuracy of 250 m. This degree or accuracy allowed the drifting of the ice to be followed. What is the accuracy of the measured geographical latitude of the station? (The length of a degree of the meridian = 111 km.)

126. In Tbilisi the star β Ursae Minoris ($\delta = +74°31'$) was observed at its lower culmination at a zenith distance of $63°47'$. What is the latitude of Tbilisi?

127. The star α Aurigae ($\delta = 45°54'$) is visible on the horizon at the moment of lower culmination. What is the altitude of the North celestial Pole above the horizon at the place of observation?

128. The altitude of a star, situated on the celestial equator, at its moment of upper culmination, is $30°$. What is the elevation of the pole at the place of observation?

***129.** We wish to determine the geographical latitude of a place by observation of the altitude of a heavenly body in culmination. Should a star close to or far from the zenith be used, to yield the most accurate measurement? Why? (See Section V.)

***130.** A man takes a stick 1 m long, and sticking it in the ground, measures the length of its shadow at midday. Taking (correctly) the value for the Declination of the Sun on that day, he determines the latitude of the position erroneously, although the calculation is made accurately. What is the source of his error?

131. The altitude of the lower edge of the Sun is measured from a ship by means of a sextant to be $84°21'$ south of the zenith, at the meridian, and the Declination of the centre of the Sun is $+18°39'$. Determine the ship's latitude, taking into account that the angular diameter of the Sun is $32'$.

132. The altitude of the centre of the Sun at midday, measured by the navigator of a liner, is $30°15'$ (taking into account all necessary corrections). The Declination of the Sun at that time, $\delta = 19°25'$. Determine the latitude of the ship.

133. The observed zenith distance of the lower edge of the Sun, at upper culmination, taking all necessary corrections into account, is $55°42'19''$. The angular radius of the Sun is $16'10''$, and the Declination of its centre $14°34'56''$. Determine the latitude of the place of observation.

134. From what latitude has the midday Sun an altitude of $4°11'$, and a Declination $+22°8'$?

135. A non-setting star has an altitude of 20° at its lower culmination, and 50° at its highest. Find the Declination of this star and the latitude of the place of observation.

Hint. Draw a plan.

136. A non-setting star is observed in Tula at its upper culmination to the north of the zenith, at a zenithal distance of 29°47′, and at its lower culmination at 41°49′. Find the geographical latitude of Tula.

137. At what place on Earth will any circle of Declination coincide with the horizon?

---

138. A star has an hour angle of 20 hr, and a zenith distance of 40°. What will its time angle be, when it reaches the same distance on the other side of the meridian?

139. What is the sidereal time of lower culmination of a star, with Right Ascension 158°27′?

140. At sidereal time 6 hr 38 min, what is the Right Ascension of a star, in upper culmination at 2 hr 10 min?

141. What is the interval between culmination of stars of Right Ascension 5 hr 29 min, and 10 hr 31 min?

142. A star culminates at 8 hr 0 min this evening. When will it culminate in 10 days' time?

143. What is the approximate time[†] of culmination of Arcturus (α = 14 hr 12 min) on February 10th?

144. At what (solar) time will Arcturus culminate on the 1st August, if its Right Ascension is 14 hr 12 min?

145. At what (solar) time will α Cygnus (α = 20 hr 39 min) culminate on the 1st October?

146. What stars cross the meridian on the 3rd October at 10 hr 30 min in the evening? Which constellations have already crossed the meridian, and are visible in the south-west?; and which are visible in the south-east? Use a star map.

147. Calculate approximately what stars will be found at their upper culmination at 10 o'clock on the evening of the 28th July.

† In this and subsequent problems mean solar time is meant.

148. What constellations will be visible at 8 o'clock this evening within 2 hr of the meridian? Find them in the sky.

*149. At what time of year is the handle of the plough situated with its handle downwards, at about 9 o'clock in the evening, given that the constellation is dispersed between $8\frac{1}{2}$ and $13\frac{1}{2}$ hr of Right Ascension.

150. On what date does Sirius, the brightest star in the sky ($\alpha = 6$ hr 42 min) culminate at midnight?

151. If a star, of Right Ascension 18 hr, is situated on the meridian at 8 o'clock in the evening then what, approximately, is the date and the month?

152. At what time on the night of the 10th October will the star Mizar ($\alpha = 13$ hr 20 min) be situated directly above the North celestial Pole?

153. The star δ Orionis rises on the 14th November at 8 o'clock in the evening. On what day does it rise at 5·30 in the evening? What, approximately, is its Right Ascension if its Declination $= 0°$?

---

154. What are the coordinates α and δ of two stars which culminate at Moscow ($\phi = 55°54'$) at 7 hr 35 min sidereal time, at zenith distances of $z = 40°$, one to the south and one to the north of the zenith?

155. A theodolite is set up in the plane of the meridian at Gorki ($\phi = 55°20'$) to observe the culmination of Ursa Majoris ($\alpha = 10$ hr 57 min 34 sec, $\delta = +62°8'$). Determine:

(1) the angle at which the tube must be inclined from the zenith;

(2) the time of culmination on a sidereal clock, the correction for which $u = -2$ min 3 sec.

156. In Kiev ($\phi = 50°27'$) the culmination of an approaching comet is observed. Along the vertical circle of the theodolite the zenith distance (to the south of the zenith) is 3°52', and on a

sidereal clock the moment of culmination is 15 hr 15 min 10 sec.
Determine α and δ of the comet.

157. An astronomer observed the passage of a luminary across
the meridian (upper culmination) at 7 hr 35 min 15·4 sec sidereal
time, and determined the zenith distance of the body as 44°15′.
The correction for the clock that evening was +0 min 33·4 sec.
What were the coordinates of the star if the latitude of the observatory is 56°20′?

***158.** A planet crosses the meridian 2 min 19 sec earlier than
a star with coordinates $\alpha = 0$ hr 19 min 4 sec, $\delta = +0°13′\!·2$.
The zenith distance of the planet at culmination is 19′·4 greater
than that of the star at its culmination. What are the coordinates
of the planet?

***159.** An astronomer wishes to determine the coordinates of
an approaching comet and with the help of a thread micrometer,
finds it locates 3′51″ to the north of a star having the coordinates
$\alpha = 19$ hr 10 min 14 sec, $\delta = -18°14′9″$. With the tube kept
motionless the comet crossed a thread set up along the circle of
Declination, 1 min 1 sec earlier than the star. What are the coordinates of the comet?

SECTION TWO PROBLEMS

***160.** In what part of the sky does the zenith distance of a
luminary change most rapidly? In what part of the sky does it
change least rapidly?

***161.** In what part of the sky do the azimuths of luminaries
change most rapidly, and in what part of the sky will they change
most slowly?

***162.** Which is the more accurate method of timing the pas-
sage of a star through the meridian — observing at the moment
when its zenith interval is least, or noting the moment when it
passes across the vertical thread of a telescope which is set along
the plane of the meridian?

164. Where, on the Earth, and for what star is the diurnal
change in its zenith distance proportional to the change in its
hour angle?

*165. From the first equation for the conversion of the equatorial coordinates α and δ into the horizontal,

$$\cos z = \sin \phi \sin \delta + \cos \phi \cos \delta \cos t,$$

obtain the formula determining the zenith distance of a luminary in upper culmination.

166. At a place in the northern hemisphere, a vertical staff of length $1 = 2 \cdot 5$ m is set up. At 3 hr 40 min stellar time after the upper culmination of the Sun it casts a shadow $1 = 3 \cdot 831$ m long on a horizontal plane. What is the geographical latitude of the place if the Declination of the Sun on the day of observation $\delta = +15°20'$?

167. Find an expression for the latitude of a place, given the Declination of a star and its hour angle at the moment when its azimuth is equal to $180°$. (Kazakov.)

Hint. Employ formulas (4)–(6), Chapter III.

168. Prove that in the course of a day the limiting values of the azimuth of a star (to the east or to the west of the meridian) having the Declination δ, are greater than the latitude of the place of observation, and are determined by the formula

$$\sin A = \mp \frac{\cos \delta}{\cos \phi}.$$

Hint. Draw up a diagram, and employ the three basic formulae of spherical trigonometry.

169. At latitude $45°$ north the maximum azimuth of a certain star about the pole is equal to $225°$. Prove that the Declination of this star is $+60°$.

Hint. Employ the formula given for the preceding problem.

CHAPTER V

REFRACTION

ON ENTERING the atmosphere of the Earth from the vacuum of space, the light from every celestial body undergoes refraction. This refraction causes the rays to be bent, and fall on the eye of the observer from a direction closer to the vertical than would be the case if there were no atmosphere. Refraction, in fact, decreases the zenith distance of a celestial body. Measurements made from direct observation of heavenly bodies must thus be corrected to exclude this effect. The apparent displacement, zero at the zenith, increases rapidly as the horizon is approached, and at the horizon itself reaches 35'. At an air temperature of $+10°C$ and a pressure of 760 mm, the angular displacement is expressed approximately by the formula

$$r = 58''\!\cdot\!2 \tan z.$$

This value, however, diverges strongly from the true value when z is large. At $z = 70°$ the formula gives a value which is in error by $1''$, and for greater values of z it cannot in general be used. For a more accurate determination of the refraction, the temperature and pressure of the air must be taken into account. Values of the mean displacement are given in Table VIII as a function of the zenith distance, corresponding to a temperature of $+10°C$ and air pressure of 760 mm. The effects of temperature and pressure are comparatively unimportant.

Problems in this section are restricted to the correction for refraction of observed altitudes of stars, and situations involving this concept. Problems on the rising and setting of heavenly bodies, allowing for the effects of refraction, are given in Chapter IX, "The Rising and Setting of a Heavenly Body".

SECTION TWO PROBLEMS

170. Does refraction generally have an effect on both of the coordinates of a heavenly body, or only on one of them, and is this always so?

171. Does refraction in general have an effect on both the ecliptical coordinates of a heavenly body, and if so, does this always hold?

172. The measured zenith distance of a star from latitude 55°45'20'', at the moment of upper culmination is 50°0'0''. Using the Table of Refraction, determine the Declination of the star.

173. At an observatory at latitude 55°45'20'' the measured zenith distance of an object in upper culmination was determined as 47°59'48''. What is the Declination of the body, taking the effect of mean refraction into account?

174. The altitude of the lower edge of the Sun at midnight, measured by the captain of a Soviet icebreaker, was 14°11'5''. The Declination of the Sun on that day was +21°19'34'', and the angular radius of the Sun 15'47''. What was the position of the vessel?

175. The observed zenith distance of the star β Ursae Minoris at upper culmination was 24°2'8'', and at lower culmination was 53°51'51''. Determine the latitude of the place of observation, and the Declination of the star, taking refraction into account.

*176. The captain of a ship found that the zenith distance of the centre of the Sun at midnight was 80°. Where, and at what time of the year, might the ship have been situated, and how far approximately (in kilometres) would the captain have been wrong in determining the position of the ship by its latitude, if he had not taken refraction into account?

*177. By how much does the effect of refraction prolong the duration of the day at the Earth's equator?

*178. Is it possible to see both the Sun and the full Moon simultaneously above the horizon?

*179. Does the effect of refraction increase or decrease the visible diameter of the Sun and the Moon near the horizon?

180. Does refraction increase the visible area of the Sun's disc when it is near the horizon?

*181. Does the apparent position of Jupiter in the sky change because the light reflected by this planet passes through its own atmosphere and is refracted?

*182. Is it necessary in practice to take into account the effects of refraction when measuring the angular separation of the components of binary stars, with a separation of the order of $1''$, and why?

*183. The difference in the azimuths of two stars was measured at a given moment, their Right Ascensions being 8 hr 50 min and 9 hr 46 min. Must this difference be increased or diminished if the effects of refraction are taken into account?

184. The star β Ursae Minoris, observed on the meridianal circle, had upper and lower culminations at $55°48'6''$ and $24°58'$ $56''$ of altitude respectively. Determine the Declination of the stars and the latitude of the place, taking refraction into account.

*185. Having received information about the discovery of a new minor planet, an astronomer decides to measure its exact equatorial coordinates that evening. Observing it on the meridianal circle he finds that the upper culmination of the planet occurs at an altitude of $37°19'55''$ at 5 hr 18 min 14 sec according to sidereal clocks which have a correction of -3 min 19 sec. Under the given conditions the correction for refraction was $1'3''$. What are the α and δ of the planet if the latitude of the observatory is $43°19'1''$?

186. Using the second formula given in the answer to Problem 215, deduce an expression for the derivative of the Declination of the Sun with time, and hence determine by how long the duration of the polar day is increased by refraction at the horizon, $35'$?

Hint. Assume that the longitude of the Sun, L, changes by approximately $1°$ a day, and that $\sin \varepsilon = 0.4$ (Parenago).

187. In Rado's Tables of Refraction, the stellar displacement is given by the formula $\varrho = \varrho_0 + \varrho_0 (A + B)$. In the Tables the mean ϱ_0 is given for zenith distance values z (every $10'$ from $z = 42°$ to $80°$); the temperature coefficient A by the argument t (in degrees centigrade) and the barometric coefficient B by the argument b (in millimetres). A measured zenith distance is $53°48'33''\cdot5$. Correct this by the formula given above for the effect of refraction, for $t = +18°\cdot4$ and $b = 746\cdot7$. In the Tables $\varrho_0 = 1'25''\cdot55$ for $z = 53°40'$, the increment for $8'33''\cdot5$ being $0''\cdot42$. $A = -0\cdot0660$, and $B = -0\cdot0175$.

188. Deduce the formula for refraction $r = 58''\cdot2 \tan z$, assuming that the surface of the Earth is covered with a layer of atmosphere of constant thickness and density. Using Fig. 10, in which KL is the surface of the Earth, $A-A$ is the border of the atmosphere, and z is the observed zenith distance of the object S.

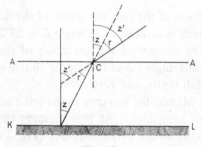

FIG. 10.

The coefficient of refraction for air is $n = 1\cdot0002825$ (at a temperature of $+10°C$ and at normal atmospheric pressure) and $\sin 1'' = 1/206,265$.

CHAPTER VI

THE APPARENT MOTION OF
THE SUN

I

DURING the course of the year the centre of the Sun moves along the ecliptic, which is inclined at an angle $E = 23°27'$ to the celestial equator. On account of the attraction of the Earth by the other planets, this angle varies during the course of the year, but within very small limits, and very slowly.

On the 22nd March, the Sun crosses the celestial equator, rising in the northern hemisphere. At that moment the centre of the Sun is at the point of the Vernal Equinox (Fig. 2 on p. 9). Three months later, on the 22nd June, the Sun reaches its most northerly position, on the day of the Summer Solstice. On the 23rd September, the Sun arrives at the point of the Autumnal Equinox, and on the 22nd December, it sinks to its southernmost point below the heavenly equator on the day of the Winter Solstice.

SECTION ONE PROBLEMS

189. When is the zenith distance of the Sun equal to 90°? When is its azimuth equal to 0°?

190. How long does it take the Sun to change its position by a distance equal to its diameter, in its annual movement along the ecliptic?

191. What are the longitude and latitude of the Sun on the 22nd June and on the 22nd December?

192. What is the longitude of the Sun on the 22nd September; 1st October; 1st January?

193. Using a star map with the ecliptic marked on it show, approximately, the point at which the Sun is situated today. On what point will it be situated in a month's time?

194. What is the Right Ascension and the Declination of the Sun on the 22nd March and on the 23rd September?

195. What are the Right Ascension and the Declination of the Sun on the 22nd June? What are they on the 22nd December?

196. What are the latitude and the longitude of the Sun when its Right Ascension is 6 and 12 hr, respectively?

197. On approximately which days of the year does the Right Ascension of the Sun make up even numbers of hours (2 hr, 4 hr, etc.)?

198. What is the height of the Sun at Moscow ($\phi = 55°45'$) at midday on the day of the Summer Solstice?

199. At the mouth of the Belomorsco–Baltinsco canal (the canal between the White Sea and the Baltic), in the town of Belomorsk the altitude of the celestial North Pole is 64°33'. What is the altitude of the Sun there at noon on the 22nd December?

200. What is the altitude of the Sun in the meridian, on the day of the Summer Solstice in Leningrad ($\phi = 59°57'$); at Tashkent ($\phi = 41°18'$)? At a latitude of $+23°27'$? At a latitude of $+66°33'$? Find the altitudes for the Winter Solstice. Why are the last two circles of latitude remarkable, and what are they called?

201. Determine the greatest altitude at midday to which the Sun can rise in your city during the summer. Obtain the Declination of the Sun from an astronomical ephemeris.

202. What is the altitude of the celestial pole in a place on the Earth's surface where the centre of the Sun at midnight is situated exactly on the horizon on the 22nd June, supposing that refraction does not take place?

203. How low below the horizon does the centre of the Sun sink at Archangelsk ($\phi = 64°34'$) at midnight of the 22nd June?

204. At what altitude is the Sun visible at the South Pole on the 22nd December?

205. What is the altitude of the pole at a place on Earth where the centre of the Sun is 69°38' at noon on the 22nd June? What is the altitude of the Sun at the same place at noon on the 22nd December?

*206. On the 23rd September the shadow of a vertical rod at noon is 0·731 of the rod's length. Determine the geographical latitude of the place, without consulting the astronomical calendar.

*207. The shadow of a post at noon in Moscow ($\phi = 55°45'$) is 0·854 of its length. On what day of the year was this observation made?

Hint. Find the Declination of the Sun and, using an astronomical ephemeris, a star map, or a globe, find the corresponding latitude, from which the day of the year can be established.

*208. At what sidereal time, and at what altitude will the Sun culminate at Simferopol' ($\phi = 45°$) on the 23rd September?

*209. When will a rod fixed vertically upright on the Tropic of Capricorn cast no shadow on a sunny day?

210. About the year 1100 B.C. Chinese astronomers discovered that at noon on the day of the Summer Solstice the altitude of the Sun was 79°7', and on the day of the Winter Solstice 31°19' (to the south of the zenith). At what latitude was the observation made? What was then the Declination of the Sun to the equator?

211. When do the Right Ascension and the Declination of the Sun change most quickly and when do they change most slowly?

212. What approximately are the astronomical longitudes of the Sun at its apogee and its perigee, if its movement along the ecliptic is taken as being constant?

Hint. The dates of the passage of the Sun through its apogee and perigee are the 3rd July and the 3rd January.

213. Does the Sun pass through the point of the Vernal Equinox on exactly the same day in March each year? If not, then why is this so, and within what limits does this date change?

Hint. Remember the construction of the calendar.

214. Does the Sun's ephemeris remain the same every year? Within what limits may it vary? (By ephemeris we mean the

Table giving the calculated values of the Right Ascension and the Declination of the Sun at noon or midnight at Greenwich on every day of a given year.)

215. Using the cosine formula for a side of a spherical triangle, deduce a formula relating the longitude of the Sun, L, to its Right Ascension α, and its Declination δ. Make the same deduction using the sine formula.

Hint. Use a diagram.

216. Prove that the equatorial coordinates of the Sun are always connected by the relationship $\tan \delta = \tan \varepsilon \sin \alpha$, where ε is the inclination of the ecliptic.

217. The coordinates of the north pole of the Milky Way are expressed as $\alpha = 12$ hr 40 min, $\delta = +28°$. When and where does the Sun cross the Milky Way in its annual movement along the ecliptic?

Hint. Find the ecliptical coordinates of the pole of the Milky Way, and hence determine the points of intersection with the ecliptic.

CHAPTER VII

THE DETERMINATION OF
TIME AND LONGITUDE

I

THE HOUR angles of a heavenly body differ in places situated on
different geographical meridians, as do the angles between the
meridians and the apparent direction of a given heavenly body.
The hour of the solar day is determined by the time angle of the
Sun, so that in different places the solar time is different. For this
reason the time, determined by the time angle of the Sun, is called
local.

The difference between the geographical latitudes of two places
on Earth is equal to the difference in their local times. Latitude is
usually calculated from the meridian of Greenwich, and is expressed in terms of time. If the latitude is westerly, it is denoted by
the letter W, if it is easterly, it is denoted by the letter E.

Generally speaking, no clock indicates the time with complete
accuracy. The problem of the determination of the exact time
amounts therefore to the determination of the appropriate correction. The correction is defined as the value which must be added
algebraically to the time indicated by the clock, to yield the true
time. The change in the clock correction in a day (a given correction minus its preceding one) is called the diurnal clock rate. If it
is sufficiently constant, then the clock correction for a given moment t can be calculated from the formula

$$u = u_0 + w(t - t_0),$$

where u_0 is the known clock correction for the moment t_0 which
most nearly precedes the moment t. If the clock has a pendulum,

44

then the period of its oscillation T is expressed by the formula

$$T = 2\pi \sqrt{\frac{l}{g}},$$

where l is the effective length of the pendulum, and g is the acceleration due to gravity.

A difference in geographical longitudes is determined by a comparison of the local time at each of two meridians. The determination of longitudes has been carried out, for example, by observing the local time of a phase of a lunar eclipse, simultaneously visible from different parts of the Earth. Nowadays radio signals of the exact time may be used for this purpose.

Sidereal days are the terms for the intervals of time between two subsequent culminations of the same type (upper or lower) of the point of the Vernal Equinox. The moment of its upper culmination is taken as the beginning of the sidereal day. The sidereal time, s, is measured by the hour angle to the point of the Vernal Equinox.

The true solar day is the name given to the interval of time between two sequent upper (or lower) culminations of the centre of the Sun. The apparent solar time (the hour of the true day) is measured by the hour angle to the centre of the Sun. It is convenient to take noon as the beginning of the day, although the conventional beginning of the day is taken as midnight. In the latter case, the solar time is equal to the hour angle of the Sun plus 12 hr.

The duration of the true solar day changes non-constantly during the course of the year, because of the speed of the movement of the Sun along the ecliptic, and the inclination of the ecliptic to the equator. In the latter effect the projection on the equator of the diurnal displacement of the Sun along the ecliptic varies throughout the year.

In order to eliminate these inconveniences, we introduce the idea of the mean Sun. That is, an imaginary point moving uniformly about the equator at the rate of one full revolution in a single tropical year.

The intervals of time between two sequent upper (or lower) culminations of the mean Sun are called *mean solar days*. The length of these intervals is thus constant. Mean solar time is measured by the hour angle of the mean Sun.

The difference between mean and real time is called the equation of time. The approximate values of the equation of time are represented graphically in Fig. 11. Exact daily values are given in astronomical calendars.

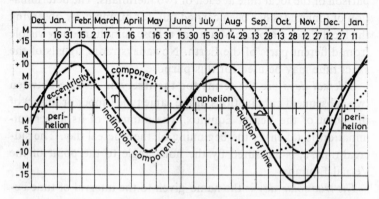

FIG. 11. The changes in the value of the equation of time in the course of a year.

The equation of time is equal to α of the true Sun, minus α of the mean Sun.

The sidereal time at the mean midday is obviously the Right Ascension of the mean Sun at the mean midday.

The conversion of sidereal time s, into mean solar time m, was covered in Chapter III. We may also use the formula

$$m = s - s_0 - (3^m\ 56^s)\ \frac{m}{24}\ ;$$

and for the translation of solar into sidereal time, the formula

$$s = s_0 + m + (3^m\ 56^s)\ \frac{m}{24}\ ;$$

where s_0 is the sidereal time at the mean midday (or at midnight, if the calculation of m is taken from midnight), and m is expressed in hours. The conversion of an interval of sidereal time into an interval of mean solar time and vice versa, is more exactly given in Tables VI and VII in the Appendix. These tables give the values for $m+(3^m\ 56^s)\dfrac{m}{24}$ for given values of $s-s_0$, and vice versa.

All the times mentioned above are local.

Universal Time (M.B. or U.T.—Russian or Latin) is the name given to Greenwich Mean Time, calculated from midnight.

Internationally, time is reckoned by zones. The sphere of the Earth is divided into twenty-four time zones, whose borders (with a few exceptions) follow meridians separated from each other by intervals of 15°. The centre of the zero band coincides with the meridian of Greenwich. The centre of the first zone falls 15° (1 hr) to the east of Greenwich, of the second zone 30° (2 hr) to the east, and so on. All places lying within a given zone calculate their time in advance of Greenwich Mean Time by the same number of hours as the number of the zone. That is, the zonal time of a place is equal to the local time of the central meridian of the given zone. *The mean local (civil) time is equal to the zonal time plus the longitude of the place from Greenwich, minus the number of hours equal to the number of the zone n.* We may write this as

$$m = T_n + \lambda - n.$$

Statutory time is normally equal to the zonal time plus one hour. It is used continuously in the Soviet Union, and in summer in some countries, to prolong the useful hours of daylight.

The International Date Line passed through the Pacific Ocean at exactly 180° latitude from Greenwich, between Kamchatka and Alaska. A new date, for example, the 1st January, 1966, begins first of all on this line, and proceeds westwards. Vessels crossing this line on a course from the west drop a date out of their reckoning; for example, on arriving at the line on the 5th March they count the next day as the 7th March. In crossing the line from the east, two days in succession are referred to by the same date.

The determination of time corrections can be carried out by many methods. For example, by noting the moment of culmination of a body of Right Ascension α. A clock correctly giving sidereal time must at that moment show the time s to be α. If the clock is set to mean time, zonal time, or statutory time, it is necessary to calculate the sidereal time of culmination before comparing it with the observed clock reading.

II

The simplest means of calculating the time by the Sun is by making an observation with Prof. S. P. Glazenapa's solar ring. The sunlight passes through a small hole in the ring, and the times are recorded when the beam falls on the same division on the scale in the ring, both before and after midday. The mean of these instants is the moment of true midday and accurate clocks

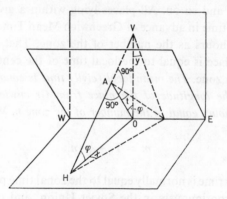

FIG. 12. Combined sun-dials.
H — the dial of a horizontal solar clock.
V — of a vertical solar clock.
A — of an equatorial solar clock.
HAV — the pointer of the solar clocks.

should show this to be 12.00 hr plus the equation of time. A more accurate determination of a time correction demands the calculation of the change in Declination of the Sun during the interval of time between observations.

Sun-dials always show the true solar time. Their indicators are rods, set up parallel to the Earth's axis (that is, in the plane of the meridian, and at an angle to the horizon equal to the latitude of the location). In equatorial sun-dials the shadow of the rod falls perpendicular to their surface, and, on vertical dials, on a vertical surface. On each of these surfaces radial lines are scribed to correspond to positions of the shadow at specified times. The hourly divisions for an equatorial dial are drawn in the direction of the shadow at midday, at angles equal to $\pm n \times 15°$ where n is a whole number. For horizontal dials, these angles x are found by the formula

$$\tan x = \sin \phi \tan t,$$

and for vertical dials by the formula

$$\tan y = \cos \phi \tan t,$$

where t is the corresponding hour of the apparent time.

For accurate estimations of sidereal time it is best to obtain the sidereal time of the local midnight from an astronomical ephemeris, where this time is given for midnight at Greenwich. If the place has a longitude λ (in hours) east of Greenwich, then the sidereal time at the local midday is equal to the sidereal time for midday at Greenwich minus (3 min 56 sec) $\lambda/24$. The equation of time for local midday also differs from that given for Greenwich by an amount equal to the difference in time, multiplied by the easterly latitude of the place in hours.

SECTION ONE PROBLEMS

218. If the sky were always covered by clouds, how would we measure time?

219. What would be the relationship between solar and sidereal time if the Earth rotated in a direction opposite to that in which it rotates at present?

220. The difference in the longitudes of two places is equal to the difference in time. Is this solar or sidereal time?

221. The zero meridian was once reckoned to pass through the island of Ferro, and on a few maps longitude is calculated from Ferro. Ferro lies 17°40′ to the west of Greenwich. What is the longitude from Greenwich of a place which lies 50° east of Ferro on a map of this type?

222. The longitude of Novocherkassk with reference to Leningrad is 9°48′. What is the difference in the local times of these two places?

223. When the time is 10 hr 17 min 14 sec in Greenwich, it is 12 hr 47 min 31 sec at Moscow. What is the longitude of Moscow?

224. A chronometer set correctly to the mean local time in Alma-Alta is taken to Pulkov. What correction must be made to the chronometer at Pulkov if the longitude of Alma-Alta is 5 hr 7 min 46 sec and of Pulkov 2 hr 1 min 19 sec?

225. At noon in Moscow, the clocks at Kazan stand at 12 hr 46 min. What is the longitude of Kazan from Greenwich if the longitude of Moscow from Greenwich is 2 hr 30 min?

226. The longitude of Moscow is 37°34′ east of Greenwich. What is the longitude east of Greenwich of a place where the clocks set to sidereal time indicate 8 hr 45 min at the same moment as those in Moscow indicate 2 hr 30 min?

227. A telegraphic signal is sent from Moscow to Gorki at 9 hr 8 min 32 sec local sidereal time. The signal was received in Gorki at 9 hr 34 min 16 sec local sidereal time. What is the difference in the longitude of these two places expressed in degrees?

228. The upper culmination of Capella ($\alpha = 5$ hr 10 min) is observed in Orla, at 4 hr 48 min according to a clock set to local sidereal time at Kiev. What is the difference in latitude of these two places?

229. In a point in Central Asia the upper culmination of Capella (α Aurigae) is observed at 2 hr 56 min according to a chronometer set to sidereal time at Pulkov. The Right Ascension of Capella is 5 hr 10 min. What is the longitude of the place of observation?

230. At the moment of culmination of the star α Orionis ($\alpha = 5$ hr 51 min) a clock, set correctly to sidereal time at Greenwich, indicates 15 hr 9 min. What is the longitude of Greenwich relative to the place of observation?

231. At the moment of culmination of α Bootis ($\alpha = 14$ hr 12 min) a clock brought from Pulkov, and set accurately to sidereal time there, stands at 6 hr 25 min. At what longitude relative to Pulkov is the observation made?

232. A traveller notes that an eclipse of the Moon begins at 5 hr 13 min local time. According to an astronomical calendar, this eclipse was scheduled to take place at 3 hr 51 min Greenwich Mean Time. What is the traveller's longitude?

233. An eclipse of the Moon on the 2nd April, 1950, began at 19 hr 3 min universal time. At what time (zonal) did it commence at Tashkent? What statutory time (1 hr forward) and local time were these? (The longitude of Tashkent is 4 hr 37 min of Greenwich. Tashkent is in Zone V.)

234. The Polar expedition led by 0. Shmidt landed on the ice from the sinking ship *Cheliuskin* on the 13th February, 1934. On the 15th February, Krenkel sent the message: "For two days the crew of the *Cheliuskin* have been living on the ice. It has been clear by night. We have determined our position by the stars, as latitude 67°17′ N. longitude 172°51′ W." What was the time on the camp clocks (local time) when Krenkel received time signals from Moscow, given at noon for Zone III? What was the zenith distance of the celestial pole? (Nabokov and Vorontsov–Vel'yaminov.)

235. On the 14th June an observation with a sextant was made from a ship of the culmination of the Sun at 8 hr 23 min according to a chronometer set in Greenwich sidereal time. The culmination took place at a zenith distance of 22°2′ (refraction being allowed for). Determine the latitude and longitude of the ship, if the *Nautical Astronomical Almanac* gives the coordinates of the Sun at the time as

$$\alpha = 5 \text{ hr } 26 \text{ min.}$$
$$\delta = +18°25′.$$

236. At apparent noon on the 22nd December the captain of a ship finds the zenith interval of the Sun to be 66°33′. A chronometer set to Greenwich Mean Time gave the moment of observation as 11·54 a.m. The time correction for that day was −9 min. Indicate the position of the ship on a globe of the world.

237. A traveller arriving at an unpopulated part of the Far North has in his possession tables of coordinates (α and δ) of stars, tables of the eclipses of the satellites of Jupiter calculated for Greenwich Mean Time for the current year, a theodolite, and star clocks, which have accidentally stopped on the way, but are in good working order. Describe in order the observations and calculations which the traveller would have to make to determine his latitude and longitude. (Shcherbakov.)

*238. Given that the diameter of Moscow is 20 km, by how much will true midday on the eastern boundary of the city precede that for the western boundary, if the latitude is 55°45′?

---

239. At midday on October 3rd the clock correction was

$$u = -26 \text{ min } 34 \cdot 6 \text{ sec.}$$

The mean diurnal clock rate is $-1 \cdot 61$ sec. Find the clock correction for 18·00 hr and for 06·00 hr on that date.

240. At noon on the 1st January the clock correction is -2 min 6·5 sec, and the diurnal clock rate $+2 \cdot 9$ sec. Find the exact time when the clocks show 9 hr 18 min 13·4 sec.

*241. At noon on the 3rd February the clock correction is 6 min 14 sec. The diurnal clock rate is -11 sec. Determine the clock corrections at noon on the 1st and 6th of February.

*242. The clock corrections at noon obtained by using a Sun ring are:

15th July	9 min 1 sec,
18th July	8 min 40 sec,
20th July	8 min 24 sec.

Determine the mean diurnal clock rate for the period between the 15th and 20th of July.

*243. In a log book the following time corrections are given, determined by radio signals of the exact time:

9th September at 06·00 hr	2 min 14 sec,
10th September at 06·00 hr	2 min 21 sec,
14th September at 06·00 hr	2 min 49 sec.

Determine the clock correction for 06·00 hr on the 12th September, for 18·00 hr on the 12th September, and for 06·00 hr on the 16th September.

244. A clock with a seconds pendulum keeps accurate time in Moscow. How much will it gain or lose per day if it is set up on the equator? The acceleration due to gravity is $g = 9.8156$ m/sec² at Moscow, and at the equator $g_0 = 9.7810$ m/sec².

---

245. By how much will a sidereal clock gain on a mean solar clock in 10 hr 30 min mean solar time?

246. What is the length of the sidereal day, in terms of mean solar time?

247. Convert the interval 15 hr 11 min 50·8 sec sidereal time into an interval of mean time, either with or without the help of Table VII.

248. Convert the interval 5 hr 32 min 15·43 sec sidereal time into an interval of mean solar time, using the Table.

249. With the help of the Table express the interval 10 hr 12 min 5·32 sec mean time in terms of sidereal time. Do the same for the interval 21 hr 22 min 43·76 sec mean time.

250. Express the interval 2 hr 23 min 24·92 sec mean solar time in terms of sidereal time.

251. Express 1465 sidereal days in terms of mean solar days.

252. At what mean local time will the beginning of the sidereal day on the 1st July occur? What is this time on the 20th August and the 5th November? (Give an approximate calculation.)

253. Calculate approximately the sidereal time for mean midnight on 1st May, and on 19th July.

254. Find the sidereal time at 10·00 a.m. mean local time on the 7th June.

255. Find the sidereal time at 3·00 p.m. mean local time on 27th December.

256. Find the sidereal time for 10·00 p.m. mean local time on the 10th May.

257. What is the zonal time in Kursk ($\lambda = 2$ hr 24 min 51 sec zone II) 18 hr 24 min 30 sec mean local time?

258. Find the Greenwich time corresponding to 12 hr 10 min 30 sec in the Tbilisi zone (Tbilisi is on Zone III).

259. What is the zonal time in Omsk (Zone V) at 18 hr 46 min

23 sec u.t. on the 1st May and what is the statutory time in Yakutsk (Zone IX) where the statutory time is equal to the zonal
time plus 1 hr.

260. In Kazan, a clock keeping zonal time shows 4·02. What is
Greenwich Mean Time at this moment? What is the mean local
time at Kazan? The longitude of Kazan is 3 hr 16 min east of
Greenwich (Kazan is situated in Zone III).

261. Using a geographical map, or a globe of the world, determine what time clocks must indicate when it is noon at Greenwich if they are set to zonal time, and to the local mean time at
the following cities: Leningrad; Moscow; Irkutsk; Kazan; Kiev;
Omsk; Kuibishev; and Vladivostok.

262. Find from a map which time zone your city is situated in.
What time will be indicated there by clocks, at Greenwich noon
today?

*263. At what zonal time in Kubishev (Zone III) will the culmination of the Sun take place on the 22nd June (longitude 3 hr
20 min 20 sec) if on that day the equation of time is +1 min
20 sec?

264. On the 15th July a sun dial indicates 4 p.m. What time
will a clock indicate at that moment, set to local mean time and
sidereal time?

265. Find the true local time, corresponding to 13 hr 15 min
28·5 sec mean local time in Moscow on the 21st January, 1931.
The equation of time for that moment is +11 min 13·97 sec.

*266. A sun-dial in Moscow on the 8th October indicates
3 p.m. If the time equation for the day is −12 min, what is the time
expressed in statutory Moscow time?

*267. A total eclipse of the sun took place at Moscow ($\lambda = 2$ hr
30 min) at 9 hr 27 min Greenwich (or Universal) time. On the
day the equation of time was −9 min. Did the eclipse take place
before the apparent noon?

*268. At the culmination of Arcturus ($\lambda = 14$ hr 12 min) on
the 15th August the sidereal clocks in an observatory gave the
time as 15 hr 18 min. Is this possible? If not, what would account
for the discrepancy between the observation and theory?

269. The star γ Ursae Minoris ($\alpha = 15$ hr 20 min 49 sec) is observed in lower culmination, when sidereal clocks give the time as 3 hr 39 min 33 sec. What is the clock correction?

270. At the moment of upper culmination of β Ursae Majoris ($\alpha = 10$ hr 20 min 49 sec) sidereal clocks stood at 10 hr 55 min 48 sec. Determine the clock correction. Determine at what time, by these incorrect clocks, the culmination of α Ursae Majoris ($\alpha = 10$ hr 57 min 34 sec) would take place.

*271. The culmination of Procyon ($\alpha = 7$ hr 36 min), observed in Moscow, took place at 1 hr 15 min on the night of 30–31 December by a clock set to statutory Moscow time. What was the clock correction?

272. On the 26th September the Sun rises at 5 hr 51 min a.m. local mean time, and sets at 5 hr 51 min p.m. What is the equation of time on that day?

273. What is the difference length between the periods from sunrise to 12 noon mean time, and 12 noon to sunset, on the 1st November, when the time correction is -16 min?

274. What, approximately, is the Right Ascension of the Sun on the anniversary of the October Revolution (7th November) if on that day the time correction is -16 min?

---

275. If we lose one solar day on a journey round the world, travelling from west to east do we also lose a sidereal day?

276. What is the greatest possible number of Sundays in February; and where and how can this occur?

277. A steamship leaves Vladivostok on Saturday, 6th November, and arrives in San Francisco on Wednesday, 23rd November. How many days has the journey taken?

278. A ship, leaving San Francisco on the morning of Wednesday, 12th October, arrives at Vladivostok after exactly 16 days. On what date, and on what day of the week, does it arrive?

SECTION TWO PROBLEMS

*279. By how long are sidereal days on Jupiter shorter than solar days, if the sidereal period of rotation of Jupiter about its axis is 9 hr 50 min 30 sec and its period revolution about the Sun is 4332·6 mean solar days? Give an expression for the difference in sidereal time on Jupiter, taking as its day periods of 24 hr.

280. How often do the ticks of two chronometers coincide, if one keeps sidereal and the other mean time, and they tick every $\frac{1}{2}$ sec?

281. How many times in the course of a mean solar day does the tick of a sidereal chronometer, which occurs every second, coincide with the tick of a chronometer set to mean solar time, if their ticks coincide at the beginning of the day?

282. A mean chronometer is compared with a sidereal chronometer whose correction is +0 min 18·4 sec. Determine the correction to the mean chronometer if at the moments of the coincidence of their ticks the chronometers show:

Sidereal			Mean		
hr	*min*	*sec*	*hr*	*min*	*sec*
5	5	33·5	12	36	50·0
5	8	34·0	12	39	50·0

and if the sidereal time at midnight is 16 hr 25 min 50·48 sec.

283. How much does a sidereal clock gain on a mean clock in 1 sec?

284. Show that at a fixed place the relationship

$$s-\alpha+\eta-t = 0$$

applies, where s is the sidereal time, α is the Ascension of the Sun, η is the equation of time, and t is mean time, calculated from midday.

285. Find with the help of Table II, the exact mean local time, corresponding to 15 hr 33 min 15·71 sec sidereal time, at the meridian $\lambda = 2$ hr 30 min 39·60 sec on the 2nd July, 1931.

286. With the help of an astronomical ephemeris determine the sidereal time at 3 hr 15 min 4 sec mean Moscow local time on the 15th July for the current year.

287. On the 11th February the Sun rose at 7 hr 6 min and set at 16 hr 24 min zonal time. What is the difference between zonal and mean local time for the given place? (On the 11th February the equation of time reaches a maximum of +14 min.)

*288. The clocks at an observatory at a latitude 22°75′ E. are set to Greenwich Mean Time. What do these clocks show at the moment of culmination of the western edge of the Sun if at that moment the equation of time is +6 min 2·88 sec and the time passage of the Sun's diameter across the meridian is 2 min 21·24 sec?

289. At Moscow ($\phi = +55°45′20″$), on the 15th May, the measured and corrected zenithal distance of the centre of the Sun is 65° 13′ 20″. At that moment the mean chronometer indicated 16 hr 51 min 7 sec and the Declination of the centre of the Sun was +18° 50′ 33″. Determine the clock correction of the chronometer with respect to mean local time, using the formula $\cos z = \sin \phi \sin \delta + \cos \phi \cos \delta \cos t$. The equation of time was −3 min 47·5 sec.

290. The image of the Sun crossed the same division of a Sun-ring on the 29th June at 9 hr 35 min 5 sec and at 14 hr 29 min 41 sec according to a clock set to local time. Determine the correction to the clock, if the time equation was +3 min 10 sec.

*291. On the 15th March, 1935, at Leningrad, the Sun was observed on the same mark of Glazenap's Sun-ring before and after midday, at the times 9 hr 55 min 26 sec, and 16 hr 18 min 40 sec. The equation of time at local mean midday was +9 min 34 sec. Determine the clock correction to zonal time for local mean solar time. (Leningrad is situated in Zone II, with $\lambda = 2$ hr 1 min 29 sec.) Determine the clock correction to statutory time.

292. In Leningrad ($\lambda = 2$ hr 1 min 1 sec; Zone II) on the 1st October, 1928, an observation was made with a Glazenap Sun-ring. The times before and after midday when the solar ray fell on the same divisions were noted by a clock.

Division number	hr	min	sec	hr	min	sec
20	9	13	12	14	27	22
20–21		16	30		24	16
21		19	52		20	33
21–22		23	51		16	50

The equation of time at midday was −10 min 17 sec. Determine the clock correction for mean local time, and for zonal time.

293. On the 5th June, 1935, an observation was made near Leningrad ($\phi = 59°40'\cdot0$) with the help of a Glazenap Sun-ring:

Division number	Times before and after midday					
	hr	min	sec	hr	min	sec
33–34	8	51	34·0	17	12	8·0
34		53	56·4		9	45·2
34–35		56	18·4		7	26·0
35		58	36·0		5	7·2
35–36	9	0	48·4		2	51·6
36		3	18·0	17	0	26·8
36–37		5	30·8	16	58	4·8
37		7	50·0		55	40·0
37–38	9	10	21·2	16	53	20·8

The equation of time was +4 min 8·0 sec. The correciton to the observed moment of midday due to the change in the Declination of the Sun during the course of the observation is given by

$$M = -A\theta \tan \phi + B\theta \tan \delta,$$

$$\log \tan \delta = 9\cdot6249$$

where θ is the hourly change in the Declination. According to the ephemeris $\log \theta = 1\cdot1259_n$, $\log A = 9\cdot4891$, and $\log B = 9\cdot1850$ on that day. Determine the correction for mean local, zonal and statutory time.

294. From the astronomical ephemeris we find that the sidereal time at mean midday on the 21st March is 23 hr 56 min 5·87 sec, and on the 22nd March is 2·42 sec. Determine, approximately, the mean time at that moment when the Sun passed through the point of the Vernal Equinox.

295. Why does the post meridian of the day begin to lengthen according to mean time, from about the 8th December, 2 weeks before the Winter Equinox?

*296. How qualitatively would the amplitude of the equation of time change if the inclination of the ecliptic to the equator increased to 30°? If it increased to 90°? Neglect the eccentricity of the Earth's orbit.

*297. What are the limits of the equation of time on Mars? Are they greater or less than on the Earth? The inclination of the axis of Mars to the plane of its orbit is 65°. The eccentricity of Mars' orbit is 0·093 and that of the Earth's orbit 0·017.

*298. From the data given above for the orbit of Mars, would mean solar time be necessary there?

*299. Design† the dial of a horizontal sun-dial for Archangelsk ($\phi = 64°34'$) and for Samarkand ($\phi = 38°39'$) and compare the two.

300. Design† the dial of a horizontal sun-dial for your town.

*301. Show that the dial of a vertical sun-dial is the projection of an equatorial dial on a vertical plane.

*302. Design vertical sun-dials for Kuibesheva ($\phi = 53°11'$) and for Yalts ($\phi = 44°30'$).

---

† Work out the angles between the midday shadow and those at other hours of daylight.

CHAPTER VIII

THE CALENDAR

I

CALENDARS may be solar or lunar, based on the following periods:

The tropical year $=$ 365 days 5 hr 48 min 46 sec

$=$ 365·24220 mean solar days.

The sinodic month $=$ 29 days 12 hr 44 min 3 sec

$=$ 29·53059 mean solar days.

For everyday convenience every calendar month and year is given a whole number of days. In order that they should agree with the periods given above, in the solar and lunar calendars, an extra day, and in the solar-lunar calendar, extra days and months are inserted in some predetermined years. The ancient Egyptian calendar contained a fixed 365 days.

The *Julian calendar* has three consecutive years of 365 days, followed by one of 366 days, known as a leap year. This calendar was first introduced in the year 45 B.C., and leap years were those whose number was divisible by four.

The *Gregorian calendar* was introduced in 1582 and has the same system of leap years as the Julian, with the exception that the years completing centuries (for example 1900) for which the number of hundreds are not exactly divisible by four, are counted not as leap years, but as ordinary years. The change was made on the 5th October, 1582, and the day following made the 15th October, to correct the error of 10 days accumulated by the Julian calendar. In subsequent years the difference between the calendars continued to grow, and at the moment stands at 13 days. In Russia, the new calendar was introduced after the Socialist Revolution, on the 1st February, 1918.

The counting of years has generally historical or religious origins, and thus varies widely between different countries. In the problems that follow, Table III in the Appendix will be useful.

SECTION ONE PROBLEMS

303. In the decree of the government (in 1918) on the introduction into Russia of the Gregorian calendar, why is mention made only of the change in the date, and why do the names of the days of the week not have to be changed? (Kamen'schikov.)

304. How many days were there in the year 1918, in the Russian Soviet Federated Socialist Republics? (Kamen'schikov.)

305. Is it possible to keep a calendar absolutely exact during the course of an unlimited period of time?

306. Why does the day of the Vernal Equinox not always fall exactly on the 22nd March?

*307. In 1937 the Vernal Equinox fell on the 21st March, at 18 hr 58 min Greenwich Mean Time. Give the dates and the moments of the Vernal Equinox in 1938, in 1939, in 1940, 1941 and in 1942.

308. What was the error of the Egyptian calendar, according to which the year was exactly 365 days? When would the Vernal Equinox occur, on this calendar, after 100 years? After how long (approximately) would the Vernal Equinox occur in autumn?

309. What are the days in the Gregorian calendar corresponding to the 15th February, 1900; 25th February, 1900; and 5th March, 1900 in the Julian calendar.

310. When, on the contemporary calendar, was a century completed from the day of the Dekabrist riot (14th December, 1825) by the Julian calendar?

311. Newton was born on 25 December, 1642, by the Julian calendar. What would this date be on the Gregorian calendar?

312. What date on the modern calendar corresponds to the 28th February, 2445, on the Julian calendar?

313. After what interval of time would the Summer Solstice on the Julian calendar fall on the 21st March?

314. What is the mean duration of the "Gregorian year" and what is its inexactitude?

315. What is the error in the Gregorian calendar in 100, 500, and 1000 years? When would the Vernal Equinox take place after these intervals of time?

316. The astronomer, Medler, in Iurev (1794–1874), proposed a calendar in which there would be 31 leap years in every 128 years. That is, 1 leap year would be dropped in every 128 years. Determine the length of the year in Medler's calendar, and the size of the error in his chronology.

317. What is the error of the Mohammedan lunar calendar, which has 19 years of 354 days, and 11 years of 355 days in every 30 years.

318. In the eleventh century, in Persia, a calendar was drawn up based on a cycle of 33 years. In this cycle 25 simple and 8 leap years were counted. Determine the length of the year, and the inaccuracy of the Persian calendar.

319. The early Athenian astronomer, Meton (in the fifth century B.C.), discovered a period in the course of which the New and Full Moon would recur on the same day of the year by the solar calendar. Find the length of this period, called "Meton's cycle", or the "Lunar circle", using the mean length of the sinodical month and the tropical year.

*320. Reckoning from the date of the October Revolution, say what would be the year of 1st November, 1958.

*321. In what year were you born, if you count the years from the date of the October Revolution? In what year, by this system, was your father born?

322. In February, 1920, there were five Sundays. When was the previous occasion on which this occurred?

*323. The year 1353 of the Mohammedan calendar began on the 16th April, 1934. In what year of this calendar is the 16th April, 1968?

*324. Given that the year 1227 of the Mohammedan era began on the 20th July, 1860, and that 34 Mohammedan lunar years are equal to 33 of our years, in what year will the numerical designation of the year by our reckoning coincide with that on the Mohammedan calendar?

CHAPTER IX

THE RISING AND SETTING
OF A HEAVENLY BODY

I

THE PROBLEMS in Section One do not require any further explanation.

II

In a place with a latitude ϕ the zenithal distance z of a heavenly body, having an hour angle t, and Declination δ, is given by the formula

$$\cos z = \sin \phi \sin \delta + \cos \phi \cos \delta \cos t. \tag{1}$$

At the moment of rising or setting of a heavenly body, its $z = 90°$ so that the formula becomes

$$\cos t = -\tan \phi \tan \delta \tag{2}$$

which gives the time angle t. t may be positive or negative, corresponding to setting and rising, respectively. The sidereal time of rising and setting $s = t + \alpha$, where α is the Right Ascension of the body. In the case of the Sun, t is obviously the apparent local solar time (calculated from midday) of sunrise and sunset. To obtain the mean local time, the equation of time for the given day must be added to t.

From the formula for the transformation of horizontal coordinates into equatorial,

$$\sin \delta = \sin \phi \cos z - \cos \phi \sin z \cos A \tag{3}$$

we obtain for $z = 90°$,

$$\cos A = -\frac{\sin \delta}{\cos \phi} \tag{4}$$

which gives the azimuths of the points of sunrise and sunset. In the two solutions of equation (4) the value of $A > 180°$ corresponds to sunrise.

Refraction raises the apparent position of a heavenly body above the horizon. At the horizon the displacement is $35'$ so that, at the moment of the visible rising and setting of a heavenly body, its true zenith distance is equal to $90°35'$. The simplified formulae (2) and (4) are thus not strictly correct, and for accurate calculation we derive for instance from (1),

$$\cos t = \cos 90°35' \sec \phi \sec \delta - \tan \phi \tan \delta.$$

For the Sun and the Moon the moments of rising and setting are taken as the moments of rising and setting of their upper edges. As the angular radius of both the Moon and the Sun is $16'$, the zenith distance of the centres of these bodies (to which the value of δ given by astronomical calendars refers) is then $90°35' + 16' = 90°51'$ (taking refraction into account). Putting $\cos 90°51' = -0.0148$, we obtain

$$\cos t = -(0.0148 \sec \phi \sec \delta + \tan \phi \tan \delta). \quad (5)$$

Substituting $z = 90°51'$ in formula (3), we obtain

$$\cos A = \tan \phi \cot 90°51' - \frac{\sin \delta}{\cos \phi \sin 90°51'}$$

or

$$\cos A = -0.0148 \tan \phi - \frac{\sin \delta}{\cos \phi}. \quad (6)$$

The moments of rising and of setting of the Sun and Moon are also influenced by the so-called diurnal parallax. However, in the case of the Sun, this effect diminishes the zenith distance by only $9''$, which is negligible, as the refraction at the horizon normally varies by a greater amount. In the case of the Moon, the parallax diminishes z by $57'$. However, we do not include any problems on calculations of the rising of the Moon, because its rapid motion means that its Declination at rising and setting must be obtained by interpolation from the Tables in the ephemeris, and on the whole the problem is too difficult for beginners.

SECTION ONE PROBLEMS

325. At what time of the day is the zenith distance of the Sun equal to 90°?

326. Is it possible for a star to rise in the north-east, and to set in

(a) the west?

(b) the south-west?

327. A heavenly body has a Declination of 0°. Determine its azimuths at its moments of rising and setting.

328. If a star rose at the point of south-east, then at what point of the horizon would it set? What are the azimuths of the points of rising and setting?

329. Between what points on the horizon do stars rise and set, if they are visible above the horizon for

(a) less than 12 hr?

(b) more than 12 hr?

330. At what time on the 21st September does a comet rise, if its Right Ascension is 4 hr and its Declination is 0°?

331. What is the azimuth of the Sun at the moment of its rising on the Earth's equator on the 22nd March, 22nd June, 22nd September and 22nd December?

332. On the 13th November the Sun's polar distance is 108°. In what latitudes does it not rise?

333. In what latitudes do the morning and evening astronomical twilights not run into each other at night? (Astronomical twilight ends when the Sun has sunk 18° below the horizon. Local twilight is taken as ending when the Sun has sunk 6° below the horizon.)

334. At what geographical latitude do the "white nights" begin? (That is, where the local twilight does not end.)

335. Two stars have equal Declination north and south. Show that the point of rising of one of them is diametrically opposite to the point of setting of the other. (Kazakov.)

SECTION TWO PROBLEMS

*336. From the astronomical ephemeris, find how many days the polar night lasts, not illuminated by local twilight. Do not make allowance for refraction.

*337. Is the length of day on the 27th August greater at Greenwich or at Irkutsk, if their latitudes are the same but Irkutsk is more easterly in longitude by 6 hr 57 min?

*338. In a certáin year the Sun passed through the point of the Vernal Equinox at 6 p.m. Greenwich Mean Time, on the 21st March. Did the Sun rise at the same moment of local time in London and Irkutsk?

Hint. Remember the change in the Declination of the Sun.

339. What approximately are the hour angle and the points of rising and of setting of the star δ Orionis in Murmansk ($\phi = 68°59'$) and at Tashkent ($\phi = 41°20'$) if the Declination of the star is $-0°21'$?

340. Determine, without calculating the refraction, the sidereal time and azimuths of the rising and setting of the star ε Geminorum ($\alpha = 6$ hr $39'\cdot7$, $\delta = +25°12'$) in Moscow ($\phi = 55°45'$).

341. Determine for Pulkov ($\phi = 59°46'\cdot3$) the sidereal time and azimuth of the point of setting of Vega ($\alpha = 18$ hr 34 min 36 sec, $\delta = +38°43'\cdot6$).

342. Calculate the exact time of rising of Sirius ($\alpha = 6$ hr 42 min, $\delta = -16°37'$) in Moscow ($\phi = 55°45'$) on the 22nd October, 1949, without accounting for refraction.

343. Calculate the sidereal and the mean local time of rising and setting of the star α Canis Minoris ($\alpha = 7$ hr 34 min 29 sec, $\delta = 5°27'\cdot5$) in Leningrad ($\phi = 59°56'\cdot5$) on the 3rd April, without accounting for refraction.

344. Without accounting for refraction, calculate the hour angle, and azimuth of the points of rising and setting of the star Regulus ($\alpha = 10$ hr 4 min 42 sec, $\delta = +12°18'\cdot3$) at Pulkov ($\phi = 59°46'\cdot3$). How long does the star remain above the horizon? At what mean solar time does it rise and set on the 20th April, if the sidereal time at midnight on this date is 13 hr 48 min 8 sec?

*345. A star is situated 15 hr below and 8 hr above the horizon of Moscow ($\phi = 55°45'$). Determine approximately the azimuth points of its setting, and its Declination.

*346. The azimuth of a star at its moment of setting is 30°. Determine its Declination, the time of its passage above the horizon, and the altitude of its culmination, for an observer situated at Voronij ($\phi = 51°7'$).

347. Show that if the diurnal passage of a star describes the angle ψ with the horizon at its rising, then

$$\cos \psi = \sin \phi \sec \delta,$$

where $\phi = $ the latitude of the place and $\delta = $ the Declination of the star.

*348. Show how the formula $\cos t = -\tan \delta \tan \phi$ is connected with the diurnal path of the Sun at various times of the year at the poles, the polar circles, central latitudes, and the Earth's equator.

349. On the 21st June the Declination of the Sun is $\delta = 23°27'$. At what latitude is the duration of that day only 3 hr?

350. Using an exact formula, calculate the length of the day, and the mean local time of rising and setting of the upper edge of the Sun at Rostov on Don ($\phi = 47°13'$, $\lambda = 2$ hr 38·9 min) on the 24th May if at that time the Declination of the Sun $\delta = 20°37'·2$.

Hint. Allow for the influence of refraction.

351. Calculate the lengths of the longest and shortest days in Leningrad ($\phi = 59°57'$) in Moscow ($\phi = 55°45'$), and in Samarkand ($\phi = 38°39'$). What is the relationship between the longest and the shortest day in any place? (Neglect refraction effects.)

352. Calculate the exact times of rising and setting of the upper edge of the Sun by local time on the longest and the shortest days in Leningrad, Moscow and Samarkand.

353. On the 4th May the Declination of the Sun, δ, is equal to $+15°0'·7$. Observations showed that on that day the Sun set 7 hr 25 min sidereal time, after its upper culmination. What is the geographical latitude of the place of observation?

354. When the Sun sinks 18° below the horizon, full night begins (astronomical twilight ends). Approximately, how long after sunset does night begin at equinox

(a) on the equator,

(b) at a latitude of 45°,

(c) at a latitude of 60°?

355. Allowing for refraction calculate the duration of astronomical twilight in Leningrad ($\phi = 59°56'\cdot5$) on the 25th March when the Declination of the Sun was $+2°1'\cdot9$.

356. At what northern latitude does the effect of refraction lengthen the day by 16 min when the Declination of the Sun is 0°.

357. Show that on the north polar circle (Arctic Circle) the absolute value of the daily change in the azimuth points of the setting of the Sun is equal to the change in its longitude during the course of a day.

358. How must two places on Earth be situated, so that at any time of any day of the year the Sun is either at or above the horizon at one of them?

359. For half the year on the north polar circle ($\phi = 66°33'$) sunrise takes place every day at exactly the same moment of sidereal time. During the other half of the year the same applies for the place at which the Sun sets. Demonstrate this without the help of trigonometrical calculations, and explain the details of the phenomenon. What is this invariant sidereal time of the rising (and setting) of the Sun? How is the ecliptic situated at that moment? On what day of the year, and in what way, does the constancy of the sidereal time of sunrise change to a constant sidereal time of sunset? How does the length of the day and the night change on the polar circle in the course of the year?

360. Show that on latitude 45° the interval of time from the moment when the azimuth of a star is equal to $-90°$, to the moment of setting, is constant for all stars.

*361. Using the formula connecting cos z with δ, t and ϕ, deduce the formula for the change of hour angle with zenith distance for the rising and setting Sun.

Hint. Differentiate the formula.

*362. From the equations connecting equatorial and horizontal coordinates,

$$\sin \delta = \sin \phi \cos z - \cos \phi \sin z \cos A$$
$$\sin z \cos A = -\cos \phi \sin \delta + \sin \phi \cos \delta \cos t$$

obtain a formula, giving the zenith distance and the sidereal time of the passage of a star across the prime vertical.

363. Determine the altitude of the star Deneb ($\alpha = 20$ hr 39·5 min $\delta = +45°2'\cdot0$) and the sidereal time of its passage across the prime vertical at Pulkov ($\phi = 59°46'\cdot3$) from the formulae given in the answer to the preceding question. Calculate the same values for the stars η Boötes ($\alpha = 13$ hr 51·4 min; $\delta = +18°45'$) and i Aurigae ($\alpha = 4$ hr 52·5 min; $\delta = +33°4'$) at Moscow ($\phi = 55°45'$).

CHAPTER X

PRECESSION

THE ROTATION of the Earth causes a slight equatorial bulge and flattening at the poles. The gravitational attraction of the Sun and Moon on the equatorial mass causes the Earth's axis to describe a conical surface in space, without changing its inclination to the ecliptic. This phenomenon is known as precession and has a period of about 26,000 years. This means that the pole changes its position among the stars along a circle of radius 23°27′, with its centre at the pole of the ecliptic (situated in the constellation Draco, α = 18 hr, δ = 66°33′). The point of Vernal Equinox, too, changes its position along the ecliptic by 50·24 sec every year in the direction of the Sun's apparent motion (to the west). The precession is still sometimes called "the precession of the equinoxes", as it causes the equinox to occur earlier than would be the case if the axis were stationary.

The period between two passages of the Sun through the points of Vernal Equinox is called the "tropical year" and is 365·2422 days.

The full period of the revolution of the Earth about the Sun with reference to the stars is called the "stellar", or the "sidereal" year. Because of the precession of the equinoxes, it is longer than the tropical year and is 365·2564 days.

The period between two passages of the Sun through perihelion is called the "anomalistic year". It is not the same as the sidereal year (it is equal to 365·2596 days) because the major axis of the Earth's orbit revolves very slowly in space relative to the stars.

Because of precession, the longitude of all stars increases by 50″·24 annually while their latitude remains unchanged. The equatorial coordinates of a star, α and δ, both change because of precession, and many Tables have been drawn up for computing these changes. A Table of this type is given in the Appendix as Table IX.

SECTION TWO PROBLEMS

364. In how many years does the Earth's precession take to move the Sun's apparent position by 5°?

365. Are the titles "The Tropic of Cancer" or "The Tropic of Capricorn" apt ones in our time?

*366. In what constellation will the point of the Vernal Equinox be situated 13,000 years from now?

*367. What two conditions are separately necessary and sufficient for the cessation of the phenomenon of precession?

368. The constellation Southern Cross has the approximate coordinates $\alpha = 18$ hr; $\delta = -40°$. The constellation Orion has the coordinates $\alpha = 6$ hr, $\delta = 0°$. How will their coordinates and the conditions of their visibility change in 13,000 years?

369. Decide which constellations now visible at London will not be visible there in 13,000 years.

*370. Using a celestial globe, determine what constellations were not visible from the spot where London now stands, 6000 years ago, when the first systematical observations were made in ancient Babylon of the movements of the planets.

*371. Would precession be faster or slower if the Earth were flattened? If the Moon were nearer? If the Earth were denser? If it revolved more rapidly?

372. The duration of the sidereal year is 365·25636 mean days. Find the duration of the tropical year, given that the point of the Vernal Equinox, precesses westwards along the ecliptic, by 50·2″ every year.

*373. Does precession affect the relationship between the solar seasons of the Earth's northern and the southern hemispheres?

*374. The ecliptical coordinates of a star at a given moment are $\lambda = 359°17'44''$; $\beta = -17°35'37''$. Determine its coordinates for a time preceding this by 10 years, 100 years, and for a moment 100 years hence.

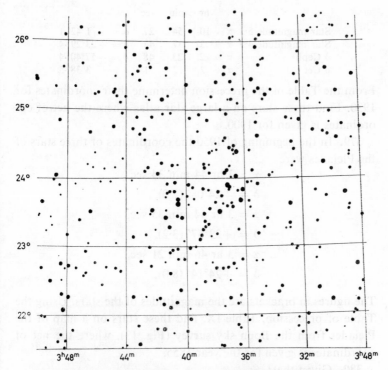

FIG. 13. A chart of the stellar cluster of the Pleiades. The net of
coordinates is for 1855.

*375. How does the phenomenon of precession qualitatively
affect the equatorial coordinates of a star?

*376. Which stars in the celestial sphere change their Right
Ascension most rapidly due to precession?

*377. In the star catalogue for the equinoxes of 1855, the fol-
lowing coordinates are given for a star of stellar magnitude 6·4;
$\alpha = 22$ hr 7 min 0 sec: $\delta = +27°53'·7$. With the help of the
Table of annual precession given in Table IX determine the coordinates of this star for the equinoxes of 1810 and 1900. Compare the difference in the position obtained with the angular
diameter of the Moon, 32'.

378. The coordinates given for some stars in 1855 were as
follows:

		hr	min	sec	
Star magnitude 5·2	$\alpha = 10$	54	27		$\delta = -\ 1°42'·1$
Star magnitude 4·5	$\alpha = 3$	37	43		$\delta = +23°29'·4$
δ Ceph	$\alpha = 22$	23	48		$\delta = +57°40'·4$
o Cet	$\alpha = 2$	12	1		$\delta = -\ 3°38'·5$

From the Table of the precession determine their coordinates for 1930. Find these stars on a large star atlas where the net of co-ordinates is given for 1900.

379. In the beginning of 1950 the coordinates of three stars of the Pleiades were

$$\alpha = 3 \text{ hr } 44 \text{ min } 34 \text{ sec,}$$

$$\delta = +24°08' \ (7·0),$$

$$\alpha = 3 \text{ hr } 44 \text{ min } 35 \text{ sec,}$$

$$\delta = +23°57' \ (3·2),$$

$$\alpha = 3 \text{ hr } 46 \text{ min } 21 \text{ sec,}$$

$$\delta = +24°14' \ (8·0),$$

The figures in brackets are the magnitudes of the stars. Using the Table of precession, Table IX, find these stars on a map of the Pleiades from the Bonn sky survey (Fig. 13), where the net of coordinates is given for the year 1855.

380. Given that:

the tropical year is 365·2422 mean solar days,
the sidereal year is 365·2564 mean solar days,
the anomalistic year is 365·2596 mean solar days.

Determine the magnitude and direction of the precession and the secular movement of the perihelion, relative to the stars.

CHAPTER XI

PROBLEMS SOLVED WITH
THE HELP OF THE CELESTIAL
GLOBE

I

THE USE of a celestial globe assists with the understanding and solution of many astronomical problems. The globe must be set within movable, graduated rings (see Fig. 14), and if accurately constructed, gives results to an accuracy of 1°.

The globe revolves on the axis PP' within the ring PZS, representing the meridian, and is supported by the rest Z', representing the nadir. Z is the zenith, and NWS the circle of the horizon, divided into degrees. Azimuths are reckoned along it from the point S to the point W. Altitudes are reckoned from the circle of the horizon, along the arc ZQ, which is divided into degrees, and turns about an axis perpendicular to the surface of the globe, and fastened to the clamp R. In the absence of this attachment, a strip of paper divided into degrees may be used instead. The circle of the meridian is also divided into degrees, and 0° can be seen on the line of the celestial equator. The clamp R can be set at any point along the arc of the meridian. If the clamp R is set at a point along the meridian 90° from the points S and N, then Z will be the zenith, and the arc ZQ will be the circle of altitude. If the clamp is fixed above the point P, then the arc RQ forms the circle of Declination (the time circle) and Declination can be reckoned along it. In general, the Declination and the Right Ascension of a body are read directly from the net of coordinates on the globe. On the horizon the points N and S are the points north and south, the points W and E, the latter not visible in the illustration, are the points of East and West. The circle *WA* on the globe is the equator, and *A* is the point of the equator. The hour angles of a heavenly body are reckoned from the net of coordinates on the globe as the angles made between the southern part, *PZS*, of the meridian, and the movable arc *RQ*, set as the circle of Declination. The hour angle can also be measured, from the point *A* towards *W* along the equator to its intersection with the circle of Declination.

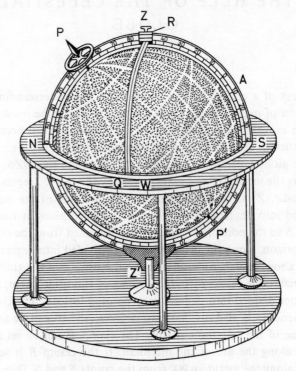

Fig. 14. A celestial globe.

The globe is set to represent the sky and celestial sphere relative to the horizon of an observer situated at latitude ϕ by rotating the circle of the meridian with the globe in its plane, until the arc *NP* is equal to ϕ. This is called setting the globe to latitude.

TYPES OF PROBLEMS SOLVED WITH THE HELP OF THE CELESTIAL GLOBE

I. *To establish the position of a constellation relative to the horizon and the meridian of an observer at a given sidereal time s*

Set the globe for the latitude, turning it within the circle of the meridian, until the circle of Declination on the globe of Right Ascension *s* coincides with the arc of the meridian, *PAS*. If *s* is not a whole number of hours, the circle of Declination is judged by eye, using the divisions along the equator.

II. *To solve the same problem for the moment of solar time, t, on a given day*

Calculate the sidereal time *s*, corresponding to the solar time *t*, on the given day, and then proceed as for the previous problem.

III. *To determine the altitude of a heavenly body, at its upper and its lower culmination*

Set the globe to the given latitude and turn it about its axis until the heavenly body stands above the arc *PZS* for upper culmination or above the arc *PN* for lower culmination. The altitude of this position is measured along the circle of the meridian from the horizon to the heavenly body.

IV. *To determine the limits of the Declination of stars which do not rise, and of stars which do not set*

We set up the globe for the latitude. The minimum Declination of stars which do not set is the distance along the circle of the meridian from the equator to the point *N*. The maximum Declination of stars which do not rise is the distance along the circle of the meridian from the equator to the point *S*.

V. *To determine whether a given star is visible in a certain place*

Set up the globe for the latitude. Find the heavenly body on the globe, turn it and see if it ever rises above the horizon.

VI. *To determine the latitudes of places where a heavenly body is just visible*

Finding the body on the globe, set it under the circle of the meridian, and turn the circle of the meridian together with the globe until the body coincides with the point *S*. The altitude of the pole *P* then gives the desired latitude.

VII. *To study the diurnal motion of various heavenly bodies for a given geographical latitude*

Set the globe to the latitude, and turn it about its axis. This shows how stars move with respect to the horizon, the zenith, and so forth.

VIII. *To find the point on the celestial sphere where the Sun is situated on a given day*

Find the coordinates α and δ of the Sun from the ephemeris, and hence plot this point in the sky using the net of coordinates on the globe. If there is no ephemeris, then multiply 59' (the mean diurnal displacement of the Sun along the ecliptic) by the number of days from the 22nd March to the given day of the year. Measure this angle on the globe from the point of the Vernal Equinox, γ, anticlockwise along the ecliptic to find the Sun's position.

IX. *To transform equatorial coordinates of a heavenly body horizontal at a given latitude and time*

Set up the globe, as described in Problems I or II; with the clamp *R* at the point *Z*. Turn the arc *RQ* to pass through the body, and hence measure *h* and *A* from it.

X. *To determine the hour angle, the solar time, and the azimuths of the points of rising and setting of a star*

Set up the globe for the given latitude. Find the body on the globe and turn it about its axis until the body lies on the circle of the horizon, in either the rising or setting position. The azimuth of this point is measured along the circle of the horizon. To find the hour angle clamp *R* at the pole *P* and set *RQ* to pass through the point of rising or setting of the body. The hour angle is then

measured along the equator from A to its intersection with RQ.
Adding the hour angle obtained to the Right Ascension of the
body gives the sidereal time, s, of rising or setting, which may be
expressed in solar time by the usual calculation. Alternatively, we
can find the position of the Sun on the globe and measure its
hour angle at the moment of rising or setting under investigation.
The apparent local time of the rising and setting of the Sun itself
is given by the hour angle of the points of its rising and setting,
measured in the same way.

XI. *The conversion of α and δ of a body to λ and β (longitude
and latitude)*

Set the pole of the ecliptic, which is marked on the globe, under
the circle of the meridian. Fasten the clamp R above this point and
rotate the arc RQ so that it passes through the body, whose position is defined by α and δ. Without disturbing the globe measure
β, the distance of the body from the ecliptic, along the arc RQ.
λ is then measured anticlockwise along the ecliptic to its intersection with the arc RQ. It is important to keep the clamp of the
arc RQ above the pole of the ecliptic.

XII. *To determine the time of culmination of a body on a given
day*

Rotate the globe to set the body under the circle of the meridian.
The upper culmination takes place at the time $s = \alpha$, where α is
the Right Ascension of the body either given or calculated from
the net of coordinates on the globe, and s is expressed in solar
time, in the usual way. Alternatively, if we know the position of
the Sun at the time, then its hour angle measured on the globe
will give the solar time of the moment of culmination of the body.

XIII. *To find the sidereal time corresponding to the given mean
time*

Mark the point on the equator distant from γ, the point of the
Vernal Equinox, by 59′ times the number of days elapsed from the
22nd March. Turning the globe about its axis, bring this point to
a position where its hour angle is equal to the given mean time.

The corresponding stellar time is obtained by measuring to the arc A (the hour angle of the point of the Vernal Equinox) along the equator.

XIV. *To find the day when the Sun rises at a given time at a given latitude*

Set the globe for the latitude. Fix the clamp R above the pole P and the arc RQ at the given hour angle. The point of intersection of the arc RQ with the horizon is the point at which the Sun rises. Turning the globe, find the point on the ecliptic, which intersects the horizon at the point of sunrise which we have found. The required day of the year is computed as 22nd March plus the number of days equal to the arc of the ecliptic (measured anticlockwise from γ), divided by 59'. The second date with this time of sunrise is found by turning the globe until the ecliptic again cuts the horizon.

Many other problems may be solved by using a celestial globe as, for example, Problems 368, 369, 370 from the Chapter on Precession.

In place of the globe various graphical aids may be employed, such as Woolfs' net, or the nets of Kavraiski and others. The simplest of these aids, the systems of rotating circles and of celestial planispheres, are described by Kamen'schikov in his *Handbook of Astronomical Problems*. In general, however, these methods give rather inexact results.

_____

The following Problems, given earlier, may be solved with the celestial globe (remember that the globe gives less accurate answers than calculation):

II. *The Celestial Sphere:* 14, 20, 24, 25, 27–32.
III. *The Systems of Celestial Coordinates:* 36–45, 47, 54–74, 84–95.
IV. *The Culmination of Celestial Bodies:* 101–24, 126–8, 137–54, 161.
V.   *The Rising and Setting of Celestial Bodies:* 325–35, 339–46, 349–55.

CHAPTER XII

PLANETARY MOVEMENT

I

THE PLANETS move about the Sun in elliptical orbits. The ellipticity of these orbits and their inclinations to the ecliptic are usually so small that for the solution of many problems planetary orbits may be considered to be circular, lying in the plane of the ecliptic. The orbits of the planets Mercury and Venus lie within the orbit of the Earth: and they are known as the inner (or inferior) planets. The remaining planets are farther from the Sun than the Earth, and are known as the outer (or superior) planets. The distance of the Earth from the Sun, 149,500,000 km, is called one astronomical unit. Mercury is never visible farther than 27°, and Venus never farther than 48° from the Sun. Because of this these planets are visible either as morning or as evening stars in the east before sunrise or in the west after sunset.

The various defined positions of planets relative to the Earth and the Sun (planetary configurations) are shown in Fig. 15, in which the position of the Earth is marked by the letter T.

If we draw a straight line $S\gamma$ (Fig. 16) from the Sun in the direction of the point of the Vernal Equinox, then the angle γSP between the line $S\gamma$ and the direction of the planet from the Sun (SP), measured anticlockwise from $S\gamma$, is called the heliocentric longitude of the planet, and is denoted by the letter l.

In Fig. 15, if the heliocentric longitude of the Earth at T is denoted by the letter L, then for the inner planets,

> in inferior conjunction $l - L = 0°$,
> in superior conjunction $l - L = 180°$,
> in western elongation $l - L = 90° - \theta$,
> in eastern elongation $l - L = 270° + \theta$,

where θ is the greatest visible angular elongation of the planet from the Sun.

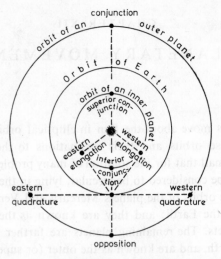

FIG. 15. Planetary configurations.

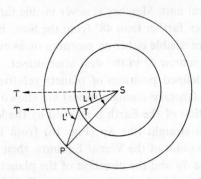

FIG. 16. The heliocentric and geocentric longitudes of a planet.

For the outer planets

$$\text{in opposition} \quad l-L = 0°,$$
$$\text{in conjunction} \quad l-L = 180°.$$

The angle γTP between the direction of a planet from the Earth and the point of the Vernal Equinox γ, measured anticlockwise, is called the geocentric longitude l' of the planet (Fig. 16). The angle l' is determined graphically in problems of this type in the following way. Two circles are drawn to scale to represent the orbits of the Earth and the planet, and $S\gamma$ fixed in an arbitrary direction. L and l then define the positions of the Earth and planet. $T\gamma$ is then drawn parallel to $S\gamma$ and l' measured by joining TP.

The heliocentric longitudes of the planets for given days of the year are published annually in the astronomical ephemeris.

If S is the period of revolution of a planet about the Sun (the sidereal period) and T is the length of its year, then P, the interval of time between two identical configurations of the planet (sinodical period), is given by the equations of sinodical movement:

$$\text{for the inner planets} \quad \frac{1}{S} - \frac{1}{T} = \frac{1}{P},$$

$$\text{for the outer planets} \quad \frac{1}{T} - \frac{1}{S} = \frac{1}{P},$$

P (for example, the interval of time between two superior conjunctions) may be found by observation.

The mean heliocentric angular velocity of a planet diminishes with its distance from the Sun, and is equal to $360° S$. The mean diurnal movements of the planets (mean angular displacement per day) are as follows:

Mercury 245'·5   Earth 59'·1   Jupiter 5'

Venus   96'·1   Mars 31'·4   Saturn 2'

Calculations made from these data are inaccurate, because in fact the planets move in ellipses with non-uniform velocities, and the planes of their orbits are slightly inclined to the ecliptic.

The motions of the planets are described by Kepler's laws as follows:

I. The planets move in elliptical orbits with the Sun as one of their principal foci.

II. The radius vector of a planet describes equal areas in equal periods of time.

III. The squares of the periods of the planets are proportional to the cubes of the semi-major axes of their orbits (i.e. their mean distances from the Sun), or

$$\frac{a_1^3}{a_2^3} = \frac{T_1^2}{T_2^2} \quad \text{or} \quad \frac{a_1^3}{T_1^2} = \frac{a_2^3}{T_2^2} = \text{constant.}$$

These equations hold also for the motions of satellites about their planets. Ellipses are the names given to closed curves, on which the sum of the distances of every point from the two points known as foci (S and F in Fig. 18) is constant. The elongation of an ellipse is characterized by the value of its eccentricity, e. If $e = 0$ then the orbit is a circle (a particular case of an ellipse). If $e = 1$, then the orbit is an infinitely elongated ellipse, or a parabola. In Fig. 18 the distance $OB = OA = a$ is known as the semi-major axis of the orbit and O is the centre of the ellipse. By definition

$$e = \frac{OS}{OA} = \frac{c}{a}.$$

The smallest distance of a planet from the Sun is $SB = a(1-e)$, and the greatest is $SA = a(1+e)$. The point B, the nearest to the Sun, is called the perihelion; the point A, the farthest from the Sun, is called the aphelion. The values of a and T for all the planets are given in Table X.

II

As the Earth moves about the Sun faster than the outer planets, there is a period near opposition when the apparent movement of an outer planet is reversed. Assuming circular orbits the length of arc of retrograde motion is given by

$$\phi = (360° - 2\theta_0) - 2n\tau,$$

where n is the mean diurnal motion of the planet, 2τ the duration of the retrograde motion in days and θ_0 the elongation of the planet at the stationary point. That is, θ_0 is the angle at the Earth between the directions of the planet and the Sun, when the planet appears stationary in the sky.

θ_0 is given by the formula

$$\tan \theta_0 = \frac{a \sin \phi_0}{a \cos \phi_0 + 1}, \quad \theta_0 < 180°$$

where a is the radius of the orbit in astronomical units. The angle ϕ_0 is found from the formula

$$\cos \phi_0 = \frac{na^2 + n_1^2}{na + n_1 a} = -\frac{na^2 + n_1^2}{a(n + n_1)},$$

where n_1 is the mean diurnal motion of the Earth.

An elliptical orbit is characterized by various elements whose significance is illustrated in Figs. 17 and 18. The orbital elements of the planets of the solar system are given in Table X.

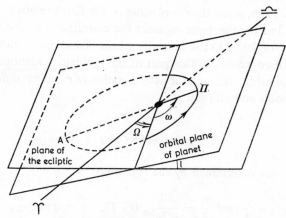

FIG. 17. Elements of planetary orbits.

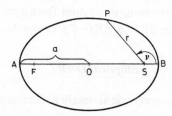

FIG. 18. The true anomaly v and the radius vector of a planet, r.

The sixth element T is one of the moments of passage of a celestial body through perihelion. For a parabolic orbit (approximated by comets) $e = 1$, $a = \infty$, and here the perihelion distance q — the distance of the apex of the parabola from its focus, the Sun — is given.

The Calculation of Ephemeris

We now show how to calculate the ephemeride or Table of orbital positions at different times, for a heavenly body. Generally, we tabulate r, the heliocentric distance, z, the geocentric distance, and coordinates α and δ (or λ and β) for various times t.

First the radius vector, r, and the true anomaly of the body, v, are found, determining its place in the orbit at the moment t_1 (Fig. 18). Then, given the coordinates of the Earth relative to the Sun, we find for the same moment the coordinates of the body (α, δ and ϱ) relative to the Earth by means of successive transformations of coordinates. This part of the problem is identical for all types of orbit, although the determination of r and v is different for parabolas and ellipses.

The Parabolic Orbit

r and v are determined by the equations

$$\tan \frac{v}{2} + \frac{1}{3} \tan^3 \frac{v}{2} = \frac{k}{\sqrt{2}q^{3/2}} (t-T), \quad r = q \sec^2 \frac{v}{2},$$

where k is the Gaussian constant (0·0172) and T is the moment of passage through perihelion. v is found from special Tables as a function of the value $M = q^{-3/2}(t-T)$, or $\log M$.

Elliptical Orbit

v is found from the eccentric anomaly E, determined by Kepler's equation

$$E - e \sin E = M$$

where the mean anomaly $M = n(t-T)$, and the mean diurnal movement $n = ka^{-3/2}$.

If e is nearly 0, E may be found by successive approximations, as follows:

$$E_0 = M + e \sin M,$$
$$E_1 = M + e \sin E_0,$$
$$E_2 = M + e \sin E_1$$

and so on, until $E_n - E_{n-1}$ is negligible. It must be remembered that in the Tables the values of sines are generally given for radians, whereas the values for E are found in degrees. This means that $e \sin E$ must be converted from radians to degrees, by multiplying by $360/2\pi$, or $57°\cdot2958$. For example, if $M = 45°$ and $e = 0\cdot66144$; $\log e = -0\cdot17951$, $\log 57\cdot2958 = 1\cdot75812$, and the logarithm of the coefficient of $\sin E$ is $1\cdot57861$. The number corresponding to this logarithm will be "e expressed in degrees". If e is large, then an approximate value for E can be found on the graph in Fig. 19. This is a sinusoid, where the ordinates are given in radians. In order to find E from a given M, taking the same values as above, note the point a on the axis of the abscissa which corresponds to the value of M ($45°$) and on the upper horizontal line find and note the point b, corresponding to $M + 100° \, e$ ($111\cdot1$). The intersection of the straight line ab with the curve at the point c gives an approximate value of E ($82'\cdot30$ in our example). If $M + 100° \, e$ does not fit in on the scale above, then it is possible to fit $M + 50 \, e$ on the "fiftieth line" or $M + 20° \, e$ on the "twentieth line" and proceed in an analogous manner. The value of E obtained graphically may be taken for E_0, and E determined by successive approximations, as above. We then find v from the equation

$$\tan \frac{v}{2} = \sqrt{\left(\frac{1+e}{1-e}\right)} \tan \frac{E}{2},$$

where v and E lie in the same quadrant, and we find r from the equation

$$r = a(1 - e \cos E).$$

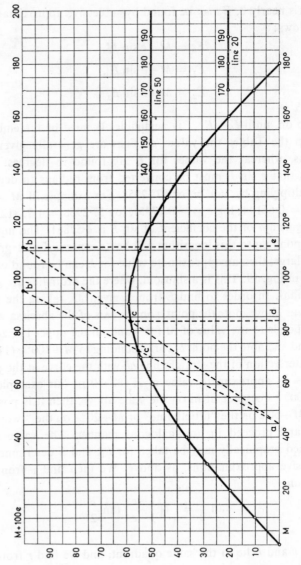

FIG. 19. Graph for an approximate solution of Kepler's equation.

The Calculation of α, δ and ϱ

We find the so-called Gaussian constants, a, b, c, A, B, C, from the auxiliary values n and N, and the inclination ε of the ecliptic:

$\tan N = \tan i \sec \Omega$ (the signs of $\sin N$ and $\sin i$ being the same),

$n = \sin i \operatorname{cosec} N$;

$\tan A = -\cot \Omega \sec i$ (the signs of $\sin A$ and $\cos \Omega$ being the same),

$a = \cos \Omega \operatorname{cosec} A$;

$\tan B = \sin \Omega \cos \varepsilon / n \cos (N+\varepsilon)$ (the signs of $\cos B$ and $\cos (N+\varepsilon)$ being the same),

$b = \sin \Omega \cos \varepsilon \operatorname{cosec} B$;

$\tan C = \sin \Omega \sin \varepsilon / n \sin (N+\varepsilon)$ (the signs of $\cos E$ and $\sin (N+\varepsilon)$ being the same),

$c = \sin \Omega \sin \varepsilon \operatorname{cosec} C$.

If the calculations are correct then

$$\tan i = \frac{bc \sin (C-B)}{a \cos A}, \text{ which may be used as a check.}$$

After this α, δ and ϱ are determined by the formulae

$$\tan \alpha = \frac{rb \sin (B+\omega+v)+Y_0}{ra \sin (A+\omega+v)+X_0}$$

$$\tan \delta = \frac{rc \sin (C+\omega+v)+Z_0}{rb \sin (B+\omega+v)+Y_0} \sin \alpha$$

$$\varrho = \operatorname{cosec} \delta \left(rc \sin (C+\omega+v)+Z_0\right)$$

where X_0, Y_0 and Z_0 are the rectangular geocentric coordinates of the Sun.

SECTION ONE PROBLEMS

381. How long would it take a train, travelling without stopping at 100 km/hr, to travel from the Earth to the orbit of Pluto?

382. To the inhabitants, if any, of Mars the solar disc has an angular diameter of 22′·7. Knowing that the linear radius of the

Sun is 109 Earth radii, find how long it takes the light of the Sun to reach Mars.

383. How long would it take to travel to Mars from the Earth in an interplanetary ship moving in an orbit, whose perihelion distance is the distance between the Earth and the Sun (1 astronomical unit), and whose aphelion distance is the distance between Mars and the Sun (1·5 astronomical units)? (Parenavo).

384. Is it possible for a transit of Mars across the solar disc to occur? Can it happen for Mercury or Jupiter?

385. Is it possible for Mercury to be visible in the evening in the east?

386. A planet is visible at a distance of 120° from the Sun. Is this planet superior or inferior?

*387. On the 19th May, 1937, an opposition of Mars occurred. In which constellation was it visible? In 1937 Venus was at her greatest evening elongation from the Sun on the 5th February. In which constellation was it situated?

*388. At what time of the year is the visibility of Mercury best in the evening?

*389. Two small planets appear simultaneously on a photograph at a distance of 3° from each other, leaving elongated traces on the negative due to their movement relative to the stars during exposure. If the traces are of unequal length, which planet is probably closer to the Earth and to the Sun?

390. By how much (in angular measure) does the Earth gain on Mars per day, viewed from the Sun? (The sidereal periods of revolution of these planets are 365·25 and 687 days, respectively.)

391. Is it possible for Mars to approach to the minimum distance from the Earth annually, that is, to be in opposition every year?

392. Determine the sidereal period of the revolution of Mars, given that its sinodic period is 780 days.

393. The sinodic period of revolution of an imaginary planet is 3 yr. What is the sidereal period of its revolution about the Sun?

394. What is the sidereal period of revolution of a planet whose sinodic period is 4 yr?

395. What are the lengths of the sidereal and sinodic periods of revolution of a planet, in a case when they are equal?

396. An opposition of Jupiter occurred on 15th June, 1937. When was the next occasion on which it happened?

*397. An observer notices that a certain planet moves to 90° east of the Sun every $505\frac{1}{4}$ days. What is the period of its revolution about the Sun?

398. An optimum evening visibility of Venus (at its maximum distance east of the Sun) was on the 5th February, 1937. When was the next occasion for optimum visibility of Venus under these conditions, if the sidereal period of the revolution of Venus about the Sun is 225 days?

399. The conditions of visibility of Venus are repeated every 8 yr, almost to the same day of the month. What is the reason for this phenomenon? (Polak.)

400. Find the mean diurnal movement of Mercury in its orbit, if its sinodic period is 115·88 mean days.

*401. To the imaginary inhabitants of Mars, the Earth, like Venus, appears as a morning and evening star. At what intervals of time is it possible to see the Earth, from Mars, as a morning star?

*402. Knowing the distance of the planets from the Sun, calculate the greatest angular separation of the Earth from the Sun, observable from Mars.

403. Calculate the greatest angular separation of the Earth and Moon seen by an observer on Mars during a mean opposition, given the distances from the Earth to the Moon and to Mars. (Polak.)

*404. The distance of Jupiter from the Sun is 5·20 astronomical units. What is the greatest elongation of the Earth (in degrees) observed from Jupiter, when the Earth is a morning or evening star?

405. The orbits of the Earth and Mars are ellipses. The orbit of Mars is noticeably elongated, so that oppositions of Mars take place at various distances between the two planets. When opposition occurs at the position of the nearest approach of the orbit, the distance to Mars (55,000,000 km) is half as great as at the least favourable opposition, and this is the best time to examine Mars through a telescope. How often do these optimum, or "great" oppositions, of Mars occur, if the period of its revolution about the Sun is 1·88 yr?

Hint. Make use of the properties of continued fractions. (Perel'man.)

406. Determine the date of the opposition of Jupiter nearest to the 1st January, 1938, knowing that on that date the heliocentric longitude of Jupiter was 306°55', and of the Earth 99°55'.

407. Determine the dates of the conjunction of Jupiter with the Sun in 1938 and 1939, knowing that the heliocentric longitudes of Jupiter and the Earth on the 1st January, 1938 were 306°55' and 99°55', respectively.

Hint. During superior conjunction the difference in the heliocentric longitudes of the planets and the Earth is equal to $(2n+1)\,180°$ $(n = 0, 1, 2, \ldots)$. The mean diurnal movement of a planet is given in the introduction to these exercises. Using this, establish and solve an equation similar to that in Problem 406.

408. Find the first day after the 1st January, 1938, when the inferior conjunction of Venus and the Sun occurred, given that the heliocentric longitudes of Venus and the Earth on the 1st January, 1938, were 260°40' and 99°55', respectively.

Hint. Establish and solve an equation, using the fact that at the moment of inferior conjunction the difference in the heliocentric longitude of Venus and the Earth is equal to 0°, 360°, or in general to $2\,n\,180°$.

409. Calculate the day nearest to the 1st January, 1938, of the easterly elongation of Venus, when it was visible in the evening, and determine the position of Venus in the sky at the moment of this elongation. Heliocentric longitudes for the 1st January, 1938 are, Venus 260°40', Earth 99°55'.

Hint. Set up and solve the equation bearing in mind that at easterly elongation the difference in the heliocentric longitudes of the Earth and Venus is $360° - 43° = 317°$, or in general ($2\ n\ 180° - 43°$). The mean diurnal movements of the planets are given in the introduction to this section.

410. Determine the date nearest the 1st January, 1938, on which the morning visibility of Venus will be optimum given that on that day the heliocentric longitude of the Earth is 99°55′, and of Venus 260°40′.

411. The heliocentric longitude of the Earth on the 1st January, 1937 is 100°, and that of Mars is 172°49′. Determine the position of Mars in the sky on the 1st May, 1937, and on the 1st May, 1939.

Hint. Determine first the true positions of the Earth and Mars in their orbits on the 1st May, given their mean diurnal movement, and then with the help of a sketch and a protractor determine the heliocentric longitude of Mars. Using a star map or a globe indicate the constellation in which Mars is situated at the given moment.

412. The heliocentric longitudes of Jupiter and the Earth on the 1st July, 1937 were 291° and 279°. Determine the visible position of Jupiter in the sky on the 1st September. Was it visible in Leningrad on that evening?

*****413.** If the orbits of the Moon about the Earth, and the Earth about the Sun are circular, is there a change in the velocity of the Moon relative to the Sun?

414. Find the points at which the rate of change in distance of a planet from the Sun is greatest, and least.

415. What is the apparent angular velocity of Mars (forward) at conjunction, and (retrograde) at opposition?

416. With what apparent angular velocity does the angular separation of Venus from the Sun change near the time of superior conjunction? The sinodic period of revolution of Venus is 584 days, and its distance from the Sun is 0·72 astronomical units.

417. With what apparent angular velocity does Venus transit the disc of the Sun during its passage? How long does its passage across the disc of the Sun last, if it is central? The distance of Venus from the Sun is 0·723 astronomical units; the sinodical period of the revolution of Venus is 584 days. The diameter of the Sun is 32′ (1/675 of a revolution).

418. Determine the distance, R, of Venus from the Sun in astronomical units, if the angle of its maximum elongation is 47°.

Hint. Take the orbit of the planet as circular. Draw up a plan of the orbits of the planets, and Venus in elongation.

419. Taking the orbit of Mercury as circular, calculate its mean distance from the Sun, given that, at its mean elongation, Mercury is 23° away from the Sun.

***420.** Determine the distance of Jupiter from the Sun in astronomical units, given the following data: In 1925 an opposition of Jupiter occurred on the 10th July. 11 yr and 315 days later (the sidereal period of the revolution of Jupiter) the geocentric difference of the longitudes of Jupiter and the Sun are established by observation as $\Delta l = 120°$.

421. Verify Kepler's Third Law for the Earth and for Neptune ($a = 30.07$ astronomical units, $T = 164.8$ yr).

422. How long would a planet take to revolve about the Sun if it were 100 astronomical units away?

423. The asteroid Pallada is on the average 2.77 times farther from the Sun than is the Earth. How long does it take to complete a revolution about the Sun?

424. What is the mean heliocentric distance of a minor planet whose period of revolution about the Sun is 8 yr?

425. The asteroid Vesta completes a full revolution about the Sun in 3.63 yr. What is its mean distance from the Sun in astronomical units?

426. What would be the sinodic period of a planet whose sidereal period of revolution about the Sun is 370 days? How close would it approach to the Earth?

Hint. The sidereal period of revolution of the Earth may be taken as 365 days, and the orbits may be considered circular.

***427.** An observer notices that a certain planet is in opposition every $665\frac{1}{4}$ days. What is its distance from the Sun in astronomical units?

***428.** What would be the semi-major axis of the orbit of a planet, whose sinodic period was 1 yr?

429. What are the limits of mean heliocentric distance of planets with a sinodic period longer than two years?

430. The period of revolution of the innermost satellite of Saturn—Mimas—is 23 hr, and of the sixth satellite—Titan—15 days, 23 hr. What relationship is there between their mean distances from Saturn?

431. The third satellite of Jupiter revolves about the planet at a distance 14·9 planetary radii, in 7 days, 3 hr 7 min. How long does the revolution of the fifth satellite take, if its distance from Jupiter is 2·52 planetary radii? What is the period of the eighth satellite, at 328 radii?

432. What is the eccentricity of the orbit of a planet, if its movement through orbit is to be uniform? (Nabokov and Vorontsov–Velyaminov.)

433. The semi-major axis of the orbit of a certain planet is equal to four astronomical units, and its eccentricity is zero. What is the length of the semi-minor axis of the orbit?

SECTION TWO PROBLEMS

434. A very bright star-like object was visible at about 7 o'clock in the evening of 1st April, exactly in the point of East. Was this a planet or a star, and on what do you base your conclusion?

435. The mean distance of Venus from the Sun is 0·72 astronomical units. Determine the greatest altitude, h, at which it can be seen, at a place of latitude ϕ at the moment of sunset, and indicate the time of year when this phenomenon occurs.

Hint. Take the orbit of Venus as circular, having an inclination of 0°.

*436. To what limits do the sinodic periods of the planets tend, as their sidereal periods of revolution tend towards infinity?

*437. Taking the orbits of the planets as circular, relate the distance between the Earth and a planet (the radii of their orbits being l and a) with the angle ϕ at the Sun between the radius vectors of the Earth and the planet. (This angle is in fact the difference between the heliocentric longitudes of the Earth and the planet.)

*438. If the orbits of the planets are circular and lie in the same plane, determine the diurnal movement in the celestial sphere at opposition of a hypothetical planet whose orbital radius is 40 astronomical units.

439. Find the connection between the periods of forward and retrograde movement of a planet for one of its sinodic revolutions P. (Kazakov.)

440. Given the distance of Jupiter from the Sun, calculate in degrees the length of arc of the retrograde movement of the planet.

441. Establish the relationship between the distance a of planets from the Sun and their mean angular velocity ω, supposing their orbits to be circular.

442. Establish the relationship between the mean linear velocity v, of the movements of planets, and their mean distances a from the Sun, supposing their orbits to be circular.

443. Suppose that the satellites of Mars, Phobos and Deimos describe circular orbits, with periods of 7 hr 39 min 13·85 sec and 30 hr 17 min 54·86 sec. Use Kepler's Third Law to determine the greatest angular separation of Phobos and Deimos at the time of opposition, if the greatest separation of Deimos is $1'23\cdot1''$.

444. In the novel *Hector Severdac*, Jules Verne describes the imaginary comet "Gallia", which has a period of revolution about the Sun of 2 yr, and a distance from the Sun at aphelion of 820,000,000 km. With the help of Kepler's Third Law check whether such a comet could exist. (Perelman.)

445. How does the period of revolution of a planet change if its semi-major axis is increased by the small quantity Δa?

446. The eccentricity of a comet's orbit e is 0·9, and its period T is 1000 yr. What are the distances of this comet from the Sun at perihelion and aphelion?

447. The eccentricity of the orbit of Mercury is equal to 0·2 of the semi-major axis, which is 0·4 astronomical units. What is the greatest and the least possible distance of the planet from the Earth in kilometres? Assume the Earth's orbit to be circular.

*448. Draw a sketch to scale in projection on the plane of the ecliptic the orbits of the Earth, and of a heavenly body having the elements $a = 2$ (in astronomical units), $e = 0.8$, $i = 7°$, $\Omega = 30°$, $\omega = 45°$.

Hint. Disregard the inclination of the orbits on the plane of the ecliptic.

*449. Draw, in projection on the plane of the ecliptic, the orbit of an astronomical body, having the elements $a = 1.5$, $i = 90°$, $\Omega = 45°$, $e = 0$. Draw the orbit of the Earth for comparison, in the same plane, on the same scale.

*450. Construct a diagram showing the orbit of the Earth, and the projection on the plane of the ecliptic of the orbit of a heavenly body having the elements: $i = 0°$, $\pi = 45°$, $e = 0.5$, $a = 1.5$. π is the angle between the directions of the point of the Vernal Equinox and the perihelion, from the Sun.

*451. Show in projection on the plane of the ecliptic the orbit of the periodic comet Enck, which has the elements: $i = 13°$, $q = 0.34$, $\Omega = 335°$, $\omega = 184°$, $e = 0.85$. Disregard the inclination of the orbit. On the same plan, draw for comparison the orbit of the planet nearest to the Sun, keeping the same scales.

*452. Draw the projection on the plane of the ecliptic of the parabolic orbit of a heavenly body, having the elements $i = 1°$, $q = 0.25$, $\Omega = 90°$, $\omega = 15°$. The inclination of the orbits to the ecliptic may be neglected. For comparison draw to scale the orbit of the Earth. Determine from the plan the distances of this body from the Earth on the 22nd June, if on that day the true anomaly of the body was $30°$; and if it was $-120°$.

453. Show that

$$\cos v = \frac{\cos E - e}{1 - e \cos E} \quad \text{and} \quad \sin v = \frac{(1-e)^{\frac{1}{2}} \sin E}{1 - e \cos E}$$

where v is the true, and E the eccentric, anomaly, and e is the eccentricity.

454. Solve by graphical methods Kepler's equation

$$E + 0.7 \sin E = 214°0'.$$

455. Calculate the exact value of the eccentric anomaly for $M = 47.3°$ and $e = 0.96713$, if its approximate value for $e = 0.96$ is 101.3.

456. Calculate the eccentric anomaly E for Mars 200 days after its passage through perihelion, using the following data: $e = 0.093$, and the period of revolution, $P = 687$ days.

457. Calculate the eccentric anomaly E of a minor planet 22·5 days after its passage through perihelion. The value of e is 0·02947 and the mean diurnal movement is $n = 14·678'$. Solve the problem directly by employing the method of successive approximation.

458. The orbit of a comet has the following elements:

semi-major axis $a = 4$ astronomical units;
eccentricity $e = 0.66144$.

Determine the true anomaly, v, and the radius vector, r, of the comet a year after its passage through perihelion.

459. The orbit of a comet has the elements:

period of revolution $P = 2$ yr;
eccentricity $e = 0.66144$.

Determine the radius vector r, and the true anomaly v of the comet a year after its passage through perihelion.

460. The orbit of a comet has the elements:

period of revolution, $P = 3$ yr;
eccentricity $e = 0.66144$.

Determine its true anomaly v, and the radius vector, r, a year after its passage through perihelion.

461. Calculate the radius vector r, and the true anomaly v of a minor planet corresponding to the value of its eccentric anomaly $E = 60°4'·5$ if for its orbit log $a = 0.4603$, $e = 0.04625$.

462. Calculate the radius vector r, and the true anomaly v of a comet whose orbit has the elements:

$a = 2.645$ and
$e = 0.2453$

for the moment when the mean anomaly $M = 332°28'·9$.

Hint. Employ the graph given in Fig. 19 (p. 88) and improve the value of the eccentric anomaly by means of successive approximations.

463. Calculate the true anomaly v and the radius vector r of a comet 63·32 days after its passage through perihelion, if the orbit is parabolic and log $q = 0$·04411. Determine the true anomaly by means of interpolation on the basis of the values of log M given below, corresponding to determined values of v:

v	61°15′	61°16′	61°17′
log. M	1·73523	1·73540	1·73558

464. Find v and r for a comet 36·55 days from its passage through perihelion moving in a parabolic orbit with a perihelion distance of log $q = 9$·5191 using the values of v and log M given below:

v	109°15′	109°16′	109°17′
log. M	2·28410	2·28434	2·28458

465. Given the elements for the minor planet Evdora (No. 217):

$$T_0 = 1880, \text{ Sept. } 1\cdot50 \qquad = 11°19'\cdot8$$
$$M_0 = 19°21'\cdot8 \qquad e = 0\cdot3713$$
$$\Omega = 164°9'\cdot3 \qquad \log a = 0\cdot4955$$
$$\omega = 136°46'\cdot4 \qquad n = 640''\cdot89$$

The equatorial right-angled geocentric coordinates of the Sun are as follows:

	X	Y	Z
September 1·5	0·9466	0·3192	0·1385
5·5	0·9670	0·2594	0·1126
9·5	0·9829	0·1985	0·0861

Calculate the ephemerides of the planet (r, ϱ, α and δ) for the year 1880 on September 1·5, 5·5 and 9·5.

466. The elements of a parabolic cometary orbit are as follows:

$$T = 1881 \text{ June } 16\cdot489 \qquad i = 63°28'\cdot7$$
$$\omega = 354°15'\cdot9 \qquad \log q = 9\cdot8658$$
$$\text{equatorial } \Omega = 270°58'\cdot0 \qquad \varepsilon = 23°27'\cdot3$$

The rectangular equatorial geocentric coordinates of the Sun taken from the almanac are as follows:

	X	Y	Z
June 23·5	0·0448	0·9317	0·4042
24·5	0·0617	0·9309	0·4039
25·5	0·0786	0·9299	0·4034

Calculate the ephemerides (ϱ, α, and δ) of the comet for 1881 on June 23·5, 24·5 and 25·5. In the Tables giving the values of log M for the function v we find

v	log M	v	log M	v	log M
15°21′	1·047712	17°28′	1·10478	19°34′	1·15583
15°22′	1·047600	17°29′	1·10520	19°35′	1·15621

PARALLAX AND ABERRATION

I

The Horizontal Equatorial Parallax

p_0 is the angle subtended by R, the equatorial radius of the earth, perpendicular to the line of vision from a distant extraterrestrial point. If the distance to the point is D, then we have

$$D = R/\sin p_0.$$

For the Moon the mean parallax $p_0 = 57'$, for the Sun the mean parallax $p_0 = 8''\cdot80$. If the parallax is expressed in seconds of arc, then we may put

$$D = \frac{R}{p_0 \sin 1''} = \frac{206\,265 \times R}{p_0},$$

and we see that the parallax is inversely proportional to the distance of the extraterrestrial observer.

If the visible angular radius of a body is ϱ, its linear radius r and its parallax p_0, then

$$r = D \sin \varrho = \frac{\sin \varrho}{\sin p_0} R,$$

or for small angles

$$r = \frac{\varrho}{p_0} R.$$

The annual parallax π is the angle subtended by the semi-major axis of the Earth's orbit perpendicular to the line of sight at a point outside the solar system. For the star closest to us (α Centauri) the annual parallax is $0''\cdot75$. If we denote the distance to the star by D, and the semi-major axis of the Earth's orbit by a, then

$$D = \frac{a}{\sin \pi}$$

or for small angles

$$D = \frac{206\,265}{\pi''}\, a,$$

where π'' is π expressed in seconds of arc. The distance corresponding to $\pi = 1''$ is called a parsec.

Thus

$$D = \frac{1}{\pi''} \text{ in parsec.}$$

(Exercises on annual parallax also appear in Chapter XXIV.)

II

The diurnal parallax P is the angle subtended by the radius of the Earth at the distance of an external body. It thus changes in the course of a day, depending on the zenith distance, z, of the body:

$$p = p_0 \sin z.$$

A zenith distance, calculated for an observer at the centre of the Earth, is called geocentric. It is always smaller than its observed value on the Earth's surface.

The horizontal equatorial parallax of the Sun, p_0, is usually determined by indirect methods. For example, the horizontal equatorial parallax of a minor planet p_M, is found during its opposition, and then:

$$p_0 = p_M \left(\frac{a'}{a} - 1 \right),$$

if the opposition occurred when the Earth was at a mean distance of a and the minor planet at a' from the Sun. Other methods of determining the parallax of the Sun are described in the text of the Problems.

The annual aberration is the apparent displacement of the stars from their normal positions on the celestial sphere in the direction of the movement of the Earth. The aberration is caused by the combination of the orbital velocity v of the earth and the velocity c of the light from the stars. Thus, as the Earth revolves about the Sun, all stars describe ellipses in the sky with semi-major axes $20''\cdot5$ and semi-minor axes $20''\cdot5 \sin \beta$, where β is the latitude of the star.

The angle $\alpha = 20''\cdot5$ is determined by the relationship $\tan \alpha = v/c$ and is called the constant of aberration.

SECTION ONE PROBLEMS

467. How long does it take a ray of light to travel from the Sun to the Earth?

468. The diameter of the Moon is $0\cdot27$ the diameter of the Earth. Ignoring the distance from the Earth to the Moon, determine the horizontal parallax of the Sun for an observer situated on the Moon. (Nabokov and Vorontsov–Vel'yaminov.)

469. What is the horizontal parallax of Mars, when this planet is closest to the Earth ($0\cdot378$ astronomical units)? The horizontal parallax of the Sun is $8''\cdot80$.

470. What is the greatest diameter of the Earth seen from Mars at a distance of $0\cdot378$ astronomical units?

471. Neptune is situated at a distance of 30 astronomical units from the Sun. What is its horizontal parallax at its mean distance from the Earth? What is the annual parallax of Neptune?

472. What is the horizontal parallax of Jupiter when it is 6 astronomical units from the Earth?

473. At the moment of opposition Jupiter is 628,000,000 km from the Earth, and its angular diameter is then $47''\cdot2$. Determine from this the linear diameter of the planet.

474. The closest approach of Venus to the Earth is 40,000,000 km at which time the angular radius of Venus is $32''\cdot4$. Determine from these data the linear diameter of the planet.

475. Given that the horizontal diurnal parallax of the Moon is $57'2''\cdot7$, and that its angular radius is $15'32''\cdot6$ calculate the distance to the Moon, and its linear radius expressed as a function of Earth radii. Calculate also its surface area and volume in comparison with those of the Earth.

476. The equatorial horizontal parallax of the Sun is $8''\cdot80$ with a maximum error of $\pm0''\cdot01$. Indicate, as a percentage, and in kilometers, the accuracy with which the distance of the Sun can be determined from this.

477. The parallax of the Sun is $8''\cdot8$, and the visible radius of the Sun is $16''\cdot1$. How many times is the radius of the Sun greater than that of the Earth? What is the solar radius in kilometres?

*478. What would be the angle of elongation of the Earth from the Sun, if it were observed from the star nearest to us, α Centauri, the parallax of which is $0''\cdot75$? Could it be resolved from the Sun, with a telescope having an objective of 1 m, ignoring brightness considerations?

Hint. See the introduction to Chapter XVIII.

*479. By how much would the pattern of the stars and constellations visible to the naked eye, change if they were observed from Pluto?

480. What is the annual parallax of the Sun? What is the distance from the Earth to the Sun in parsecs?

SECTION TWO PROBLEMS

481. What is the parallax of the Moon at a latitude of $35°$?

482. At the moment of culmination the observed zenith distance of the centre of the Sun was $50°0'\cdot0$. Correct this observation for the effects of refraction and parallax.

483. The observed zenith distance z of the upper edge of the full Moon is $64°55'33''$, and the apparent radius of the Sun is $15'51''$. Making the necessary corrections for refraction and parallax, find the geocentric z' of the centre of the Sun.

484. By how much is the horizontal polar parallax of the Moon less than its horizontal equatorial parallax? The same for the Sun? (see Chapter XIV).

485. The centre of the Earth, the centre of the Moon (which has a visible radius of $16'$) and a distant star lie on a straight line in the equatorial plane. From what latitude on the meridian of the Moon's culmination will the star be visible to a terrestrial observer? The parallax of the Moon is 57'. (Polak.)

*486. Does the diurnal parallax of the Moon have an effect on its apparent angular diameter?

487. On the 7th January, 1904, the angular radius of the Moon was found to be $\varrho = 16'\cdot20$, and its parallax $p = 59'51''$. Determine the angular radius of the Moon when its parallax was $p = 3422''$.

---

488. Show that the difference in the apparent position of the Sun caused by parallax for two observers simultaneously observing it from two points has its maximum of $2p_0$.

*489. The minor planet Adonis can approach to within 15,000,000 km of the Earth, and its parallax can be measured to an accuracy of $0''\cdot05$. What is the maximum error in the calculation of the parallax of the Sun from these data?

*490. Is it possible to use the measurement of the parallax of Jupiter or of other superior planets, to determine the distance of the Earth from the Sun?

*491. It is observed that the eclipses of the satellites of Jupiter, which should repeat themselves at equal intervals of time, actually take place increasingly later relative to theoretical prediction, as Jupiter crosses from the point of opposition to the Sun to the point of conjunction. After this the delay diminishes until at the next conjunction the theoretical and observed times of the eclipses again coincide. The greatest value of this delay caused by the change in the distance between the Earth and Jupiter, is 998 sec, with a possible error of 4 sec. From these data and knowing the speed of light from laboratory experiments, determine the distance from the Earth to the Sun.

*492. Determine the distance from the Earth to the Sun, and its parallax, given that the constant aberration is $20''\cdot47$, the speed of light is 299,774 km/sec and the equatorial radius of the Earth is 6378·4 km.

*493. How is it possible to determine the velocity of the Earth in its orbit from observation of the radial velocity of a star lying in the plane of the ecliptic?

*494. Given that the observed radial velocity of all stars lying on the ecliptic oscillates in the course of a year between the limits of ± 30 km/sec, determine the distance from the Earth to the Sun.

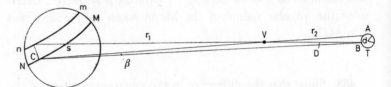

FIG. 20. Determination of the parallax of the Sun from the observation of the passage of Venus across the Sun's disc.

*495. On the 3rd June, 1769, the parallax of the Sun was determined by Galileo's method, observing the passage of Venus across the disc of the Sun. In Varda (Sweden) the passage lasted for 5 hr 53 min 14 sec and in the islands of Tahiti 5 hr 30 min 4 sec. In Fig. 20, s is the centre of the Sun, M, N and m, n are chords described by Venus (V) across the disc of the Sun for observers situated on the Earth at the points A and B. The chords are taken as rectilinear, and the diameter of the Sun as 32′. From the figure it can be seen that $D/\beta = r_1/r_2$ where r_1 is the distance from the Sun to Venus, and r_2 is the distance from Venus to the Earth. By Kepler's Third Law $r_1/r_2 = 72/28$. It follows that the parallax of the Sun is

$$p = \beta \frac{r}{d} = D \frac{28}{72} \frac{r}{d},$$

where r is the radius of the Earth, and d is the length of the base AB. In the given case the length of the base must be determined, finding the two points of observation on a map. To find the chords MN and mn, which are required for the calculation of D, the angular velocity of the movement of Venus across the disc of the Sun can be taken as 240″/hr. Determine from these data the parallax of the Sun, correct to three significant figures.

496. Why do we use Venus and not Mercury to determine the parallax of the Sun by Galileo's method?

497. What error in the determination of the distance to the Sun D, is caused by an error of 1 per cent in the value of the ratio of the mass of the Earth to the mass of the Sun in the dynamical method of determination of the solar parallax? The formula for this method is

$$D^3 = \left(\frac{M+1}{4\pi^2}\right) f T^2 r,$$

where M is the mass of the Sun in terms of Earth masses, f is the gravitational constant, T the number of seconds in the year, and r the radius of the Earth.

*498. At the moment when the Moon enters its first quarter the angle SME (see Fig. 21) between the directions from the Moon M

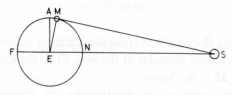

FIG. 21. Aristarchus' method for the determination of the distance to the Sun.

to the Sun S and the Earth E is equal to 90°. Knowing from observation that the period from new Moon to the first quarter is approximately 0·6 hr less than that from the first quarter to the full Moon, and knowing the sinodic period of revolution of the Moon, estimate the distance from the Earth to the Sun in comparison with its distance from the Moon.

AE in Fig. 21 is perpendicular to ES. This method was employed in the third century B.C. by the Greek astronomer Aristarchus in the first comparison of the distances to the Moon and to the Sun. However, he erroneously adopted the given difference in time as 12 hr and obtained a very inaccurate result. What was Aristarchus' result? By how many times is the Sun farther than the Moon, if the true value of this time interval is employed?

*499. Fig. 22, taken from Copernicus' book, presents a plan explaining the method used by Aristarchus to determine the distance to the Moon (M), in terms of the radius of the Earth (KE) knowing that the angular radii of the Sun and the Moon are 15′, and angular radius of the Earth's shadow at the distance of the Moon (determined at an eclipse of the Moon), $MR = 40′$ and that $DK/KM = 390$. (Aristarchus erroneously obtained a value of 19 for this ratio.) Re-employ Aristarchus' method and

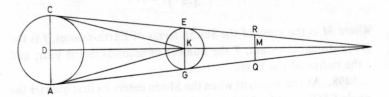

FIG. 22. Aristarchus' method for the determination of the distance to the Moon.

determine the distance KM from the Earth to the Moon. On the diagram, CA is the diameter of the Sun, EG is the diameter of the Earth, and M is the Moon.

500. Which methods of determining the distance from the Earth to the Sun do not demand a knowledge of the dimensions of the Earth?

SECTION TWO PROBLEMS

(ABERRATION)

501. A star has an astronomical latitude $\beta = 0$. At what points in the Earth's orbit is the aberrational displacement of this star zero? (Scherbakov.)

502. Let the positions of a star on its aberrational ellipse be P and Q when the Sun is at perihelion and at aphelion. Using Kepler's Law of Area show that the true position R of the star on the straight line PQ is such that $PR/RQ = (1+e)/(1-e)$ where e is the eccentricity of the Earth's orbit.

Hint. See the text of Problems 712 or 713.

*503. Imagine that the Earth moves about the Sun in a circle at a non-constant velocity. Would the aberrational orbits of a star situated at the pole of the ecliptic be circular?

504. The diurnal revolution of the Earth also produces an aberration, the so-called diurnal aberration. Calculate its value at the equator, where the linear speed of rotation is 0·464 km/sec. What would be the diurnal aberration at one of the poles of the Earth?

*505. Show that for an observer at latitude ϕ all stars under the influence of diurnal aberration describe an ellipse with the semi-major axis

$$\frac{2\pi R}{c} \cos \phi,$$

where R is the radius of the Earth in kilometres and c is the speed of light in km/day.

*506. Calculate the maximum diurnal aberration of a star, at latitude ϕ. In which position of the stars and on which of the equatorial coordinates, α and δ, does this aberration have its greatest effect?

CHAPTER XIV

THE EARTH

THE EARTH moves about the Sun in an ellipse. It is in perihelion on about the 2nd January, and in aphelion on about the 4th July. As the eccentricity of the orbit is very small, the change in temperature due to this phenomenon is negligible. The inclination of the Sun's rays at the surface of the Earth is the prime cause of temperature and climatic conditions on the Earth. From Kepler's Law (faster in perihelion, slower in aphelion), we see that the lengths of the seasons are not equal. The semi-major axis of the Earth's orbit revolves slowly in space, so that the dates of perihelion and aphelion drift slowly with time.

Evidence for the movement of the Earth about the Sun are the phenomena of annual parallax and annual aberration. The deviation of a freely falling body towards the West, and the rotation of the plane of oscillation of a free pendulum towards the West (Foucault's experiment) may be taken as evidence for the rotation of the Earth about its axis. The magnitude of the deviation of a falling body towards the West in millimetres is $0.022\ h\sqrt{h}$ cos ϕ, where ϕ is the latitude of the place of observation and h is the height of the fall in metres. The plane of oscillation of Foucault's pendulum rotates through an angle of $15° \sin \phi$ in an hour.

The curvature of the Earth is demonstrated by the change in the distance, D, to the line of the horizon seen by observers at different heights h above the surface of the Earth, in the formula

$$D = 3.57 \sqrt{h}$$

or, allowing for refraction by the Earth's atmosphere

$$D = 3.80 \sqrt{h}$$

where D is expressed in kilometers, and h in metres. In addition to this the visible horizon falls below the astronomical one by a value x, called the depression of the horizon:

$$x = 1.93' \sqrt{h},$$

or taking refraction into account

$$x = 1.80' \sqrt{h}.$$

These values are proportionally related to the Earth's radius, R, as

$$\frac{x}{360°} = \frac{D}{2\pi R}.$$

To determine the Earth's radius, R, the length of arc of the meridian S is measured between two points whose latitudes ϕ_1 and ϕ_2 are determined by astronomical observation. It is obvious that

$$\frac{S}{2\pi R} = \frac{\phi_1 - \phi_2}{360°}$$

whence we obtain R. The arc S is measured by means of a method known as triangulation. A relatively short line, the base, is measured directly and then the angles with the base of the lines of sight of a distant (terrestrial) object. Using a series of triangles, any arc length can be measured fairly well, and by means of such measurements the flattening of the Earth at the poles was discovered. The flattening may be characterized by the ratio of oblateness, $\dfrac{(a-b)}{a}$, where a and b are the equatorial and polar radii of the body. For the Earth the ratio is $\dfrac{1}{298}$. This oblateness is caused by the centrifugal force of the rotation of the Earth. For a body of mass m, the centrifugal force is equal to

$$J = m\omega^2 r,$$

where ω is the angular velocity, and r the distance from the axis of rotation. The centrifugal force acts against the gravitational attraction of bodies towards the centre of the Earth. The acceleration g due to the force of gravity may be computed by determining the period T of oscillation of a free pendulum.

For a mathematical pendulum

$$T = 2\pi \sqrt{l/g},$$

where l is the length of the pendulum. At latitude ϕ we expect the centrifugal acceleration of a body to be

$$g = g_{90} - \omega^2 R \cos^2 \phi,$$

where g_{90} is the acceleration due to gravity at the poles. At latitude $45°$ at sea level this gives $g = 980 \cdot 6$ cm/sec^2. However, observed values of g differ from this showing an even greater change with latitude. This can be explained if the surface of the Earth is ellipsoidal as the acceleration of gravity is inversely proportional to the square of the distance to the Earth's centre. Klero deduced the following formula for the compression ratio of the Earth:

$$\frac{5}{2} \frac{j_0}{g_0} - \frac{g_{90} - g_0}{g_0},$$

where g_{90} and g_0 refer to the poles and the equator, and j_0 is the centrifugal acceleration at the equator. There still remain small differences between the observed and calculated values of g, which are explained by the inequality of the distribution of masses about the surface of the Earth (the anomaly of gravity), and the divergence of the form of the Earth from that of a true ellipsoid with two axes.

A plumb-line does not always give the direction of the centre of the Earth, because the Earth is not spherical, and a line perpendicular to its surface in general does not pass through its centre. The angle between the radius of the Earth at a point and the plane of the equator is called the *geocentric latitude*.

The angle between the plane of the equator and the normal (perpendicular) to the surface of the Earth is called the geodesic, or geographical, latitude. The latitude determined by the observation of the altitude of the pole is called the astronomical latitude, and corresponds to the angle between the plane of the equator and a plumb-line.

The form of the Earth diverges slightly from that of an ellipsoid of rotation, and its true form is known as a *Geoid*. The axis of the Earth changes its position slightly in the body of the Earth. This has been discovered by systematic determinations of the latitudes of observatories, which appear to change, although only within very small limits. Figure 23 shows the drift in position of the poles over a period of a few years.

Physical conditions on the Earth's surface are dependent in the main on the properties of its surrounding atmosphere.

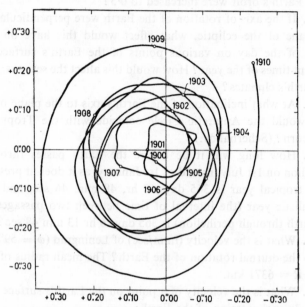

FIG. 23. The movement of the pole over the surface of the Earth.

SECTION TWO PROBLEMS

507. What would be the velocity of the Earth about the Sun if its orbit is uniform and circular, with a radius of 149,500,000 km, and a period of $365\frac{1}{4}$ days?

508. By how much would the length of the year alter if the distance of the Earth from the Sun were increased by 1,000,000 km? Assume that the orbital velocity of the Earth is unchanged (Perelman.)

509. Calculate how many days spring, summer, autumn and winter last in the Northern Hemisphere. Explain the inequality in the lengths of the seasons of the year. Why is summer in the Northern Hemisphere longer than winter?

510. If the eccentricity of the Earth's orbit were zero, then how would the lengths of the seasons of the year differ from those which exist?

511. How would the seasons of the year alter if the eccentricity of the Earth's orbit were increased to 0·5?

512. If the axis of rotation of the Earth were perpendicular to the plane of the ecliptic, what effect would this have on the length of the day on various points of the Earth's surface at different times of the year? How would this affect the seasons, and the Earth's climates?

513. At what inclination of the Earth's axis to the plane of its orbit would the Antarctic Circle coincide with the Tropic of Capricorn? (Scherbakov.)

514. How long will it be before the Earth passes through perihelion on 1st July instead of 1st January, as it does at present, if the tropical year is 365 days, 5 hr, 48 min, 46 sec, and the anomalistic year (the interval of time between two passages of the Earth through perihelion) is 365 days 6 hr 13 min 48 sec?

515. What is the velocity (in m/sec) of Leningrad ($\phi = 59°57'$) due to the diurnal rotation of the Earth? The mean radius of the Earth $R = 6371$ km.

516. What is the velocity of a point on the Earth's surface due to the diurnal rotation of the Earth:

        (a) on the equator,

        (b) at latitude $\phi = 48°24'$,

taking the radius of the Earth to be 6371 km?

517. At what latitude is a place situated if its movement due to diurnal rotation is half that of Moscow ($\phi = 56°$)? Twice that of Kola ($\phi = 69°$)? (Kamen'schikov.)

518. The diurnal rotation of the Earth has been shown recently to be slowing down in the course of the centuries. Will astronomical phenomena in the future appear to be faster or slower than before?

519. If the heavens are regarded as rotating, rather than the Earth, then what would be the speed of the star α Centauri in its diurnal revolution about the Earth? (The light from this star takes 4 yr to reach us, and its Declination is $-60°$.)

_____

520. At what latitude will the westward deviation of a body falling from a given height be greatest?

521. Calculate the deviation to the west of a body, falling from a tower 100 m high, on the equator.

522. Calculate the angle of rotation of Foucault's pendulum per hour for latitudes $30°$, $60°$, $45°$, $75°$, $89°$, $90°$, $0°$, and that of your own city.

523. Two ships, x and y, are sailing along the 48th parallel of northern latitude, and the 15th parallel of southern latitude, respectively. If at each moment they are on the same meridian, what is the speed of ship x if the speed of ship y is 15 knots (15 nautical miles per hour; a nautical mile is the length of an arc of $1'$ at the equator)?

524. During clear weather, is it possible to see the shore of the Crimea, 600 km away, from Mount Elbrus (altitude 5630 m)?

525. What is the distance of the horizon from the summit of the highest mountain in the world, Everest, whose height is 8840 m?

526. From what distance can a seafarer see a fire beacon standing 100 m above the level of the sea?

*527. What was the distance of the horizon for the crew of the Soviet Stratostat which rose to an altitude of 22 km? What is the horizon distance for a man 1.7 m tall standing on a flat plain?

528. What would be the lowering of the horizon of the sea to an observer at the top of Yaila (in the Crimea) whose height is 1000 m?

529. Two observers at the equator, during September, watch the setting of the Sun. One of them makes the observation from a boat, the other from an aeroplane flying at an altitude of 10 km. How much later does the Sun set for the pilot of the aeroplane?

530. Determine the radius of the Earth if, from a mountain 1000 m high, the lowering of the horizon is $1.01°$.

Neglect refraction by the Earth's atmosphere.

531. Calculate in metres the length of a nautical mile which is equal to the length of an arc of 1′ at the equator, given that the length of the equator is 40,076,594 m.

532. During the significant degree measurement of the arc of the meridian, carried out by Pulkov astronomers under the directorship of W. Struve, it was established that the distance between Fugleness ($\phi = 70°50′$) and Staronekresovski ($\phi = 45°20′$) is 2822 km. Determine from this the radius of the Earth, assuming it to be a sphere. (Blazko.)

533. From the Lapland and Peruvian surveying expeditions in 1736 and Picar's measurement in France in 1677 the following values were obtained for the length of a degree:

$$
\begin{array}{lll}
\text{In Peru} & \phi = -2° & 110{,}578 \text{ m} \\
\text{France} & \phi = +49° & 111{,}213 \text{ m} \\
\text{Lapland} & \phi = +66° & 111{,}950 \text{ m}
\end{array}
$$

Calculate the values of the radius of curvature of the Earth for the latitudes of Peru, France and Lapland.

534. Do errors accumulate in triangulation with the length of the distance measured? Does the absolute error in astronomical determinations of the angular length of an arc increase with its length?

535. To what accuracy must a base of length 10 km be measured so that the error of this measurement may not lead to an error in the measurement of the Earth's circumference greater than 1000 m?

536. If the Earth is represented by a globe of diameter of 3 m how would the oblateness of the Earth be represented?

537. The Newtonian proof of the oblateness of the Earth presupposes that the Earth rotates. What proofs do not depend on the knowledge of the Earth's rotation?

538. Two identical trains travel at exactly the same speeds, in opposite directions, east to west, and west to east. Which of the trains is heavier? (Perelman.)

539. How great is the centrifugal acceleration of a body placed at sea-level on the equator? The radius of the Earth $R = 6,378,400$, and the period of its rotation $T = 86,164$ mean solar sec.

540. What is the acceleration of gravity at the equator if a pendulum with a period of 1 sec there has a length of $l = 991 \cdot 03$ mm?

541. At the equator the acceleration due to the Earth's gravity g_0 is $9 \cdot 781$ m/sec^2, and at latitude ϕ, $g = 9 \cdot 781 \, (1 + 0 \cdot 00512 \sin^2 \phi)$. Calculate the length of a second's pendulum in Dneipopetrovsk ($\phi = 48°24'$).

542. Taking the length of a degree of the meridian to be $111 \cdot 7$ km, determine approximately the linear amplitude of oscillation of the poles of the earth from Fig. 23 (p. 113). The angular inclination of the pole from its mean position is shown on the axes of the coordinates.

---

543. If the surface of the Earth were free of water, what would be the effect of this on the mean temperature, on the diurnal range of temperature in a given place, and on its range over the whole surface of the Earth?

545. Compare the illumination of areas of equal size at the equator, on the Tropic of Cancer and at the North Pole when the Sun attains its greatest height above the horizon in these places.

*546. What is the theoretical relationship between the amounts of sunlight falling on a horizontal surface at midday at Saratov ($\phi = 51°32'$) on the 22nd June and on 23rd December?

*547. Compare the amounts of heat falling on the Earth on the days of the Summer and Winter Solstices at latitudes 65°, 45°, $23\frac{1}{2}°$ and 0°. Compare these ratios with the data known from geography.

*548. Compare the quantities of heat received per unit surface in Moscow ($\phi = 55°45'$) on the days of the Summer and Winter Solstices and on the days during which the Sun passes through perihelion (in winter) and the days when the Sun passes through aphelion (in summer). The eccentricity of the Earth's orbit, $e = 0 \cdot 017$. How many times greater is the influence of the inclination of the rays of the Sun than the influence of the change in the distance of the Sun from the Earth at this latitude?

549. What is the Right Ascension of a point on the celestial sphere in whose direction the Earth moves in its orbit on the 21st June?

550. Which of the proofs of the revolution of the Earth about the Sun also gives the dimensions of its orbit?

*551. Determine the eccentricity e of the Earth's orbit, given from observation that the greatest visible diameter of the Sun, $p = 32'36''\cdot4$ and the least, $q = 31'31''\cdot8$.

552. What is the explanation of the fact that from January to July we are nearer to the Sun at noon than in the evening, while from July to January we are nearer to it in the evening than at noon? (Perelman.)

553. What is the relationship between the sizes of the areas of the three basic climatic zones of the Earth, tropical, temperate and polar?

*554. Does the movement of the perihelion of the Earth's orbit through the centuries caused by planetary perturbations have any effect on the duration of the seasons of the year?

555. Given that the duration of a sidereal year, in which the Earth completes a full revolution (360°) about the Sun relative to the stars, is 365·25636 mean days, and that the perihelion of the Earth's orbit relative to the stars moves by 0·0033° every year, find the duration of an anomalistic year (that is the interval of time between two successive passages of the Sun through perihelion). Determine the interval of time in which the apsides of the Earth's orbit will return to their present position; that is, will complete a revolution of 360°.

556. In a repetition of Foucault's experiment a physical pendulum was used, consisting of a thin wire and a brass sphere. The weight of the wire may be ignored in comparison with that of the sphere which was $m = 28$ kg, situated at a distance of $K = 53$ m from the axis of rotation. The density of brass is $\delta = 8\cdot4$.

What is the distance from the centre of the swing of the pendulum to the centre of the sphere?

557. Prove that the distance between two seaports, A and B, lying on latitude 60°, and having a difference in longitude of 60°, is shorter along the arc of the great circle than along the arc of parallel 60°.

Hint. Make use of Fig. 24. The mean radius of the Earth
$R = 6371$ km.

558. A pilot needs to know the distance between the towns a
and b so as to estimate his fuel supply. Their geographical coordinates are:

$$\phi_1 = 24°18',$$
$$\lambda_1 = 133°30' \text{ E},$$
$$\phi_2 = 36°47',$$
$$\lambda_2 = 125°24' \text{ W}.$$

Assume the Earth to be a sphere of radius 6371 km.

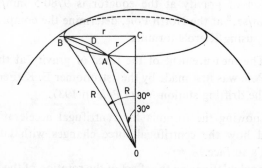

FIG. 24. The arc of the parallel is longer than the arc of the great
circle.

559. A ship sails from a port with coordinates $\phi = 38°42'\cdot5$;
$\lambda = 9°11'\cdot5$ E. along the arc of the great circle holding a course
of S 22°47' W. Where, and on what course, does it cross the
equator? How many kilometres has it to sail to the equator?
When will it reach the equator if its speed is 22·2 km/hr?

560. A ship sails from a point with coordinates

$$\phi_1 = 39°20',$$
$$\lambda_1 = 110°10' \text{ E.},$$

to a point with coordinates

$$\phi_2 = -44°30',$$
$$\lambda_2 = 46°20' \text{ W}.$$

Show that if it sails by the shortest possible route not intersecting parallel $-62°$, than the length of its route is 5847·6 nautical miles.

561. It is sometimes said that the proof of the sphericity of the Earth from eclipses of the Moon is incorrect, in that the shadow of the Earth does not fall on a plane surface, but on the spherical surface of the Moon, so that the edge of the shadow is not an arc of a circle. Refute this objection. (Polak.)

562. Given that the acceleration due to centrifugal force at the equator is 33·9 mm/sec^2, and knowing from observation that the acceleration of gravity at the equator is 9780·5 mm/sec^2 and 9832·2 mm/sec^2 at the North Pole, determine the compression of the Earth, using Klero's formula.

Note. The measurement of the force of gravity at the North Pole was first made by the astronomer E. K. Fedorov on the drifting station *North Pole* in 1937.

563. Knowing the formula for centrifugal acceleration ($u = v^2/r$), find how the centrifugal force changes with latitude on the Earth's surface.

564. In calculations on the effect of the rotation of the Earth on the effective force of gravity, why is it necessary to multiply the equatorial acceleration a_0 twice by cos ϕ? (Polak.)

565. On the equator the gravitational acceleration is 9·7805 m/sec^2. How many times faster would the Earth have to rotate for an object on the equator to have no weight?

566. Let g be the acceleration due to gravity at sea level. What would it be at a height h above sea-level, if the radius of the Earth is R?

567. Suppose that time can be measured to an accuracy of 1/10 sec. How accurately could g be measured with a second's pendulum in the course of 10 days?

568. Compare the practical advantages of the method of a swinging balance, and the method based on the attraction of mountains, in the determination of the mass of the Earth. Which of these is the better method?

569. Are the astronomical and geocentric latitudes the same for all points on the Earth's surface?

570. Do the lengths of a degree of geocentric and astronomical latitude change by equal amounts?

571. Show that the deviation of a plumb-line from the radius of the sphere of the Earth, due to the rotation of the Earth, reaches its greatest value at (approximately) 45°, and determine this value. (Bachinskii.)

*572. Which layers of the atmosphere (in height) have a noticeable effect in diffracting the light of the Sun, if the appearance of astronomical twilight, due to this diffraction, ends when the

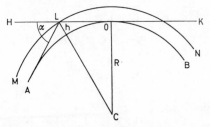

Fig. 25. The determination of the limit of the atmosphere from the diffused light of the Sun.

height of the Sun beneath the horizon is 18°? Deduce a formula for this, making use of Fig. 25. AOB is the surface of the Earth, with its centre at C. O is the observer, HK is his horizon, and h is the height of MLN, the critical layer of atmosphere. The angle α is the negative height of the Sun at the end of twilight.

*573. At what height is the layer of the atmosphere which refracts the light of the Sun during local twilight, if the latter ends when the Sun is 6°·5 below the horizon?

*574. The solar energy falling on 1 cm² of the surface of the Earth, perpendicular to the Sun's rays, at the mean distance of the Earth from the Sun is 1·94 cal/min. This is called the "solar constant". The Earth reflects 37 per cent of the energy falling on it back into space (mostly from clouds).

Given the radius of the Earth, R, and assuming it to be a completely black body, calculate the mean temperature of the

Earth, T, from the Stefan–Boltzmann Law

$$E = 5^{\circ}\!\cdot\!72 \times 10^{-5} T^4,$$

where E is the energy in ergs radiated by 1 cm^2 of black body in T sec. The mechanical equivalent of heat $q = 4 \cdot 19 \times 10^7$. Compare the value obtained with the real mean temperature of the Earth ($+14^{\circ}$C).

CHAPTER XV

THE MOVEMENT AND PHASES
OF THE MOON

THE CHANGES in the phases of the Moon are due to the fact that we see one side of the Moon, illuminated by the Sun from various angles during the course of its revolution about the Earth. This period of revolution is the stellar, or sidereal month, and has a mean value of 27·32 days. The interval of time between two identical phases of the Moon is the *Sinodical* month, with a mean value of 29·53 days. The sinodical month is longer than the sidereal because of the revolution of the Earth about the Sun. The plane of the lunar orbit intersects the ecliptic at an angle of 5°8′. The Moon moves against the background of the stars along a line representing the projection of its orbit on the celestial sphere. This motion has a speed of 13°10′35″ per mean solar day. The Moon changes its position by approximately ½°, or its own angular diameter per hour. In the course of its movement across the sky the Moon can obstruct our view of stars — a phenomenon known as occultation. Lunar days, or the intervals of time between culminations of the Moon, have a mean duration of 24 hr 51 min. The Moon revolves about its axis with exactly the same period as it revolves about the Earth.

The Moon moves about the Earth in an ellipse, in agreement with Kepler's laws. Its perigee is the point on its orbit closest to the Earth, and its apogee is the most distant point of its orbit. The line joining these two points (the line of the Apsid) rotates in space in the plane of the Moon's orbit to the East, making one complete revolution in approximately 9 yr.

The line of nodes of the lunar orbit (the line of intersection of the plane of the lunar orbit with the plane of the ecliptic) also rotates towards the west (in the plane of the ecliptic) with a period of $18\frac{2}{3}$ yr. In other words, the nodes of the Moon's orbit, or the points of the celestial sphere at which the Moon crosses the ecliptic, move steadily to the west. The interval of time between the passage of the Moon through the same node is called the Draconitic month, and is 27·21 days. The times of the eclipses depend upon these factors.

The irregularity of the movement of the Moon through its orbit, combined with its uniform rotation about its axis, the inclination of the axis to its orbit, the inclination of its orbit to the ecliptic, the phenomenon of parallax, and other conditions, allow us short glimpses from time to time of a small portion the other side of the Moon which, generally speaking, is always turned away from the Earth. These appearances are called Librations. Quite recently the normally unviewable hemisphere of the Moon was photographed from a rocket launched by the U.S.S.R.

SECTION ONE PROBLEMS

575. How long would a cannon shell take to cross the space between the Earth and the Moon (384,400 km) if the initial speed of the projectile (800 m/sec) remained constant?

576. How would you explain the origin of the expression "the first quarter" of the Moon?

577. Is the Moon waxing or waning when the convex part of the Moon is to the right of the diameter joining the points of the Moon's crescent? When is it to the left of this diameter? (The observer is in a northern latitude.)

578. Can stars be seen between the horns of the crescent Moon?

579. What determines the direction of the horns of the crescent of the new Moon?

580. Why does a perpendicular drawn to the line joining the horns of the crescent Moon under no circumstances pass through the Sun? (Perelman.)

*581. Is it possible anywhere on Earth to see the crescent Moon sinking into the sea like a little boat, with its points uppermost?

582. What would the phase of the Earth be to an imaginary inhabitant of the Moon during the new Moon? During the full Moon? What would the general relationship be between the phases of the Earth and the phases of the Moon?

583. The Moon is observed in its first quarter on the 25th December, 1922. What was the phase of the Moon on the 25th December, 1923.

584. Taking into account the inclination of the lunar orbit to the ecliptic, determine the limits of the changes in the Declination of the Moon.

585. Taking into account the inclination of the lunar orbit ($5°8'$) calculate the maximum possible altitude of the Moon above the horizon in Kola ($\phi = 68°53'$), Kharkov ($\phi = 50°00'$) and in Tashkent (ϕ 41°20').

586. Is it possible for the Moon to pass through the zenith anywhere in England? In what latitudes is this possible?

*587. Between what limits does the azimuth of the points of the rising of the Moon change for an observer living on the Earth's equator?

588. Why does the crescent of the "new Moon" appear particularly high in the sky in the spring?

589. Why is the waning Moon (after full Moon) poorly visible in the spring, while in the autumn it is easily observable — that is, it rises early and high in the sky?

590. The Moon in its first quarter is visible on the meridian. What is the time approximately?

591. The full Moon rises in March. What is the time, approximately?

592. In what phase is the Moon, if it culminates at 6 o'clock in the evening by apparent solar time? What is its phase if it culminates at midnight by apparent solar time?

593. At what time, approximately, and at what time of year, does the Moon culminate highest above the horizon

(a) when it is full;

(b) when it is in its last quarter;

(c) when the "earthlit" Moon is visible in the evening?

594. At what time of the year does the full Moon culminate farthest from the horizon for us in the Northern Hemisphere? At what time of the year does the "new Moon" move farthest from the horizon for us?

595. Where, approximately, on Earth, and at what time of the year, does the full Moon remain above the horizon for more than a day?

596. Is the full Moon visible in June to an observer at the terrestrial North Pole?

*597. Is it possible anywhere on Earth not to see the Moon during a fortnight of completely clear weather.

598. Does the Moon rise every day?

599. If a sidereal month lasted 60 days, what would be the interval of time between two successive culminations of the Moon?

600. A lunar occultation of a star lasted for 20 min. Was the occultation central? Take the diameter of the Moon to be $\frac{1}{2}°$. (Nabokov and Vorontsov Velyaminov.)

601. The mean diurnal motion of the Moon is $13°10'35''$. What is the mean duration of a sidereal month?

602. What would the length of a sinodical month be, if a sidereal month were 60 days?

603. What would the visible diurnal movement of the Moon be if the sidereal month were exactly equal to a stellar day? How would it move if the sidereal month were less than a stellar day, for example, 20 hr? (Kamen'schikov.)

604. What would the sinodic period of revolution of the Moon be if it revolved about the Earth from east to west with exactly the same speed as it does at present?

SECTION TWO PROBLEMS

605. Given the angle between the directions of the Moon and Sun from the Earth, deduce a formula for the illuminated fraction of the diameter of the Moon perpendicular to the line joining its horns.

606. Show that the visible lunar terminator (the line separating

the illuminated and dark portions) is a half ellipse, if the phenomenon of parallax is neglected.

607. What are the limits of angular distance of the Moon from
the Sun

(a) in opposition;

(b) in conjunction;

(c) in quadrature?

608. Give the main reason why the period from the "new
Moon" to full Moon should sometimes be a day longer than the
period from the full Moon to the following "new Moon".

609. If the Moon rose at 8 hr 45 min one evening when,
approximately, did it next rise? How (qualitatively) does this
time change if the Declination of the Moon increases during that
time?

610. Under what conditions will the daily delay in the rising of
the full Moon be at its least just before the Autumnal Equinox?

*611. In the calendar for 1937 the phases of the Moon are
given as:

19th March, 15th June, 12th September	First quarter.
23rd June, 17th December	Full Moon.
5th March, 27th September, 24th December	Last quarter.

Give, approximately, the hours on these dates when the light of
the Moon interferes with the observation of faint stars.

612. What is the lowest latitude on the Earth from which it is
possible to see the Moon above the horizon continuously for
48 hr? Do not take refraction and parallax into account.

613. At what place on Earth does the Moon rise on two consecutive days at the same moment of sidereal time?

614. How do the phases of the Moon appear to an observer at
the North Pole?

*615. In June of a certain year the culmination of the full
Moon is observed in Simferopol ($\phi = 45°$) at a height of $16°$ above
the horizon. Is it possible for the full Moon to culminate at $26°$,
at this place during June? If so, how and after how many years
would it occur?

616. Why does the Moon occult without exception, every star with astronomical latitude within ±6°38′?

Hint. The inclination of the Moon's orbit is variable, having a maximum value of 5°20′.

617. Calculate, correct to 1/100 of a day, the length of an anomalistic month, or the period of longitudinal libration (i.e. the interval of time between the passages of the Moon through perigee), given that the perigee of the Moon's orbit moves continuously to the east, completing a revolution in 3232 days (about 9 years). (Polak.)

*618. Owing to the parallax of the Earth's rotation an observer has slightly different views of the Moon at rising, culmination, and setting. What is the maximum width of the supplementary visible lunar strip, in selenocentric degrees, if the equatorial horizontal parallax of the Moon is 57′?

Hint. Draw a diagram.

619. Calculate the period of libration in latitude (the Draconitic month). Why is the Draconitic month shorter and the anomalistic month longer than the stellar month? (Polak.)

CHAPTER XVI

ECLIPSES

A LUNAR eclipse can take place only when the Moon is full, close to a node of the lunar orbit, that is, close to the plane of the ecliptic. An eclipse of the Sun can take place only at the "new Moon", and under the same conditions. These conditions are fulfilled at approximately six-monthly intervals. Because of the movement of the node of the lunar orbit the interval is 10 days shorter than half a year. In each of these two eclipse periods during the course of the year there can be a maximum of three eclipses (solar—lunar—solar), and a minimum of one solar and no lunar eclipses. The diameter of the shadow of the Earth at the distance of the Moon is greater than the diameter of the Moon. Entering the shadow of the Earth, the Moon is visible in eclipse simultaneously from all parts of the dark side of the Earth. A complete eclipse of the Sun is visible only on those parts of the Earth where the small spot of the Moon's shadow falls, and is visible in different places at different times, as they successively come into the shadow. Where the penumbra of the Moon's shadow falls on the Earth, a partial solar eclipse occurs. If the Moon is in apogee during an eclipse of the Sun, its apparent diameter is smaller than the Sun's is, and only an annular eclipse of the Sun takes place. The width of the belt which the shadow of the Moon traces on the Earth (in which a full eclipse is observed) is small, so that in a fixed place on Earth eclipses of the Sun occur more rarely than eclipses of the Moon, although for the Earth as a whole the reverse is the case.

In the course of 18 yr, 11 days (10 days, if there have been 5 leap years in that interval) the Sun passes through the nodes of the Moon's orbit nineteen times (19 Draconitic years). That is, a period of 242 Draconitic months, or 223 sinodic months. In the period of 18 yr and 11 days the relative positions of the Sun, the Earth and the Moon repeat themselves, and the cycle of the eclipses is thus repeated, although solar eclipses occur in different places in each period. This period is called a "saros".

The conditions for the occurrence of an eclipse are determined by the inclination of the lunar orbit to the ecliptic, the apparent diameter of the Moon and of the Sun (their parallax), the speed of the revolution of the lunar modes and several other lesser considerations.

SECTION ONE PROBLEMS

620. What would an imaginary observer situated on the Moon see during an eclipse of the Sun?

621. When would an observer on the Moon see a total eclipse of the Sun by the Earth? What would an observer on the Earth see at this time?

622. Why is an annular eclipse of the Moon not possible?

623. What distinguishes a phase during an eclipse of the Moon from one of its normal phases?

624. Is it possible for a total eclipse of the Moon to be observed at local midday?

625. A situation arises where the Moon, in total eclipse, rises before sunset, so that both Sun and Moon are simultaneously visible, and it follows that the Sun must be visible from the Moon while the Moon is in eclipse. How can this be explained?

626. Is it possible for the middle of a total eclipse of the Moon to be observed at 4 a.m. local time?

627. A complete eclipse of the Moon on the 4th June, 1909, began at 1 hr 44·6 min a.m. Pulkovo time. When did it take place by Moscow local time, if the longitude of Moscow with respect to Pulkovo is 29 min to the east?

628. If in the course of the current year an eclipse of the Moon has occurred in August, is it possible for another lunar eclipse to occur in June next year? Could it occur in October this year and, if not, why not?

*629. Under what conditions would a total central eclipse of the Moon have its longest duration?

630. Is it possible for Jupiter to be covered by the Moon during a lunar eclipse? Could Venus be covered at this time?

631. What type of eclipse, solar or lunar, is most often observed in London? In Edinburgh?

632. Is it possible to observe an eclipse of the Sun from the Earth at midnight?

633. Why are the spots of light in the shadows cast by leaves crescent-shaped during partial phases of a solar eclipse?

634. Does the eastern or the western edge of the solar disc first appear to touch the Moon during an eclipse of the Sun?

635. Can an annular eclipse of the Sun occur when the Moon is in perigee? In apogee?

636. By how many times is the light of the Sun weakened during the brightest annular eclipse?

Hint. The angular diameters of the Sun and the Moon on this occasion may be taken as 32'·6 and 29'·4, respectively, and the surface of the Sun may be assumed to have an even brightness. (Polak.)

637. What would occur at every new Moon if the plane of the orbit of the Moon coincided with the plane of the Earth's orbit?

*638. How would the conditions for the occurrence of an eclipse be changed if the nodes of the Moon's orbit ceased to change position, and the inclination of the lunar orbit increased to 30°?

*639. Where is it possible to observe eclipses most frequently, in the polar or the equatorial regions (between the tropics) of the Earth? Do not take considerations of cloud cover into account.

*640. In the year 1917 the following eclipses occurred: a total eclipse of the Moon visible in America; a partial eclipse of the Sun on the 23rd January, visible in eastern Europe and in eastern Siberia; a partial eclipse of the Sun on the 19th June visible in north polar regions; a total eclipse of the Moon on the 4th June visible in Europe; a partial eclipse of the Sun on the 19th July visible in Antarctica; an annular eclipse of the Sun on the 14th December visible at the South Pole of the Earth; a total eclipse of the Moon on the 28th December clearly visible in America.

In the year 1935 the following eclipses took place:
a partial eclipse of the Sun on the 5th January visible in the Southern Hemisphere;
a total eclipse of the Moon on the 19th January, visible in the U.S.S.R.;
a partial eclipse of the Sun on the 3rd February visible in Northern America;
a partial eclipse of the Sun on the 30th June visible in the extreme north of the U.S.S.R.;
a total eclipse of the Moon on the 16th July visible in America;
a partial eclipse of the Sun on the 30th July visible in the Atlantic Ocean;
an annular eclipse of the Sun on the 25th December visible at the South Pole;
on the 8th January, 1936, there was yet another total eclipse of the Moon visible in the U.S.S.R.

Compare these two cycles of eclipses, and check whether the period of saros is maintained. Investigate the way in which the conditions of visibility of the eclipses is maintained. Explain why the intervals between the fourth and fifth eclipses in 1935 seems to be greater.

Hint. Take into account that the dates are given by Universal Time, but the moments of the eclipses are not given.

641. In 1941 there were two solar and two lunar eclipses:

on the 13th March a complete lunar,
on the 27th March an annular solar,
on the 5th September a total lunar, and
on the 21st September a total solar eclipse.

Predict on the basis of the saros the next occasion on which these eclipses will be repeated, and when they last occurred.

*642. Determine from a map showing the path of a total eclipse of the Sun when by local time the middle of the eclipse occurs, and what its maximum phase is in London. Determine the same for Johannesburg, Sydney and Toronto. Such maps are sometimes given in handbooks of astronomy and in all astronomical almanacks.

SECTION TWO PROBLEMS

*643. A traveller reported that during a solar eclipse he saw the waning of the disc begin from its lowest point. Could he really have observed such a phenomenon, and if so where, and at what time?

644. Is it ever possible for the shadow of the Moon to move westward over the Earth's surface during a solar eclipse?

645. Why is it not possible for eight eclipses to occur within a calendar year? (Polak.)

*646. Making use of Fig. 26, in which O and E are the centres of the Sun and the Earth, express the length of the conical

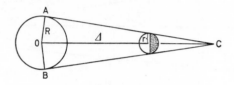

FIG. 26.

shadow of the Earth $EC = l$ in terms of the radii, R and r, of the Sun and the Earth, and the distance from the Earth to the Sun $OX = \Delta$. Express this length also in terms of r, the visible angular radius of the Sun, S, and the solar parallax p.

647. Let the radius of the Earth be r, the radius of the Sun be $R = 109 \, r$, the distance between the centres of the two bodies $L = 23{,}680 \, r$ and the distance of the Moon from the centre of the Earth $l = 60 \, r$. Determine the radius y of the cross-section of the Earth's shadow at a distance l from the Earth's centre.

648. Given the following values:

The distance of the Sun from the Earth $R = 15 \times 10^7$ km
The distance of the Moon from the Earth $l = 36 \times 10^4$ km
The diameter of the Sun $a = 14 \times 10^5$ km
The diameter of the Moon $b = 35 \times 10^2$ km

Calculate the area in square kilometres of the shadow of the Moon on the Earth's surface, assuming the latter to be flat.

649. Using the data from the preceding problem, with the exception of *l*, which becomes 38×10^4 km, find whether it is possible for a total solar eclipse to occur.

*650. It is calculated that the semi-major axis of the Moon's orbit is gradually increasing. When it has increased in size by 10 per cent, will total solar eclipses occur on the Earth?

*651. For an eclipse of the Sun to occur, the Moon must pass through the cone *ABCD* (Fig. 27) which encloses the Earth *E* and the Sun *S*. In the given instance the angle between the centres of the Moon, *M* and the Sun *S*, measured from the centre of the

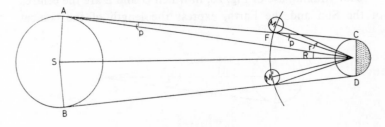

FIG. 27.

Earth, is *MES*. It is made up of the angle *MEF* (the angular radius of the Moon), the angle *AES* (which is *R*, the angular radius of the Sun) and the angle *FEA*. The latter is equal to the difference between the angles *CFE* and *FAE*, which are in fact equal to the horizontal parallaxes of the Moon and the Sun. That is, $MES = r + R + P - p$ and, owing to the change in the distance from the Moon to the Sun, it varies between $1°34'13''$ and $1°24'19''$. Find the angle *M'ES* in an analogous way, determining the limiting conditions for the occurrence of a total eclipse.

*652. Given that the angle *MES* in the previous example and in Fig. 27 may reach $1°34'13''$, determine the maximum distance along the plane of the ecliptic of the centre of the Earth from the ascending node at which an eclipse of the Sun is possible. The inclination of the lunar orbit $i = 5°9'$.

*653. Using a method similar to that of Problem 651, determine from Fig. 28 the mean value of the angle *MEN*, the so-called "radius of the Earth's shadow", determining the conditions for the occurrence of a lunar eclipse. In this figure O, E and M are the centres of the Sun, the Earth, and the Moon.

Keeping the previous notation, and given that the mean value of $r = 15'40''$, the mean value of $R = 16'2''$, the mean value of $P = 57'2''$ and the mean value of $p = 8''{\cdot}8$ compare the conditions for the occurrence of eclipses of the Sun and Moon, and hence decide which type of eclipse must in general occur more frequently.

*654. Knowing from the preceding problem that the angle MEN is equal to $41'9''$, determine A, the greatest distance of the

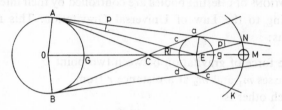

FIG. 28.

Moon from the node of its orbit, at which an eclipse of the Moon is possible.

    Hint. The angle i gives the greatest distance of the centre of the Moon from the ecliptic. The inclination of the lunar orbit is $i = 5°9'$.

CHAPTER XVII

GRAVITATION

I

THE MOTIONS of celestial bodies are controlled by their interaction according to the Law of Universal Gravitation. This may be stated as:

the force of gravitation between two point masses m_1 and m_2 at a distance r from each other is

$$F = f \frac{m_1 m_2}{r^2},$$

where the coefficient f (it is sometimes designated k^2) is called the constant of gravitation, or the gravitational constant. In the c.g.s. system of units, $f = 6 \cdot 673 \times 10^{-8}$. If we take the mass of the Sun as the unit of mass, and the semi-major axis of the Earth's orbit as the unit of distance, and the mean solar day as the unit of time, we obtain for the constant the value $k = \sqrt{f}$, known as the Gaussian constant, equal to $0 \cdot 01720210 \approx 1/58$.

The acceleration g, which a body of mass M imparts to a body of mass m at a distance r, is given by the formula

$$g = f \frac{M}{r^2}.$$

If we consider celestial bodies to be spheres with their densities increasing towards their centres, then they exert a gravitational force on points on their surfaces or further away, as if all their mass were concentrated at their centres.

From the Law of Universal Gravitation, Kepler's Third Law can be deduced in a more exact form than that obtained directly from observation by Kepler himself:

$$\frac{a^3}{a_1^3} = \frac{T^2(M+m)}{T_1^2(M+m)},$$

where M is the mass of the central body, and m and m_1 are the masses of bodies revolving about it with periods T and T_1 in ellipses of semi-major axes a and a_1. This relationship holds if a, T, m, and M in the numerators refer to one pair of bodies (for example to the Sun and the Earth), and a_1, T_1, m_1, and M in the denominator, refer to another pair of bodies (for example to Neptune and its satellite). Hence, we have the possibility of determining the masses of heavenly bodies relative to the masses of the Earth and the Sun. For instance, we can compare the movement of the Moon about the Earth with the movement of a satellite about a planet and then determine the planet's mass, neglecting the masses of the satellites in comparison with the masses of the central bodies. The mass of the planet, M_p, is given by the formula

$$M_p = \frac{T^2}{T_1^2}\frac{a_1^3}{a^3}M,$$

where T_1 and a_1 are the period and the distance of the satellite from the planet, M is the mass of the Earth, and T and a refer to the Moon. We could also use M as the mass of the Sun and let T and a refer to the Earth.

If the movement of a planet (or a satellite) is circular, then the acceleration is $\omega^2 r$, where ω is the angular velocity, and r is the radius of the orbit.

II

The velocity v of a body of mass m under the influence of gravitation in an orbit with a semi-major axis a at a distance r from the central body is given by the formula

$$v^2 = k^2(M+m)\left(\frac{2}{r} - \frac{1}{a}\right),$$

where M is the mass of the central body. If m is significantly less than M, then it may be neglected in the formula. It then follows from the above formula that the value of the semi-major axis a depends only on the velocity v of the satellite body.

Putting $k^2(M+m) = \mu$, the velocity in a circular orbit of radius a is

$$v_c = \sqrt{\frac{\mu}{a}},$$

and in a parabolic orbit the velocity at a distance r is

$$v_p = \sqrt{\frac{2\mu}{r}}.$$

Then if

$$v_c < v < v_p,$$

the body describes an ellipse and if

$$v > v_p$$

the body describes a hyperbola.

In order for a body to fly to infinity from the surface of a planet it must receive a velocity greater than or equal to v_p for the surface of the planet. If a is the radius of a planet and a body near its surface is given a velocity v_c relative to the planet, the body will revolve about, or orbit, the planet close to its surface.

Kepler's Second Law is mathematically expressed as

$$\tfrac{1}{2}r^2\frac{dv}{dt} = \text{const.}$$

where the left-hand side is called the sectorial velocity. r is the radius vector of the body moving in orbit under the influence of gravity from a centre, and v is its true anomaly.

The perturbing force of a third body represents the small geometrical difference in the forces with which this body acts on the perturbed and on the central body. It varies in inverse proportion to the cube of the distance between the perturbed and the perturbing bodies.

The tidal force at any given point on the surface of a planet (the force causing ebb and flow) represents the difference in the forces with which the body causing the tidal floods attracts the centre, and a given point of the surface of the planet. The tidal force is also inversely proportional to the cube of distance.

SECTION ONE PROBLEMS

655. Which is greater; the acceleration communicated to the Earth by the Sun, or the acceleration communicated by the Earth to the Moon, and by how many times?

656. The masses of the Earth and the Moon have a ratio of 81:1. The distance between their centres is 382,420 km. Where is their common centre of gravity situated?

657. Two celestial bodies A and B have masses m and m'. Their mutual separation is r. At what point on the straight line joining their centres would a given body have to be placed to be attracted to each of them with the same force? Calculate this position if A is the Earth and B is the Moon. Their separation is equal to sixty Earth radii; the mass of the Moon is $1/81$ of the mass of the Earth.

*658. Deduce a formula giving in days the time t of falling of any celestial body towards a central body, by analogy with the falling of a comet through a very elongated ellipse, whose semi-major axis is equal to the initial distance a between the bodies.

659. How long would the Earth take to fall into the Sun, if it ceased to move about it? (See Problem 658.)

660. How long would the Moon take to fall on the Earth, if its movement were interrupted? (See Problem 658.)

661. How long would Pluto take to fall its distance to the Sun's surface? (See Problem 658.)

662. Calculate the mass of Neptune relative to the mass of the Earth, knowing that its satellite is 354,000 km from the centre of the planet, and its period of rotation is 5 days 21·0 hr.

Hint. Carry out the calculation by comparing the movement of Neptune's satellite with the movement of the Moon about the Earth.

663. Determine the mass of Uranus in units of the mass of the Earth comparing the movement of the Moon about the Earth with the movement of Uranus' satellite, Titania, which revolves about the planet with a period of 8 days 17 hr 0 min at a distance of 438,000 km.

664. Calculate the mass of Mars relative to the mass of the

Earth, from the movement of its satellite Phobos, for which $a = 9300$ km and $t = 0.32$ days. The corresponding values for the Moon are 385,000 km and 27·3 days.

665. Determine the mass of Mars relative to the Sun, given that the distance of Phobos, a satellite of the planet, is 9380 km, and the time of a sidereal revolution of Phobos is 0·31892 days. The distance of Mars from the Sun is 227,000,000 km and the sidereal period of revolution of Mars is 686,980 days.

666. Calculate the mass of Jupiter, given that the distance of the first satellite of Jupiter from the planet is 422,000 km, the period of its revolution about Jupiter is 1·77 days, the distance of the Moon from the Earth is 384,000 km, and the period of revolution of the Moon about the Earth is 27·32 days.

667. Using the exact form of Kepler's Third Law determine the mass of Jupiter, taking the mass of the Sun to be 1, the mass of the Earth to be 0:

$$T_1 = 4332.6 \text{ days,}$$

$$a = 5.2028,$$

$$T = 365.26 \text{ days.}$$

668. Determine the mass of the Sun M in comparison with the mass of the Earth m, comparing the movement of the Moon about the Earth with the movement of the Earth about the Sun.

$$T = 365.256 \text{ days (sidereal year),}$$

$$t = 27.3217 \text{ days,}$$

$$R = 149,500,000 \text{ km (the Earth),}$$

$$r = 384,400 \text{ km (the Moon).}$$

669. Find the mass of the Sun, if the angular velocity of the Earth about the Sun is 1° per day, the gravitational constant $= 6.7 \times 10^{-8}$ cm³/gm sec², and the distance from the Earth to the Sun $R = 1.49 \times 10^8$ km.

670. How does the accumulation of meteoric substance by a planet affect the semi-major axis of its orbit?

SECTION TWO PROBLEMS

671. What would the mass of the Earth have to be (compared with its real mass) for the Moon to revolve about it with its present period, but at twice the distance?

672. How must the mass of the Earth change for the Moon to revolve about it, at its present distance, in 2 days?

673. By how much must the mass of the Earth decrease for the Moon to fly away from her for ever?

674. What would be the parabolic velocity at the distance of the Earth from the Sun, if the mass of the latter increased 100 times?

675. Could the Sun hold our Earth, moving around it in orbit with a velocity of 29·76 km/sec, if the mass of the Sun decreased by half?

676. Would the movement of the Earth be affected if the Sun attained a diameter the same as that of the Earth's orbit, without altering its mass?

677. Determine what tangential velocity a projectile requires to travel around the Earth near its surface, without falling. (The radius of the Earth $R = 6371$ km; the mass of the Earth is $5·97 \times 10^{27}$ g.)

*678. If a velocity of 7·906 km/sec is given to a body in a horizontal direction, it does not fall back to the Earth, but becomes its satellite, circling our planet at its surface. What would the period of revolution of this satellite be?

679. Calculate the parabolic velocity at the surface of the Moon. ($R = 0·27$ of the radius of the Earth; the mass is $1/81$ of the mass of the Earth.)

680. Calculate the parabolic velocity at the surface of the Sun, if the radius of the Sun $R = 1/215$ of an astronomical unit, or 696,000 km.

681. What must the velocity of a body be if it is to circle the Sun at its very surface? Solve this problem with the help of Kepler's Third Law, with the velocity to be determined as the lowest velocity at which a body will not fall on the surface of the Sun.

682. What is the period of revolution of a body moving in a circle at the surface of the Sun?

Hint. Make use of Kepler's Third Law.

683. If the Earth had a satellite with a period of revolution of 8 lunar months, what would its distance be?

684. At what distance from the surface of Mars must a satellite be situated if it is to revolve about the planet with the same period as the planet's own rotation. Take the necessary data from the Table at the end of the book.

685. What velocity is required by an interplanetary rocket ship, to move from the surface of Mars to another planet? Take the necessary data for Mars from the Table at the end of the book.

686. The value of the diameter of a certain planet is found by multiplying the diameter of the Earth by p. The density of this planet is found by multiplying the density of the Earth by q. Disregarding axial rotation, calculate the acceleration of a body falling freely at the surface of this planet.

687. If the diameter of an asteroid is equal to 0·01 of the diameter of the Earth, and its density is the same as the mean density of the Earth, what is the acceleration of gravity at its surface, in comparison with that on the Earth?

688. If a jumper on the Earth remains in the air for 1 sec how long would the same jump last on the surface of the asteroid mentioned in the preceding problem?

689. The radius of the Moon is 1740 km, and its mass is 1/81 of the mass of the Earth. How great is the length l' of a second's pendulum on the Moon's surface, and what period of oscillation t' would a terrestrial second's pendulum have on the Moon? The acceleration due to gravity on the surface of the Earth $g = 9·81$ m/sec²; the radius of the Earth R is 6371 km.

690. A shell leaves an artillery weapon on the Earth with a velocity of 900 m/sec. With what velocity would it leave on the Moon, where any body weighs six times less than it does on Earth? Ignore the resistance of the air on the Earth.

691. Calculate the acceleration due to the force of gravity on the surface of Mars, if its radius is 3430 km and its mass is $6·4 \times 10^{26}$ g.

692. What is the acceleration due to the force of gravity on the surface of the Sun if its radius is 109 times greater than the radius of the Earth, and the density of the Sun is one-quarter that of the Earth?

693. If the diameter of the Sun were doubled, and its mean density unaltered, then how would the acceleration due to the force of gravity on its surface change?

694. What would the acceleration due to gravity be on the surface of the Sun if it increased in diameter to the size of the Earth's orbit keeping its present mass of $1 \cdot 98 \times 10^{33}$ g.

695. Determine the acceleration of gravity on the surface of Jupiter (g) in comparison with its value on the surface of the Earth (g_0), given that the mass of Jupiter m is 317 times, and its radius R is 11 times greater than that of the Earth.

696. The radius of Jupiter R is 71,800 km, the distance of its fourth satellite from its centre is nR (where $n = 26 \cdot 2$), and the period of its revolution t is $16 \cdot 69$ days (in days of 86,400 sec). Calculate the acceleration g on the surface of Jupiter.

697. Compare the acceleration due to gravity on the surface of the Sun itself, and at the distance of the Earth from the Sun if the radius of the Sun is $R = 7 \cdot 0 \times 10^5$ km and the radius of the Earth's orbit $r = 1 \cdot 5 \times 10^8$ km.

698. Determine the diameter, volume and density of Neptune and the acceleration due to gravity at its surface, taking its mean visible diameter to be $2'' \cdot 3$, the mass of the planet to be $17 \cdot 12$ times the mass of the Earth, the parallax of the Sun to be $8'' \cdot 80$ and the mean distance of Neptune from the Sun to be $30 \cdot 07$ astronomical units.

699. Calculate the gravitational constant f in the c.g.s. system, postulating that the density of the Earth, $\delta = 5 \cdot 5$ g/cm^3, the radius of the Earth $r = 6371$ km, and the acceleration due to gravity is 981 cm/sec^2.

700. Determine the value of the Gaussian constant, k in the Law of gravitation, taking the semi-major axis of the Earth's orbit as a unit, the mass of the Earth m as equal to $1/354{,}710$ of the mass of the Sun, and the sidereal year as $P = 365 \cdot 2563835$ days. (The numerical values are those used by Gauss.)

Hint. Denote the mass of the Sun by M and use Kepler's Third Law in its exact formulation.

701. How would the movement of the planets of the solar system change if the mass of the Sun was suddenly halved?

702. How would the orbit of the Earth alter if the mass of the Sun suddenly doubled?

703. By how long would the period of revolution of Jupiter be lengthened if its mass became insignificantly small?

Hint. Jupiter is 1/1048 of the mass of the Sun.

704. What would the length of the year become if the mass of the Earth were reduced a million times?

705. By how much would the length T of a day alter, if meteoric dust falling on the surface of the Earth covered it evenly with a thin layer of mass $m = 138 \times 10^{11}$ tons? The mass of the Earth may be taken as equal to $M = 5 \times 10^{21}$ tons and the moment of inertia of the layer of meteoric dust relative to the Earth's axis as $2/3 \, mR^2$, where R is the radius of the Earth.

706. A meteoric body, having zero velocity relative to the Sun, and situated at infinity, begins to fall towards the Sun. What is its velocity of falling, v, when it reaches a distance of one astronomical unit from the Sun?

Hint. The orbital velocity of the Earth is $v_0 = 30$ km/sec.

707. With what velocity would the Earth fall into the Sun if it became stationary in its orbit? The distance from the Sun to the Earth $R = 1 \cdot 5 \times 10^8$ km; the radius of the Sun $r = 7 \cdot 0 \times 10^5$ km and the angular velocity of rotation of the Earth about the Sun $\omega = 1°$ per day.

708. What orbit would a meteoric body describe, entering the solar system with an infinitely great speed?

709. A certain body situated at a distance of $0 \cdot 7184$ astronomical units from the Sun has a velocity of $33 \cdot 2$ km/sec about the Sun. Determine the shape of the conical section described by the body. Do you know what this body is? (Ivanov.)

710. A comet moves about the Sun, having at a given moment a velocity of $565 \cdot 4$ km/sec. Its radius vector is equal to $0 \cdot 005543$ astronomical units. Determine the eccentricity of the comet's orbit. (Ivanov.)

711. Determine the semi-major axis, the period of rotation, the eccentricity, and the perihelion distance of an imaginary comet, at a distance of one astronomical unit from the Sun, which has a velocity corresponding in direction to a circular orbit, but ten times too small. (Polak.)

712. Prove that for a body describing an elliptical orbit the ratio of its maximum velocity (at perihelion) to its minimum (at aphelion) is that of its greatest distance from the Sun to its least.

713. If v_1 and v_2 are the velocities of a planet in perihelion and aphelion, then

$$(l-e)v_1 = (l+e)v_2,$$

where e is the eccentricity. Prove this.

714. A comet moves in an ellipse, and has an eccentricity of 0·5. Compare its linear and angular velocities at perihelion and aphelion.

715. Compare the linear and angular velocities of a comet at perihelion and aphelion if it moves in an ellipse with an eccentricity of 1/3. Do the same for an ellipse with an eccentricity of 0·75.

716. If the linear velocity of a comet in aphelion is four times less than in perihelion, what is the eccentricity of its orbit?

717. Prove that the geometrical mean of the greatest and smallest velocities of movement in an ellipse, of semi-major axis a, is equal to the velocity of movement in a circle of radius a. At what point of the elliptical orbit will a body have this velocity?

718. At what point in an orbit is the actual linear velocity of a planet equal to its mean velocity?

719. When it is at the end of its semi-minor axis, the angular velocity of a planet is not equal to its mean angular velocity. Why is this so?

720. A comet moves in a parabola with a perihelion distance of one astronomical unit. How long would it take to describe 90° after perihelion (from P to Q in Fig. 29)?

721. Prove that a comet moving in a parabola with a perihelion distance q must take 109·61 $q^{3/2}$ days to describe 90° after perihelion.

722. Two meteoric bodies, M_1 and M_2, move in the same ellipse, with the Sun at one focus S. The distance between them is so small that the arc of the ellipse M_1M_2 may be regarded as a straight segment. The distance M_1M_2 is d when its centre is situated at perihelion P. Supposing that the meteoric bodies move with the same sectorial velocities, determine the distance M_1M_2 when its centre passes through aphelion A, denoting SP by R_1 and SA by R_2. (Meshcherskii.)

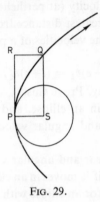

Fig. 29.

723. Determine the distance between the Earth and the Moon given that:

the radius of the Earth R_1 = 6370 km,
the mean density of the Earth δ_1 = 5·5,
the period of rotation of the Moon T = 27·3 days,
the gravitational constant, f = 6·7×10⁻⁸ cm³ g⁻¹ sec⁻².

724. What initial velocity v_0 does a body on the Earth's surface require to reach a height equal to the radius of the Earth?

Hint. Take into consideration only the force of attraction of the Earth, which changes in inverse proportion to the square of the distance of the body from the centre of the Earth. The radius of the Earth is 6·37×10⁸ cm, and the acceleration due to gravity at the surface of the Earth is 980·6 cm/sec². (Meshcherskii.)

725. What initial speed v_0 is necessary to fire a projectile from the surface of the Earth in the direction of the Moon in order to reach the point where the forces of attraction of the Earth and the Moon are equal. The movements of the Earth and Moon, and air resistance, may be ignored. The acceleration due to gravity at the surface of the Earth $g = 9 \cdot 8$ m/sec^2. The ratio of the masses of the Moon and the Earth is $1/80$; the distance between them $d = 60R$ where R is the radius of the Earth (6000 km). The value of f, the gravitational constant is obtained from the formula for two attracting masses M and m,

$$g = f\left(\frac{M}{R^2} - \frac{m}{(d-R)^2}\right).$$

(Meshcherskii.)

726. Prove that the locus of the points at which the forces of attraction of the Sun and the Earth are equal is a sphere of radius

$$\frac{R\sqrt{SE}}{S-E}$$

with its centre lying on the straight line joining the Sun and the Earth, at a distance of

$$\frac{ER}{S-E}$$

from the centre of the Earth on the side opposite to the Sun. S and E are the masses of the Sun and the Earth, and R is the distance from the Earth to the Sun. Express the two quantities given above in kilometres.

727. Find the strength of the maximum perturbing force D_s of the Sun on the Moon compared with the attractive force A_s of the Sun and the attractive force A_e of the Earth.

Note. Denote the distance from the Sun to the Earth by R, the distance of the Moon from the Earth by r, the distance from the Sun to the Moon by ϱ and the Sun and the Earth by S and M.

728. Find the ratio of the greatest possible gravitational influence of the Sun on the Moon to the least possible influence of the Earth on the Moon.

729. Show that if the Moon is regarded as revolving about the Earth, perturbed by the influence of the Sun, then the maximum perturbation will occur in those positions of the Moon where the perturbing effect of the Earth is at a minimum, if we regard the Moon as moving about the Sun, and being perturbed by the Earth.

730. Jupiter completes a full revolution about its axis in 10 hr. Find the ratio of the weight of a body on the equator to that at the poles, looking up the radius of Jupiter R, its mass M, and the gravitational constant f.

Hint. Resolve the ratio of the accelerations by means of Newton's binomial theorem.

731. The Moon in apogee is 1/9 further away than it is in perigee. By what percentage is the tidal force greater in perigee?

732. By how many times are the tides during syzygy theoretically greater than during the quadratures of the Moon? Syzygy occurs when the Moon is in conjunction or opposition.

733. At what time of the year is the tidal force of the Sun greatest, and at what time of the year does it have its least effect? Compare these two values. (Parenago.)

Hint. The eccentricity of the Earth's orbit is 1/60.

CHAPTER XVIII

ASTRONOMICAL INSTRUMENTS AND METHODS

II

A. The objective of a telescope forms a real image at its prime focus of the object under observation, and this image is observed through the eye-piece. One degree of the celestial sphere covers a length in the focal plane of the telescope equal to 1/57 of the focal length F of the objective or the mirror. The magnifying power of the telescope is equal to the focal length F of the objective or the mirror, divided by the focal length f of the eye-piece; and the optical length of the tube is $F+f$.

The *resolving power* of a telescope is the smallest angular separation of two stars simultaneously visible which do not fully merge with each other. The resolving power is given in general as $S = 11''\cdot6/D$, in which D is the diameter of the objective in centimetres; or by the formula $S = 4''\cdot56/D$, in which D is expressed in inches.

B. The brightness of a star is expressed in stellar magnitudes. The ratio of the brightness of stars differing by one stellar magnitude is 2·512. If two stars have apparent intensities I_1 and I_2, and their stellar magnitudes are equal to m_1 and m_2, then

$$\log \frac{I_1}{I_2} = 0\cdot4(m_2 - m_1) \quad \text{or} \quad (m_2 - m_1) = 2\cdot5 \log \frac{I_1}{I_2}.$$

The *penetrating power* of a telescope is the limiting magnitude of stars just visible in the telescope on a completely clear dark night. It is given approximately by the formula $m = 7\cdot5 + 5 \log D$, where D is expressed in centimetres, or by the formula $m =$

9·5+5 log D, where D is the diameter of the objective in inches.

C. The velocity of motion of a light source along the observer's line of vision causes a shifting of the lines in its spectrum from the places which they occupy in the spectrum of a light source which is motionless with respect to the observer. This means that the wavelength of the light changes. The wavelength increases, or the spectral lines move towards the red end of the spectrum, if the light source is moving away from the observer. Conversely, light from a source moving towards the observer is blue shifted. This is known as the doppler effect, and if the wavelength changes from λ to λ', then

$$\lambda - \lambda' = \lambda(v/c) \quad \text{or} \quad v = (\lambda - \lambda')c/\lambda.$$

v is the velocity of the light source which is positive when the light source is receding from the observer, and c is the velocity of light. The wavelengths of light are commonly expressed in microns (μ), in millimicrons (mμ), and in angstroms (Å). 1 Å = 0·1 mμ = 0·0001 μ = 0·0000001 mm. The number of oscillations of a light wave per second is the frequency $v = c/\lambda$. This is an important concept and will be used frequently in the remainder of this book.

D. The coordinates of a star are normally determined by means of the instrument known as the meridian circle. For the determination of time corrections the transit circle is used, set up in the same way as the meridian circle — that is, so that the tube moves only in the plane of the meridian. The axis of rotation of both instruments is the east–west line.

For the measurements of small differences in the coordinates of stars a micrometer is used. The micrometer is a box containing cross-hairs (or spiders' web filaments) which can be moved across the focal plane of the telescope by operating calibrated micrometer screws.

E. Through a telescope stars are visible as tiny discs with a faint ring of light around them, due to diffraction of the light by the edges of the objective.

F. The objective of a telescope, or astrograph (for photographing stars), is characterized by its diameter D and by its power, or focal ratio, D/F.

G. An estimate of the brightness of a celestial body may be made simply by visual comparison of its intensity with the intensity of the stars close to it in the sky, whose stellar magnitudes are known. Two comparison stars are chosen, in whose range of brightness the unknown star lies, and its brightness estimated as a decimal part of the interval. If we denote the unknown brightness of v, the star brighter than it by a, and the star weaker than it by b, then the required magnitude can be worked out as follows:

Suppose for example that the intensity of v appears to be mid-way between a and b, so that we write $a5v5b$. If the difference between a and v is $1\frac{1}{2}$ times as great as the difference between v and b, then we write $a6v4b$, and so on. The required magnitude m_v of the star v can then be found by the formula

$$m_v = m_a + \frac{m_b - m_a}{10} k,$$

if the description is of the form: $akvlb$, where k and l are numbers whose sum, $k + l = 10$.

H. Spectra are normally studied principally from their photographs. The accuracy of the measurement of wavelength in a spectrum depends mainly on the "scale" of the photograph, or spectrogram. The greater the distance on the photograph between a pair of lines of given wavelengths, the greater is the linear dispersion, as it is called. In a spectrum obtained with a prism, the dispersion is a function of the wave length, and is determinable experimentally. On photographs of stellar spectra the red end of the spectrum is always sharply cut off, while the violet end gradually fades out. The latter is relatively brighter compared with the red end of the spectrum for white stars than for yellow, and this effect is even more pronounced for red stars. Among the lines in stellar spectra the most pronounced are the Balmer series of hydrogen lines along the whole spectrum, and two broad lines close to one another in the ultraviolet end of the spectrum,[†] produced by ionized calcium.

SECTION TWO PROBLEMS

734. If a triangular piece of paper is stuck on the objective of a telescope pointed at the Moon, how will the appearance of the Moon change for the observer?

735. If you held your finger in front of the objective of a telescope, would a man looking through the telescope see it?

736. What is the theoretical resolving and penetrating power of a telescope with an 8 cm objective (about 3 in.)?

737. Using the formula for the resolving power of a telescope, determine theoretically the angular distance between the centres of two stellar discs just distinguishable from each other in a telescope with a 24 in. objective.

738. What were the resolving and penetrating power of the 75 cm objective telescope, which was in the Pulkovo Observatory until its destruction?

*739. What magnifying power is required for the angular size of Jupiter (apparent diameter 40″) to appear the same as that of the Moon seen with the naked eye?

740. If the eye-piece at the focal length of a 160 cm objective gives an angular magnification of 200, then what magnification will it give at the focal length of a 12 m objective?

741. If an eye-piece used with an objective of focal length of 1 m gives a magnification of 50 times, then what value will the same eye-piece give with an objective with a focal length of 5 m?

742. The largest refractor in the world in Yerkes Observatory, U.S.A., has a focal length of 19·5 m. What focal lengths of eye-pieces give magnifications of 300, of 1000, and of 3000 times with this refractor?

743. What is the linear diameter of an image of the Sun at the focus of an objective with a focal length of 40 cm? The Sun's angular diameter is 32′.

[†] A few problems in this section demand a basic knowledge of geometric optics, usually given in any High School course in physics.

744. If the angular diameter of the Moon is 31′, then what is the diameter of its image with an objective of focal length 254 cm?

745. What is the focal length of an objective giving an image of the Moon with a diameter of 15 mm?

746. At its nearest approach to the Earth the planet Mars has an angular diameter of 24″. What is the diameter of the photographic image obtained with a refractor with a focal length of 19·5 m?

747. The diameter of a telescope is $1\frac{1}{4}$ m, and its focal ratio is 1/5. What is the linear diameter of the image of Mars at its focus, at a time when the angular diameter of Mars is 25″?

748. How much brighter is a star of the first magnitude than the faintest star visible with the naked eye (that is, a star of the 6th magnitude)?

749. How many times brighter is a star of the 1st magnitude than the faintest star at present measurable (21st magnitude)?[†]

750. The brightness of a certain variable star changes over a range of 7 stellar magnitudes. By how many times is the intensity of the light increased?

751. Between the 20th and 22nd February, 1901, the intensity of a nova star in the constellation of Perseus increased by 25,000 times. What was this change in brightness in stellar magnitudes?

752. If the distance to a star of the 4th stellar magnitude is halved, what will its visual stellar magnitude become?

753. By how much will the stellar magnitude of a star alter if it comes nearer by 40 per cent of its distance? If it goes farther away by the same amount?

***754.** The visible stellar magnitude of Deneb is 1·33, and of Sirius 1·58. How much brighter than Sirius would Deneb appear if they were at the same distance? It is known that Sirius is 75 times closer to us than Deneb.

***755.** Suppose that a certain star goes through a periodic pulsation of its surface while at a constant temperature (that is, at constant brightness per unit surface area of the star). The ratio

[†] With the 5 m telescope at the Mount Palomar Observatory stars of the 22nd magnitude have been measured, and a few of the 23rd.

of the radii of the star in the extreme positions of the pulsation is 1/2. What is the amplitude of the change in the total brightness of the star, in stellar magnitudes?

756. How many stars of the sixth magnitude would equal the brightness of a star of the 1st magnitude?

757. How many stars of zero magnitude give as much light as all the stars from the 10th to the 11th magnitudes (546,000)?

Hint. Take the mean stellar magnitude of the stars between the 10th and the 11th magnitudes to be 10·5.

758. What approximately is the number of stars of zero magnitude which would equal the light of all stars from the 19th to the 20th magnitudes, if their number is $4·4 \times 10^8$?

759. There are 2000 stars of the 6th magnitude in the northern sky. By how many times is their combined light greater than that of Sirius, whose brightness is 1·6 stellar magnitudes?

760. In the spectrum of a star the calcium lines with a wavelength of 4227 Å are displaced towards the violet end of the spectrum by 0·70 Å. Determine the velocity of the star along the line of vision of the observer, and whether it is approaching or receding.

761. What is the frequency of the light in the calcium line mentioned in the previous problem?

762. What is the change in angstroms in the wavelength of the sodium D line ($\lambda = 5896·16$ Å) for a velocity of 160·9 km/sec?

763. The frequencies ν of red and violet light are 451×10^{12} and 783×10^{12}, respectively. What are the corresponding wavelengths? Take the speed of light to be 300,000 km/sec.

*764. In the spectrum of a nova in Hercules in 1934 the dark lines were displaced from their normal places towards the violet end of the spectrum. The line $H\gamma(\lambda = 4341$ Å) was displaced by 10·1 Å. If the lines were caused by absorption by gas expelled from the star, what was its velocity of expulsion?

765. Show that if the tube of a theodolite is pointed towards an object on the Earth, and the tube is then turned about its vertical axis by 180° and again pointed at the object, then half the sum of the two readings on the vertical circle gives the setting at which the tube is pointed at the zenith. Also that half the difference of these readings gives the zenith distance of the object.

766. What is the distance between two adjacent marks on a meridianal circle 1 m in diameter if they are made every 2′? What is the linear value of 1″ on the same circle?

767. Why is it important that both ends of the axis of a transit instrument have exactly the same diameter?

768. How is the observation of the meridianal passage of a star affected if the west bearing of a transit instrument is too high?

769. What would the effect on the transit observation of a star to the south of the zenith be if the eastern bearing of the transit instrument is moved to the north of its correct position. What is the effect of this condition on a culmination to the north of the zenith, and how does it depend on the Declination of the star?

770. What error in the recorded moment of passage of a star would be caused by an incorrect positioning towards the west of the central thread of a transit circle? Would the error be the same for stars with the same Declination? What would happen if the axis of the instrument were rotated through 180°?

*771. A star passes across the field of vision of a stationary telescope in t sec. What is the angular diameter d of the field of vision of the telescope if the Declination of the star is δ?

772. Determine the angular distance between the two vertical threads in the focus of the eye-piece of a meridianal circle if the interval of time between the passage across these threads of the star δ Ursae Minoris is 184 sec. The Declination of the star is +86°36′·6.

773. Does the effect of one revolution of a screw of a micrometer depend on what eye-piece (i.e. magnification) is used in the telescope?

774. The thread of the micrometer screw of an apparatus is 0·5 mm. What angle does this correspond to in the focal plane of a telescope with a focal length of 65 cm?

775. The threads of a micrometer are such that for a telescope of focal length 150 cm a star in its diurnal motion moves from one thread to the next in 15 sec. How long would this take if the focal length of the telescope were 450 cm?

776. What would the appearance of the Moon be seen through a telescope with half its objective covered? How would this affect the appearance of the diffraction discs and rings of a star?

777. What would the image size of the Sun be, through an aperture of diameter $d = 0.0006$ m on a wall situated at $b = 4$ m from the aperture, if the apparent diameter of the Sun is $\alpha = 32'$?

778. The data on the focal length of an astronomical refractor are as follows:

$$\text{objective } F = 160 \text{ cm};$$

$$\text{eye-piece } f = 8 \text{ cm}.$$

What is the angular diameter β of the lunar disc, through the telescope, if the visual diameter of the Moon is $2\alpha = 32'$? What is the length of the tube?

779. The concave mirror of a Newtonian telescope has a focal length of $F = 60$ cm. The distance of an object observed is $a = 500$ m. Say:

(a) At what point on the axis of the tube must one place a small plane mirror, so that the image will be situated 15 cm from the axis?

(b) What is the reduction obtained?

(c) What is the angular magnification obtained on looking at the small image through a magnifying lens of focal length $f = 3$ cm so that the final image is formed at the distance of clearest vision, $S = 24$ cm?

780. In an optical instrument the objective consists of two convex lenses joined together, with focal lengths of F_1 and F_2. What is the focal length F of the system?

*781. Plate I (at the end of the book) shows the appearance of the enlarged images of stars, taken for various distances of the photographic plate from the objective. Which of the plates was taken "in focus"?

*782. The rays of the solar corona, seen during a total eclipse of the Sun, extend 2–3 solar radii above the Sun's limb. Using apparatus of 150 cm focal length, what size photographic plate is needed to record these rays?

*783. There are two astrographs (equatorially mounted photographic telescopes) in an observatory. The first has an objective of 16 cm diameter and a focal ratio of 1 : 4; the second an objective of 16 cm diameter and a focal ratio of 1 : 20. Which of the astrographs will be most profitably employed:

(1) to take a photograph of the tail of a comet;
(2) to photograph the mountains of the Moon;
(3) to obtain a photograph of a shooting star;
(4) to photograph Sun-spots;
(5) for an exact photographic determination of the position of a star in the Pleiades;
(6) to obtain a photograph of the nebula in Orion?

*784. Two planetary nebulae have the same linear dimensions, structure appearance, and total observed brightness, but one is twice as distant as the other. What is the ratio of their surface brightnesses?

785. What is the ratio of the brightnesses of the components of the double star γ Andromedae (see Problem 1059 and the answer to it) in visual intensity, and photographically recorded intensity?

786. Calculate the combined visual stellar magnitude of the binary star γ Andromedae if the visual stellar magnitudes of the components are separately 2·28 and 5·08?

787. Determine the combined stellar magnitude of a double star, consisting of components of second and fourth magnitude.

788. The star α Centauri is double, and its compound magnitude is given as 0·06. The stellar magnitude of the brighter component is 0·33. What is the stellar magnitude of the fainter component?

*789. At what distance must one place an international candle (neglecting absorption of light by the atmosphere) in order to obtain the same illumination as a star of the eighth magnitude ($1·4 \times 10^{-9}$ lux)?

*790. Sirius, the brightest star in the sky, produces an illumination at the Earth of 9×10^{-6} lux, and a star of the sixth magnitude an illumination of 8×10^{-9} lux. What is the stellar magnitude of an international candle at a distance of 1 km? At a distance of 1 m?

791. Determine the stellar magnitude of the variable star v if the records of visual observation are as follows:

$$a\ 4v1c \qquad\qquad b1c\ 4d$$

and if the stellar magnitude of the comparison stars are

$$a = 9{\cdot}2; \qquad c = 9{\cdot}8;$$
$$b = 9{\cdot}4; \qquad d = 9{\cdot}9?$$

792. Determine the best stellar magnitude of the variable star v, from the following records of observations, as the mean of the four separate estimates:

$$a\ 7v\ 3b \qquad a\ 9v\ 1d \qquad c\ 8v\ 2d \qquad c\ 7v\ 3b$$

The stellar magnitudes of the comparison stars are:

$$a = 3{\cdot}74; \qquad c = 4{\cdot}00;$$
$$b = 4{\cdot}61; \qquad d = 4{\cdot}57.$$

*793. We know that extra-galactic nebulae are moving away from us at tremendous speeds, measured in thousands, and even tens of thousands of kilometres per second. What effect has this on the separation of lines of the spectrum obtained with a prism, for instance, Hα and Hδ?

*794. The dispersion of the spectrogram of a star is 60 Å/mm at Hγ. This line in the spectrum of the star is displaced from its normal position by 0·005 mm towards the violet end of the spectrum. What, from Doppler's principle, is the radial velocity of the star in km/sec? The laboratory value for the wavelength of Hγ is 4341 Å.

*795. Suppose that the dispersion of a spectrograph is linear, and that the whole visible spectrum of a star has a length of 5 cm on a photographic plate. What would the linear displacement on the plate be of a spectral line which has a laboratory wavelength of 5000 Å, if the star is approaching us at a speed of 10 km/sec?

*796. Measure the spectrogram of the star Procyon on Plate II (see end of the book), using the photographs above and below it, of the arc spectrum of iron, taken for comparison. The wavelengths of the lines in the arc spectrum are given in angstroms. Estimate the mean dispersion for all parts of the spectrum — the number of angstroms contained in 1 mm on the scale of the spectrogram, and measure the displacement of the lines of iron in the spectrum of the star, relative to the lines in the comparison spectrum, to an accuracy of 1 mm. Measurements must be made from the centres of the dark lines in the spectrum of the star to the centres of the bright lines in the comparison spectrum. This displacement, divided by the dispersion (angstroms per 1 mm for the given part of the spectrogram) gives the difference in wavelengths of the line, for the star and those obtained in the laboratory. Hence, determine the velocity of Procyon relative to the Earth.

Note. Use several lines and for a final result use the mean of the velocities obtained.

*797. In Plate III (see the end of the book) photographs of the spectra of two stars are reproduced. At which end of the picture is the red end of the spectrum, and which of the two stars has a whiter light than the other?

*798. To which chemical element can most of the lines in the spectrogram of the star ζ Tauri (Plate IV) be ascribed?

*799. Plate V is a reproduction on the same scale as the spectra of Vega (spectral class A) of the nova discovered in 1934 in the constellation Hercules. Identify the lines in the spectrum of the nova. In the spectrum of Vega, the last absorption line visible at the red end of the spectrum is the hydrogen line Hβ; the remaining lines are also hydrogen.

*800. In Plate VI (upper) the spectrum of the star ε Orionis (spectral class B0) shows hydrogen lines, whose wavelengths are Hβ = 4861, Hγ = 4341, Hδ = 4102, Hϵ = 3970 (in angstroms). Draw up from these data the dispersion curve, and determine from it the wavelength of the three other lines (marked with dashes) by carefully measuring their position in the spectrum.

Identify these lines with the help of the lines given for the chemical elements in the Table at the end of the book (Table XV).

> *Note.* A dispersion curve shows the variation of wavelength in the spectrum with linear distance in the spectrum, reckoned from some arbitrarily selected zero.

*801. Carry out the exercises in the same way as above for the star α Centauri, whose spectrum is given in Plate VI (lower).

802. White light falls on a crown glass prism with angle of refraction $\gamma = 60°$. The refractive indices for red and for violet light are $n_r = 1 \cdot 524$ and $n_v = 1 \cdot 543$. The red rays are the least deviated by the prism. What is the angle δ between the red and violet rays after passing through the prism? What would the length of the spectrum of a star be, from the red to the violet, if this prism were placed in front of a photographic camera with a focal length of 57 cm?

803. White light falls at an angle of incidence $\alpha = 40°30'$ on a flint glass prism with an angle of refraction $\gamma = 53°$. What is the angle of dispersion between the red and violet, if their refractive indices are $n_r = 1 \cdot 6$ and $n_v = 1 \cdot 64$?

804. White light falls on the face of a flint glass prism with an angle of refraction $\gamma = 36°$ in such a way that the red rays emerge from the prism in a direction perpendicular to its other surface. Calculate the direction δ_v of the violet light, and the angular dispersion of the prism.

The refractive indices for red and violet light are $n_r = 1 \cdot 602$ and $n_v = 1 \cdot 634$, respectively.

805. The Fraunhofer lines B, E and H in the red, green, and violet parts of the spectrum have indices of refraction $n_r = 1 \cdot 526$, $n = 1 \cdot 533$, $n_v = 1 \cdot 547$, or $n_r' = 1 \cdot 695$, $n' = 1 \cdot 712$, and $n_v' = 1 \cdot 751$ in crown and flint glass, respectively.

The angle of refraction of a flint glass prism $\gamma' = 12°$. What is the angle of refraction γ of a crown glass prism used in conjunction with this, so that the red and violet rays leave the system parallel? What is the deviation δ_g of the green and the deviation δ_r of the red rays?

CHAPTER XIX

THE MOON

THE PROBLEMS in this section do not require introduction. It should, however, be noted that there is no atmosphere on the Moon, so that phenomena which are explained by its presence do not occur there. In its revolution about the Earth the Moon keeps the same face towards us, but its entire surface is successively exposed to the Sun. Exact numerical data on the Moon may be found in Table XIII at the end of the book.

SECTION ONE PROBLEMS

806. How many revolutions about its axis does the Moon complete relative to the Sun in a year?

*807. What is the length of a sidereal day on the Moon? How long do the days and nights last there?

808. The Moon takes at least 2 min to rise, observed from the Earth. How long does the Earth take to rise for an observer on the Moon?

809. What is the position of the Earth in the sky, seen by a hypothetical observer located near the centre of the visible hemisphere of the Moon? How will libration affect the apparent position of the Earth?

*810. How does the position of the Earth in the sky seen from the Moon alter, due to libration, if the observer is located on the edge of the hemisphere of the Moon which is visible to us?

811. Describe how the "diurnal" and "annual" movements of the Earth and Sun appear to an observer on the Moon. Neglect the effect of libration on the Moon.

*812. Would it be possible to see the Earth from the Moon at the moment of "new Earth"? (The Moon is not visible from the Earth at the moment of "new Moon".)

813. The Earth has a reflective capacity six times as great as that of the Moon. By how many times is the illumination provided by the Earth on the Moon greater than the illumination provided by the Moon on the Earth? The diameter of the Moon is 0·273 times that of the Earth.

814. By how many times is the light of the Moon at full Moon weaker than that of the Sun if the stellar magnitude of the Moon is −12·5 and that of the Sun −26·7?

*815. Give one of the reasons why the light of the Moon in its first or last quarter is less than half of the light at full Moon.

816. Will the Sun appear the same from the surface of the Moon as it does from the Earth?

817. When the meteor shower of the 11th and 12th August is observed on the Earth, can it also be observed on the Moon?

*818. Is it possible to observe lunar auroral displays on the Moon?

819. How many times less is the force of gravity on the surface of the Moon than on the surface of the Earth, if the mass of the Moon is 1/81 and its radius 1/3·7 of the Earth's?

820. If a man can jump ½ m on Earth, how high could he jump if the force of gravity on the Earth were reduced to that of the surface of the Moon?

821. What weight would a spring balance give on the Moon for a man who weighs 60 kg on the Earth? What weight would a lever balance register?

822. The angular diameter of the crater Copernicus on the Moon is 40″. The distance of the Moon from the Earth is 386,000 km. What is the linear diameter of Copernicus?

SECTION TWO PROBLEMS

*823. At the limit of the full Moon mountains are visible "in profile", protruding from the edge of 0·4″. From general information about the Moon determine the height of the mountains in kilometres.

*824. Using the photograph of the Moon given on Plate VII measure the length of the shadow on the inner slopes of the ring-shaped mountain wall surrounding the plain of the crater Theophilis (in the centre of the photograph) and determine the approximate height in kilometres. At the moment the photograph was taken the height of the Sun above the horizon at this spot on the Moon's surface was

$$h = 0°43'.$$

The angular radius of the Moon is $15'30''$ and its distance 386,000 km. The angular diameter of the crater Theophilis is $59''\cdot5$.

Note. Do not forget to allow for the shortening of length perpendicular to the line of sight due to the curvature of the Moon's surface.

Determine the value of this shortening by measuring apparent diameters of the crater and treating its true form as a circle.

*825. On Plate VII measure the distance AK from the summit of the lunar mountain K which is visible as a bright spot against a dark background, to the terminator on the photograph. The scale is given in Problem 824. From the astronomical almanac, the parallax of the Moon on that day was $1°0'$ and its angular radius was $15'30''$. Hence determine h, the height of the lunar mountains, in kilometres. (Galileo used this method to measure the height of the mountains of the Moon.)

826. The root mean square velocity of a molecule of hydrogen is

$$v = 485 \sqrt{\left(\frac{14\cdot4\,T}{273}\right)} \quad \text{m/sec}$$

where T is the absolute temperature. If the temperature at lunar midday rises to 120°C, do many molecules of hydrogen leave the Moon under these conditions if the velocity of escape on its surface is 2·4 km/sec?

CHAPTER XX

THE PLANETS

THE PROBLEMS in this section are based on general information on the nature of the planets, and on a knowledge of topics covered in previous sections. Where necessary, data are obtainable from the Tables at the end of the book.

The solar constant (for the Earth), referred to in these problems, denotes the quantity of energy falling during 1 min on 1 cm² of surface perpendicular to the Sun's rays, neglecting absorption by the Earth's atmosphere, at the mean distance of the Sun from the Earth.

The solar constant is 1·94 cal/cm²/min.

SECTION ONE PROBLEMS

827. In what respects are the planets all alike? In what respects are the four inner planets alike, but different from the four outer planets? In what respects are the four outer planets alike, but different from the four inner planets?

828. What would be the angular diameter of the Earth seen in transit across the Sun from Jupiter? The distance of Jupiter from the Sun is 5·2 astronomical units, and the diurnal parallax of the Sun is 8″·80 on the Earth.

829. What is the angular diameter of Venus seen from the Earth in its superior conjunction, and during its transit across the disc of the Sun? What is the angular diameter of the Earth at these times from Venus? The Moon from Venus?

The distance from Venus to the Sun is 0·72 astronomical units; the diameter of Venus is 0·99 of the diameter of the Earth; the parallax of the Sun is 8″·80; the diameter of the Moon is 0·27 of the diameter of the Earth.

830. Prove that at the moments of mean opposition, Mars from the Earth has almost exactly the same angular diameter as the Moon from Venus. Why, under these conditions, must the Moon seen from Venus seem brighter than Mars seen from the Earth?

831. On the 2nd May, 1896, the angular radius of Jupiter was found by measurement with a micrometer to be $17''\cdot75$. The distance to the planet calculated from its orbital elements was $5\cdot431$ astronomical units. The parallax of the Sun was $8''\cdot80$. Determine the diameter of Jupiter in comparison with that of the Earth.

832. At the nearest approach of Mars to the Earth (56,000,000 km) its angular diameter is $25''$. What is its linear diameter?

833. If the angular diameter of Venus is $1'$, and its linear diameter 12,000 km, what is its distance from the observer?

834. At what angular distance from the Sun is the Earth seen by an observer on Mars? On Neptune?

835. Supposing that the human eye can resolve objects separated by an angle of $2'$, calculate in kilometres the dimensions of the smallest details on Mars which are distinguishable through a telescope with a magnification of 600 during an opposition of Mars, when its angular diameter is $25''$. Is it probable that the "canals" of Mars could have been constructed artificially of this width? We may note that magnifications greater than 600 times are not of practical use in observation of Mars, because of turbulence in the Earth's atmosphere.

836. How may the surface of the planet Mars be divided into climatical regions if its axis lies at an angle of $65°$ to the plane of its orbit?

837. Describe the climatical conditions on the planet Jupiter, given that its axis of rotation is almost perpendicular to the plane of its orbit.

838. Describe climatical conditions on the planet Uranus, given that the axis of its rotation almost coincides with the plane of its orbit.

839. How many times is the sunlight on Saturn weaker than that on Earth?

840. The comparative distances of the planets Mercury, Venus,

Earth, Mars and Jupiter from the Sun may be expressed by the series 0·4; 0·7; 1·0; 1·5; 5·2. What is the series giving the mean intensity of sunlight falling on these planets?

841. What is the angular diameter of the Sun observed from Neptune? How much weaker is solar illumination on Neptune than on the Earth?

842. What is the solar constant on the planet Mars? The mean distance of Mars from the Sun is 1·52 astronomical units.

843. If the Earth and Neptune are situated on the straight line from the Sun to the nearest star, how much brighter will the star seem from Neptune than from the Earth?

844. The stellar magnitude of the Sun observed from the Earth is −26·7. What is the magnitude of the Sun seen from Neptune? How many times brighter than Sirius is the Sun seen from Neptune?

845. The stellar magnitude of Vega is +0·1, and that of Venus at its maximum brightness −4·3. How many times brighter than Vega is Venus?

846. If Jupiter were situated twice as far from the Sun as it is now, then how much fainter would it seem to us in opposition?

847. Why would the Earth seen from Venus appear brighter than Venus seen from the Earth? Is this always so?

Hint. Take the diameter and reflectivity of both planets to be the same.

*848. The apparent brightness of a planet depends on its distance from the Sun and from the Earth. Which of the two planets, Jupiter and Pluto, show the greater variation in brightness, observed from the Earth, if the semi-major axes of the orbits of these planets are 5 and 40 astronomical units, respectively?

*849. Suppose that the whole mass of the rings of Saturn were gathered into one large satellite, revolving about the planet at the distance of the centre ring, and having the same density as the particles making up the rings. Would the intensity of illumination at night on the surface of Saturn then be greater or smaller in places where the rings are easily visible from the planet?

SECTION TWO PROBLEMS

850. Why does the terminator of Venus observed from the Earth have the form of the arc of an ellipse?

851. At what configuration does the disc of an outer planet have its major phase and how does the Earth appear from this planet at this time?

*852. From Fig. 30, calculate the phase of an outer planet P (the angle TPS) for a given angle at the point T (the Earth) and for given heliocentric distances ST and SP. When is it greatest, and what is this maximum, for Mars, Jupiter and Saturn?

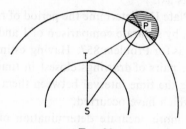

FIG. 30.

*853. The equatorial diameter of the planet Saturn is 120,600 km and its compression is 1/10. What is the polar diameter of Saturn?

854. The equatorial and polar angular radii of Jupiter at its mean distance from the Earth are 18″·71 and 17″·51. Determine the oblateness of the planet, and compare it with that of the Earth.

855. Find an approximate law by which the temperature of an absolutely black body may be found from its distance in astronomical units from the centre of the Sun.

856. Calculate the temperature of an absolutely black spheroid situated at the same distance from the Sun as the planet Mercury, given that the solar constant for the Earth is 1·94 cal/cm²/min.

857. The two pictures of Mars given in Plate VIII were taken through a telescope at times 2 hr apart. By identifying the common details on them, estimate the angle of rotation between exposures and determine approximately the period of diurnal rotation of Mars.

Note. When estimating the angle of rotation do not forget that the visible disc of the planet is a projection of its surface on the plane of the picture. You will notice that two such observations in the course of a single night do not allow us to distinguish a time of rotation of Mars of a few hours, from a few days.

*858. Does the diurnal rotation of the observer with the Earth have any effect on the determination of the period of rotation of a planet about its axis?

*859. Using Plate IX, determine the period of rotation of Jupiter about its axis by separate comparison of 1 and 2, and 5 and 6 in the same way as for Problem 857. Having estimated it approximately from the pairs of drawings closest in time, use drawings 3 and 4, dividing the time interval between them by the number of revolutions which have occurred.

This yields a more accurate determination of the period of rotation.

860. Suppose that the period of rotation of Mars is established by comparison of the sketches made by Huygens on the 28th November, 1659, and sketches made on the 22nd August, 1924.

By how much would the calculated value of the period of rotation of Mars be altered, if Huygens had erred in the dating of his sketches by one day?

861. By how many kilometres per hour does the linear velocity of the white spot on the equator of Jupiter, which has a period of rotation of 9 hr 50 min, exceed the speed of another spot, lying on the same latitude, but having a period of rotation of 9 hr 55 min?

*862. At what distance would one have to place an international candle for it to give the same illumination as Venus, at its greatest intensity (an illumination of 8×10^{-5} lux)?

*863. During the major opposition of 1924 the visual magnitude of Mars was $-2\cdot8$. Its distance from the Sun r was 207,000,000 km, and ϱ, the distance from the Earth, was 56,000,000 km. What will the stellar magnitude of Mars be during an opposition when it is at its furthest from the Earth at a distance $r' = 246,000,000$ km from the Sun, and $\varrho' = 100,000,000$ km from the Earth?

*864. Derive a formula giving the stellar magnitude of an outer planet m at a distance r from the Sun and ϱ from the Earth, if at mean opposition, $r_0 = a$, $\varrho_0 = a-1$ (a is the semi-major axis of its orbit in astronomical units), and the visual stellar magnitude of the planet is m_0.

*865. Calculate from the formula derived in the previous problem the stellar magnitude of a minor planet at a distance of $r = 4\cdot0$ from the Sun and $\varrho = 6\cdot0$ from the Earth, if the semi-major axis of its orbit $a = 3\cdot0$, and the stellar magnitude at mean opposition is $12\cdot0$.

866. What is the sinodic period of Deimos for an observer on Mars?

*867. Phobos, the inner satellite of Mars, is at a distance of $2\cdot8$ radii from the planet's centre. The diameter of Mars is twice the diameter of the Moon. By how many times does the angular diameter of Mars, seen from Phobos, appear greater than the diameter of the Moon to us?

*868. Phobos is situated at a distance of $2\cdot8$ planetary radii from the centre of Mars. Given the diameter of Mars, its distance from the Sun, the diameter of the Moon, and the diameter of Phobos (15 km), determine how much weaker the light is cast by Phobos on Mars during its "full moon", than the full Moon illumination on Earth. Assume the reflectivity of the Moon and of Phobos to be the same. How much does the brightness of Phobos seen from Mars vary at its "full moon" moving from horizon and to zenith?

*869. What is the interval of time, in Martian solar days, between two successive upper culminations of Phobos, observed from Mars? The period of rotation of Mars about its axis with respect to the Sun is 24 hr 37 min mean solar time. The sidereal period of rotation of Phobos is 7 hr 39 min mean solar time.

870. Do the satellites of Jupiter enter the eastern or the western edge of its disc in their passage across it?

871. When Jupiter is visible in the evening, do the shadows of its satellites precede or follow the projections of the satellites themselves across the side of the planet during their transit of Jupiter?

872. What apparent motion would the fifth satellite of Jupiter have to an observer on the planet, if its period of rotation is 12 hr and Jupiter's period of rotation is approximately 10 hr? (Polak.)

873. The longitudes of the three Galilean satellites of Jupiter, seen from the planet, are always related by the formula

$$l_1 + 2l_3 = 3l_2 + 180°.$$

What are the positions of these satellites when no satellites are visible along a line joining the Sun and Jupiter? (Polak.)

*874. Prove that if the slit of a spectrograph is set up along the equator of a swiftly rotating planet and our line of sight lies along the plane of the equator, then stellar spectral lines are straight but inclined to their normal positions.

CHAPTER XXI

COMETS

A COMET is made up of a small star-like luminous nucleus, surrounded by a less compact luminous head, and a diffuse tail, streaming away from the Sun. The tail is often absent in weak and telescopic comets. Comets move about the Sun in conformity with Kepler's Laws; some of them move in ellipses, periodically returning to the Sun (periodic comets), but most of them in parabolas.[†]

Only the nuclei of comets appear to be solid. The heads and tails consist of very diffuse gases and particles, possibly very fine dust. These gases appear to fluoresce in the light of the Sun in the same way as gas in a Geistler tube — the light is not simply reflected. If the comet were luminous only through reflected light its intensity would change in inverse proportion to the square of its distance from the Sun. In fact it changes much faster than this. From observation we obtain a mean law of inverse proportionality to the power of four of the distance from the Sun. The gases are injected into the head and tail of the comet by the nucleus, from which they evaporate under the action of the Sun. The radiation of the Sun exerts a force on the molecules of the tail which is stronger than that produced by the gravitational attraction of the Sun. For this reason, the Sun tends to deflect the tails of comets, and they are almost always turned away from the Sun.

Many of the problems concerning comets are constructed from material presented in preceding sections.

---

† The orbits of comets which are considered to be parabolic are probably in fact very extended elliptical orbits.

SECTION ONE PROBLEMS

*875. How is it possible to distinguish a tailless comet from an ordinary nebula?

876. It was once thought that comets were phenomena in the Earth's atmosphere. What observations would be sufficient to disprove this hypothesis?

877. Is it possible to determine the length of a comet's tail in kilometres with great accuracy?

*878. From the picture of Donati's comet, in 1858 (Plate X), determine the length of the comet's tail in kilometres, given that the distance of the comet from the Earth was 57,000,000 km.

Hint. Assume the tail to lie in a plane perpendicular to the line of vision.

879. Is it possible for a periodic comet to keep its appearance unchanged forever?

880. From Kepler's Third Law, calculate the period of a comet whose aphelion is at a distance of 140,000 astronomical units. This is about half the distance to the nearest known star.

881. The semi-major axis of the orbit of the comet Eucke is 2·22 astronomical units, and its eccentricity 0·847. Draw the orbit of this comet, and determine from your plan its distance from the Sun at its perihelion and its aphelion. (Nabokov and Vorontsov Velyaminov.)

*882. On its approach towards the Earth and the Sun the brightness of a certain comet decreased. How can this phenomenon be explained?

*883. One of the comets discovered by G. N. Neujmin passed through perihelion on the 9th March, 1916. Later observations of a comet with similar orbital elements, passing through perihelion, were made on the 16th January, 1927, 22nd June, 1932, and 1st May, 1943. If these are separate appearances of the same comet, what is its period of revolution about the Sun?

SECTION TWO PROBLEMS

884. Will the orbits of a periodic comet be exactly the same on successive returns to the Sun?

885. How do comets with orbits which almost coincide over a range of hundreds of millions of kilometres from the Sun, have periods differing from each other by hundreds of years?

886. Calculate the distance of the comet 1866 I from the Sun in aphelion from the following data:

eccentricity $e = 0.905$,

perihelion distance $q = 0.976$ astronomical units.

887. The comet 1882 II had a period of revolution $T = 770$ yr and a perihelion distance of 0.0078. Find

        (1) the semi-major axis;
        (2) the eccentricity;
        (3) the velocity in perihelion;
        (4) the velocity in aphelion.

*888. Comets with very similar elements passed through perihelion on 31st August, 1790, 24th February, 1858 and 11th September, 1885. If this is the same comet, then what is its period of revolution about the Sun, and what is the semi-major axis of its orbit?

*889. The orbits of two comets lie in the plane of the ecliptic, and have perihelion distances of 0.5 and 2.0 astronomical units. Each of these comets has a tail 150,000,000 km long. Is it possible for the Earth to pass through the tail of either of these comets?

890. On what factors does the apparent angular length of a comet's tail depend?

*891. Suppose that a comet is moving in an elliptical orbit, which is nearly a parabola. How will the semi-major axis of this orbit be affected by a small increase of velocity at perihelion?

892. The velocity of a comet moving through a parabolic orbit is inversely proportional to the square root of its distance from the Sun. At the distance of the Earth a comet has a velocity of 40 km/sec. What is the velocity of the comet at a distance of 100,000 astronomical units from the Sun, if its orbit is parabolic?

893. The great comet of 1882 approached to 0·00775 a.u. from the Sun and split into four small comets. What was the linear velocity at perihelion of those of its components which had periods of revolution of 769 years?

894. Another component of the disintegrated comet of 1882 has a period of revolution of 875 years. How much greater was its speed at perihelion than the fragment in the above example?

895. Suppose that two small masses move about the Sun in the same extended orbit, with one situated a little ahead of the other. How will their relative distance vary as they move in orbit? Could this provide an explanation for changes in the dimensions of comet heads?

Hint. Use Kepler's Law of areas.

896. Suppose that the particles constituting the head of a comet have almost exactly the same point of perihelion, but slightly different points of aphelion. How will the dimensions of the comet alter as it moves in orbit?

897. From the theory of tail formation given, is it possible for the tail of a comet to be equally long when the comet is approaching the Sun, and when it is moving away from it?

898. What would the trajectory of comet-tail particles be, if the force of repulsion acting on them from the Sun were equal to the force of gravitation?

899. What (qualitatively) would the trajectory of the particles of a comet-tail be, if the force of solar repulsion acting on them exceeded the attraction towards the Sun?

900. What would the trajectory of the particles of a comet-tail be if the force of solar repulsion acting on them were a thousand times greater than the attraction towards the Sun?

901. What would the trajectory of the particles of a comet-tail be if the force of repulsion from the Sun were a small fraction of the force of gravitation?

***902.** If the Earth is not situated too close to the plane of a cometary orbit then it is possible to determine the shape of its tail and classify it according to an approximate sequence due to F. A. Bredichin. There are three types:

Type I tail lies along the radius vector from the Sun;
Type II curves significantly away from this direction;
Type III sharply bent away from the radius vector.

Any point on the projection of the radius vector on the celestial sphere satisfies the equation

$$\tan \delta = \frac{[\tan \delta_0 \sin(\alpha_1-\alpha)-\tan \delta_1 \sin(\alpha_0-\alpha)]}{\sin(\alpha_1-\alpha_0)}$$

where α and δ are the coordinates of the point of this projection, α_0 and δ_0 the coordinates of the Sun, and α_1 and δ_1 are the coordinates of the nucleus of the comet.

These may have to be converted in practice to the equinox of the year for the corresponding coordinate nets on which the comet is sketched. Set down the appropriate value of α and calculate the corresponding δ for two or more points. Plot these coordinates on the drawing of the comet, and they should form a straight line with the nucleus of the comet.

Following these instructions, determine the types of the tails of the comet 1910 I, sketched on the stellar map (Fig. 31). At the moment of sketching (6·17 February, G.M.T.), the coordinates of the nucleus of the comet were

$$\alpha_1 = 326°14',$$
$$\delta_1 = \quad 5°36'.$$

The coordinates of the Sun were

$$\alpha_0 = 318°43',$$
$$\delta_0 = \quad 15°59'.$$

As the tail of the comet always points away from the Sun, it is obvious from the map that α must not be taken less than 21 hr 46 min or $326\frac{1}{2}°$. (S. P. Orlova.)

903. By how much does the brightness of a comet change if its distance from the Earth Δ, and its distance from the Sun r both decrease by a factor of 2. The apparent luminosity of comets varies as $l/r^4\Delta^2$.

904. What is the change in apparent magnitude of a comet on recession from the Earth and the Sun by a factor of 2, if its

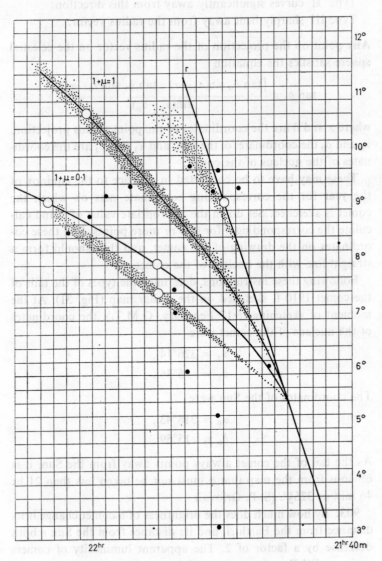

FIG. 31. A drawing of the 1910 comet, with three tails.

brightness varies as

$$\frac{I_1}{I_0} = \frac{\varDelta_0^2 r_0^4}{\varDelta_1^2 r_1^4}$$

where $\varDelta$ is its distance from the Earth and r is its distance from the Sun?

*905. At a distance $\varrho = 0.5$ from the Earth, and $r = 1.5$ from the Sun, the integrated brightness of a comet is equal to that of a star of magnitude 8·0. If the brightness of the comet changes by the law $l/r^4\varrho^2$, calculate the stellar magnitude which the comet would have had at a distance of $\varrho = 1$ and $r = 1$.

*906. The brightness of the nucleus of a certain comet falls by a factor of 16 as it increases its distances from the Sun and the Earth by a factor of two. What are the proportions of reflected sunlight to luminescence in the light of the comet?

*907. How does observation of the changes in brightness of comets make it impossible to consider these celestial bodies as self-illuminating gaseous spheroids, of the same type as stars?

*908. Molecules of cyanide (CN) are emitted from the surface of the cometary nucleus at a temperature of 200°C under the heating action of the Sun's rays. Would they leave the nucleus of the comet if the diameter of the particles were of the order of 100 m, and the density $\delta = 2.7$ g/cm^3?

*909. What would become of the nucleus of a comet if it consisted of a collection of meteoric particles, and passed frequently within a short distance of the Sun?

910. According to the hypothesis put forward by the astronomer S. K. Vsekhsvyatskov, periodic comets are formed from substances thrown up by powerful eruptions on Jupiter. What would the minimum initial velocity of the erupted substances from such an upheaval have to be, if the resistance of the atmosphere on Jupiter is ignored?

CHAPTER XXII

METEORS AND METEORITES

I

METEORIC bodies are particles of dust and rock moving through space. The great majority of them are very small and those that fall into the Earth's atmosphere with sufficient velocity ignite and vaporize, never reaching the Earth's surface. These are shooting stars or meteors. Heavier meteoric bodies fly through the atmosphere in the form of burning spheroids, known as fire-balls or bolides. In exceptional cases, a heavy body falls to the Earth, and is termed a meteorite.

If the paths of meteors across the sky are observed during a single night, and drawn on a star chart, then sometimes the majority of these paths, produced backwards, intersect at almost a single point. This point is called the Radiant. Streams of meteors, named after the constellation in which their radiants are situated, take part in the diurnal rotation of the celestial sphere, indicating that their origin is extraterrestrial. The fact that the paths of meteors meet at the point of the radiant means that meteors travel in parallel paths. The apparent divergence is due to perspective. Meteors belonging to a definite radiant are often observed in the course of a single day, or on a few definite dates in the year, every year. This means that the paths of these meteoric bodies in space intersect the Earth's orbit at certain points, which the Earth passes through on the same date each year. These streams of meteors move about the Sun in swarms or in streams, in orbits described by Kepler's Laws.

II

Swarms of meteors periodically returning to the Sun are gradually scattered along their orbits by the tidal forces exerted by the Sun and the planets. Meteors travelling through space in isolation and not related to a radiant are termed sporadic.

The heights of the points of appearance, and of extinction, of meteor trails can be determined in the following way. Two observers are situated at points A and B, where the distance AB and the angle between AB and the meridian are known. They observe and record on a star map the same meteor. Because of parallax, a given point on the meteor trail will have the horizontal coordinates h_1 and A_1 for observer A, and h_2 and A_2 for observer B. Figure 32 shows the base AB, with the meridians at A and B assumed parallel. From the point A we draw a straight line with azimuth A_1 and from the point B a straight line with azimuth A_2, to their intersection at the point C. From A and B we also draw the straight lines AE_1 and BE_2 at angles h_1 and h_2 to the lines AC and BC, respectively. From E_1 and E_2 we draw perpendiculars to AC and BC, respectively. The lengths CE_1 and CE_2 correspond to the heights above the surface of the Earth of the points on the meteor trail whose coordinates were used. If the observations were exact then $CE_1 = CE_2$. If they are not, the best value is the mean.

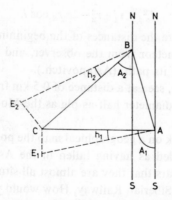

FIG. 32. The determination of the height of a meteor.

SECTION ONE PROBLEMS

911. How is it possible to prove that in fact stars do not fall from the sky?

*912. When a meteor track appears so bright that it obscures the other stars, how will this appear to an observer watching the Earth from the Moon?

913. Meteors from the swarm of the Leonids have a radiant with a Right Ascension of 10 hr and are observed on the 14th November. At what time of the night is their radiant visible?

914. Given that the period of the Leonid meteor stream is $33\frac{1}{4}$ yr, determine the semi-major axis of its orbit.

*915. Estimate the approximate width of the meteor stream of the Perseids in kilometres, if they are observed from 16th July to 22nd August.

*916. On the star map (Fig. 33) the paths of meteors observed in the course of a single evening are traced out. Determine the position of the radiant and its equatorial coordinates (using a stellar atlas or a star chart).

*917. Photographs of meteors show that their radiant occupies a certain area in the sky – that is, their paths, when produced back, do not meet exactly at one point. What does this fact indicate?

918. Prove that the true length of the path of a meteor in the atmosphere is

$$L^2 = r_1^2 + r_2^2 - 2r_1 r_2 \cos l,$$

where r_1 and r_2 are the distances of the beginning and the end of the path of the meteor from the observer, and l is the apparent angular length of its path. (Astapovitch.)

*919. A bolide, seen at a distance of 0·5 km from the observer, had an apparent diameter half as big as the Moon. What was its real diameter?

920. If we mark on a geographical map the points of landing of meteorites recorded as having fallen in the Asiatic part of the U.S.S.R., it appears that they are almost all situated close to the line of the Great Siberian Railway. How would you explain this? (Astapovitch.)

*921. Two meteors, moving in the plane of the ecliptic with a speed of 30 km/sec perpendicular to the radius vector of their orbits relative to the Sun, enter the atmosphere of the Earth in opposite directions. The initial directions of their velocities in the atmosphere are tangential to the Earth's surface. What will be the fate of these meteorites?

Note. Do not take the resistance of the atmosphere into consideration.

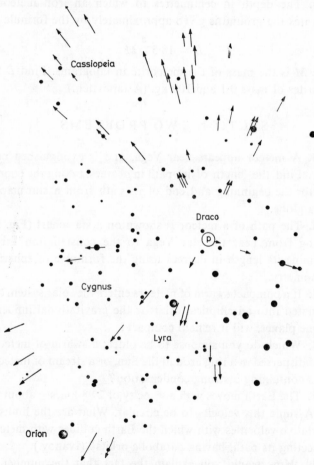

FIG. 33. Paths of meteors plotted on a chart.
Constellations on chart: Cassiopeia; Draco; Cygnus; Lyra; Aquila.

922. What is the kinetic energy of a meteorite with a mass of 1 g travelling with a speed of 60 km/sec? (Astapovitch.)

923. Because of the resistance of the air the velocity of falling meteorites close to the Earth's surface is constant, and is given by

$$v = 35 \cdot 5 \sqrt[6]{M} \text{ m/sec}$$

where M is the mass of the meteorite in grams. Find the velocities of fall of meteorites of weights of 1 mg and of 1 g. (Astapovitch.)

924. The depth in centimetres to which an iron meteorite penetrates the ground is given approximately by the formula

$$D = 18 \cdot 3 \sqrt[3]{M}$$

where M is the mass of the meteorite in kilograms. Find D for meteorites of mass 0·1 and 100 kg. (Astapovitch.)

SECTION TWO PROBLEMS

925. A meteor appears near Vega, and is extinguished near Altair. Find the length of its path in degrees, taking the coordinates for the beginning and end of its path from a star map or from a globe.

926. The path of a meteor is shown on a star chart (Fig. 33) crossing from near the star Vega to the constellation Libra. Determine its length in degrees using the formulae of spherical trigonometry.

927. If a compact swarm of meteors enters the solar system and is deviated into an elliptical orbit by the gravitational influence of some planet, will it remain compact?

928. Which do you suppose to be older: a swarm of meteoric bodies dispersed in a ring around the Sun, or a stream of meteoric bodies containing a strong condensation?

929. The Earth moves with a velocity of 29·8 km/sec about the Sun. Assume this velocity to be circular. What are the limits of the relative velocities with which the Earth collides with meteors intersecting its path, having parabolic orbits? (Ivanov.)

*930. How would you explain the fact that the number of sporadic meteors increase towards morning?

931. Why does a meteoric stream, evenly dispersed along its orbit, generally meet the Earth only once in the year?

932. Prove that if w is the mean angular velocity of a meteor, r is its distance from the observer, and ψ is its angular distance from the radiant, then the linear velocity of the meteor is given by

$$v = \frac{r}{\sin \psi} w$$

where w is small. (Astapovitch.)

*933. Calculate the intensity of the light of a meteor in international candles, if it travels at a height of 100 km above the surface of the Earth with the brightness of a star of the first magnitude, and if the stellar magnitude of an international candle at a distance of 1 km is 0·8.

934. Prove that observers standing back to back see all meteors appearing above an area of radius 300 km. If they observe, on the average, 30 meteors an hour, then how many meteors altogether fall to the Earth in the course of a single day?

935. On the 9th October, 1933, an abundant shower of meteors was observed everywhere. At its maximum, close to the zenith, 500 meteors were observed in 1 min. Assuming that the observers at a station could observe all the meteors appearing above an area of radius 300 km, determine the mean distance between the meteors, if their velocity, relative to that of the Earth, was 40 km/sec.

936. If the Earth is struck daily by 20,000,000 meteors, determine the number of meteors contained in space within a cube with a side of 1600 km.

937. How many times per day would the Earth collide with meteors if space were filled so that the distance between neighbouring meteors was 160 km?

*938. Determine by the graphical method described on p. 179 the height of a meteor above the surface of the Earth from the following data:

Observers A and B are situated at a distance of 42 km from each other, and the line joining them intersects the meridian at an angle of 45°. For the mean path of a meteor, observer A

found the coordinates to be $h_1 = 35°$, $A = -65°$, and observer B found them to be $h_2 = 45°$, and $A_2 = 72·5°$.

939. On the 11th August, 1937, a meteor appeared above Moscow ($\phi = 55°48'·4$; $\lambda = 37°54'·6$) with the coordinates

$$A = -52°·1,$$

$$h = 24°·2.$$

The same point was observed at Vladimir ($\phi = 56°3'·5$; $\lambda = 40°14'·0$) to have the coordinates

$$A = -9°·8$$

$$h = 31°·9.$$

Find the length b and the azimuth a of the base of observation, and then determine H, the height of the appearance of the meteor above the Earth's surface by a graphical method. (Astapovitch.)

*940. The study of the structure of iron meteorites shows that they seem to have been formed under conditions where masses cool very rapidly, in a weak gravitational field, but under enormous pressure. What significance, in the light of these data, has their chemical composition for a study of the inner parts of the Earth?

941. In the town of Nikolaevsk-on-the-Amur ($\phi = 53°8'$) on the 25th November, 1916, at 11 hr 49 min there appeared in the sky a bright fire-hall (bolide), which fell to the ground in the form of two meteoric masses weighing 50 and 200 kg. Determine the constellation from the direction of which the meteorite fell to the Earth.

Hint. Translate solar into stellar time. (Kamen'chchikov.)

*942. Calculate the probability that a meteorite falling vertically on the Earth should hit a certain man on the head, given that the surface area of the Earth is $5·1 \times 10^{18}$ cm^2.

943. What fraction of the energy of a meteor travelling at a velocity of 60 km/sec is sufficient for its complete evaporation if the combustion of 1 g of a stone meteor uses up 10^9 ergs of energy? Where does the remaining kinetic energy of the meteorite go?

944. On the 1st March, 1929, in western Siberia, the meteorite "Khmelkiva" fell to Earth. At what height above the Earth did it cease to glow, if observations made in three different places, at the moment of the extinction of its light, were as follows? (Astapovitch.)

Settlement	Height of point of extinction (degrees)	Distance "d" (km)
Ekaterinskoe	12	34·8
Sishchikov	30	13·0
Oopari	20	30·0

CHAPTER XXIII

THE SUN

I

THE SUN appears as an incandescent gaseous spheroid, which does not revolve as a solid body. Its maximum angular velocity of rotation is at the equator. The period of revolution of various parts of the Sun, relative to the stars, is called the stellar (or sidereal) period of their rotation. At the equator this is about 25 days. The sinodical period of rotation of the Sun about its axis is the period of its rotation about its axis relative to the Earth (which revolves about the Sun in the same direction as the Sun rotates about its own axis). The sinodical period of rotation of the Sun is about 27 days at its equator.

Spots on the surface of the Sun are relatively cool (4700°C) regions of gas. The spots are generally vortices, so that their centres often lie below the surrounding bright surface, or photosphere. The photosphere is surrounded by the atmosphere of the Sun, or chromosphere, and above this rise the streamers of hot gas known as prominences. The number of spots changes and the general solar activity varies over a period of about 11 years.

The polar aurora of the Earth occur high in the stratosphere and are produced by electric and magnetic interactions of corpuscular radiation from the Sun. This radiation arises in the main part from sunspot areas, and auroral activity changes with the Sun-spot cycle.

II

The equator of the Sun is inclined to the ecliptic at an angle of 7°10'·5, and the longitude of its ascending node is 73°47'. The spots slowly change their positions among their surroundings.

Among the Fraunhofer lines observed in the solar spectrum are some produced by light absorption in the Earth's atmosphere. The study of solar energy and the determination of the temperature of the Sun are based on the Laws of photometry and radiation taught in school physics courses.

SECTION ONE PROBLEMS

945. The diurnal horizontal parallax of the Sun is $8''{\cdot}8$, and the angular radius of the Sun is $16'{\cdot}0$. Find from this the linear radius, the surface area, and the volume of the Sun in comparison with that of the Earth.

946. How much time would it take to fly round the equator of the Sun at a speed of 200 km/hr? The necessary data may be obtained from the Table at the end of the book.

947. A Sun-spot maximum occurred in 1938. Were there many spots in 1950 and in 1954?

*948. From Plate XI, determine the Wolf *(sic)* number characterizing the action of the Sun on the day on which the photograph was taken.

Note. The degree of the covering of the Sun by spots is characterized by Wolf's number, $W = n + 10 N$, where n is the number of separate spots, and N is the number of groups of spots, including isolated spots.

949. What is the angular diameter of a Sun-spot which has a linear diameter equal to that of the Earth?

950. Given that the smallest object which can be seen must have an angular diameter of not less than $2'$, calculate the diameter of the smallest Sun-spot which can be seen with the naked eye through a dark glass.

951. If the smallest Sun-spot visible to us has a diameter of $0''{\cdot}7$, what is its linear diameter?

*952. From a photograph of the Sun (Plate XI), given its angular diameter ($32'$) and parallax ($8''{\cdot}8$), determine by means of measurement the linear dimensions of the largest Sun-spot in comparison with the diameter of the Earth.

953. Why was auroral activity in 1937 much greater than in 1933?

*954. Measure, on Plate XIII, the position of any detail of the prominence, and estimate its velocity in km/sec.

955. Spectra from areas in the neighbourhood of Sun-spots often show the red hydrogen line Hα ($\lambda = 6563\cdot0$ Å) shifted towards the red. If the measured wavelength appears to be 6566·0 Å, what is the radial velocity of the hydrogen at these points?

956. By how many angstroms does the wavelength of the green-blue hydrogen line Hβ ($\lambda = 4861\cdot5$ Å) change at a point of the solar disc, where the hydrogen is moving away from us at a velocity of 137 km/sec?

957. What is the apparent magnitude of the Sun observed from the nearest stars? (This distance is about 270,000 astronomical units.) (Polak.)

958. How much meteoric substance must fall daily on 1 m² of the Earth's surface at a speed of 40 km/sec to generate a quantity of heat equivalent to that provided by the Sun, which is about 5 great cal/min on 1 m².

959. The solar constant is 1·94 cal/cm²/min, and in the mean the Earth gets from the Sun 5 great cal/min/m². How many kilograms must fall annually on the Earth with a velocity of 40·2 km/sec on every square metre, to supply the same heat received during the year by 1 m² of the Earth's surface?

960. What mass, falling from a height of 100 m, will convert into heat, kinetic energy equivalent to the energy from solar illumination on 10 m² of the Earth's surface in the course of an hour?

Note. Assume that 50 per cent of the radiation is absorbed by the atmosphere. The mechanical equivalent of heat is 427 kg. m.

SECTION TWO PROBLEMS

961. What is the astronomical latitude and longitude of the point of intersection of the axis of rotation of the Sun with the northern celestial hemisphere?

962. If the time of rotation of a Sun-spot at a latitude of 45° is 28·09 days, then what is its sinodic period of rotation, visible to us?

963. The interval of time between two photographs of spots is 2·0 days and they reveal an angle of rotation relative to the central meridian of 24°. Determine the sidereal and the sinodic period of the rotation of the Sun about its axis.

*964. From measurements on Plate XII, which is a sketch of the positions of Sun-spots, determine the sinodic and the sidereal periods of rotation of the Sun about its axis.

965. A. A. Belopol'skii determined by spectral analysis, that points on the Sun's equator revolve with a linear velocity of 2 km/sec. What is the sidereal period of revolution of the Sun about its axis?

*966. On the equator of the Sun the mean angular velocity is 14·37° a day. In 25·05 days one of the spots, visible close to the equator, described an arc of 361·5°. What was the speed of displacement of this spot relative to the gases surrounding it, in kilometres per second?

967. For the angle of the diurnal rotation of Sun-spots the formula

$$\xi = 14\cdot37° - 2\cdot79° \sin^2 \phi$$

was established, where ϕ is the heliographical latitude of the spot. What are the periods of rotation of the Sun at the equator, at a latitude of 30°, and at a latitude of 45°?

968. In how long will a spot at the equator of the Sun overtake, by a single revolution, another spot situated at latitude 30°? The periods of rotation of the Sun at these latitudes are equal to 25·05 and 26·34 days, respectively.

*969. As a spot rotates with the Sun towards the edge of the solar disc, the part of its penumbra or outer portion, nearest the centre of the disc, becomes invisible. This has been interpreted as indicating funnel-shaped spots (Fig. 34).

Determine the depth bc of a Sun-spot in kilometres (Fig. 35), given the distance to the Sun. In the case of the spot given, the angular distance from the centre of the solar disc, at which the wall of the funnel $a'b'$ coincides with the line of vision, measured with a micrometer, was 10'. The quantity $a'c' = ac$, by the same measurement was equal to 10''. In the triangle $a'b'c'$ the side $a'b'$ may be taken as parallel to the line OA, where the observer is at A, and the centre of the Sun is situated at O.

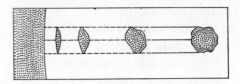

FIG. 34.

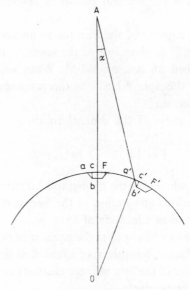

FIG. 35.

*970. In Plate XIV spectra from the Sun are reproduced. The uppermost was taken when the Sun was at a zenith distance 30°, and the lower at a zenith distance 87°. The lower strip of the spectrum is a continuation of the upper one, and lines situated in the upper strip on the right are repeated on the left of the lower strip. By comparing these spectra, find what lines of the spectrum of the Sun can be designated as telluric (that is, are produced by the absorption of sunlight in the Earth's atmosphere).

*971. In the spectrum of the chromosphere, taken with an objective prism during a total eclipse of the Sun, the emission lines of the chemical elements can be observed in the form of narrow crescents. The reasons for this phenomenon are clear from Fig 36, where S is the centre of the Sun and L the centre of

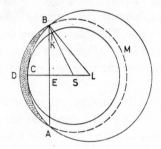

FIG. 36.

the Moon. The shaded area of the chromosphere is not covered by the Moon. Each line on the spectrogram will appear as an arc, and if a line is produced at a definite height M in the chromosphere, the length of the arc in the spectrogram will indicate that height. From Fig. 36 derive a formula for the height $h = BK = DC$ from the lengths of the arcs (chords) AB on a photograph, if the radius of the Sun is r and of the Moon R.

972. Calculate, in international candles, the output of light from the Sun, if the illumination given by it at the mean distance of the Earth is 135,000 candles. Calculate also the output from one square centimetre of the Sun's surface.

973. Making use of the data given in Problem 972, express the total light output of the Sun in lumens, and the surface brightness in lamberts.

974. On the basis of the data in the preceding exercise calculate in lamberts the surface brightness of an ideal white surface (of albedo 1) situated at the distance of the Earth from the Sun.

975. Determine the "light efficiency" of the Sun, and compare it with artificial sources of light, giving 1–2 candles/watt. The full power of the radiation of the Sun may be taken as equal to $3\cdot79$ 10^{26} W.

976. Given that the solar constant is $1\cdot94$ cal/cm^2/min, calculate the total of the Sun's energy output in terms of horsepower.

977. Calculate the thickness of a layer of ice surrounding the Earth, which the Sun's radiation, perpendicular to the Earth's surface, could melt in 1 hr. The solar constant is $1\cdot94$ cal/cm^2/min.

978. Suppose that a layer of ice 15 m thick envelopes the surface of the Sun. Calculate the time necessary for this layer to be thawed out.

979. Given that 1 kilowatt-hour of electric energy costs 20 copeck (1 rouble = 100 copecks), and that the solar constant is $1\cdot94$ cal/cm^2/min, calculate the value of the solar energy incident on Earth per sec.

980. The maximum energy in the solar spectrum is found at a wavelength of 4700 Å. Determine the temperature of the Sun according to Wien's Law.

$$\lambda_{\max} = \frac{c}{T}.$$

(The constant for this law is $0\cdot288$.)

*981. Wien's formula

$$E = c \times \lambda^{-5} e^{-c_2/\lambda T}$$

is an approximation to Planck's exact formula. Using it, determine the temperature of the Sun, given that a measurement with a spectrobolometer, gave the energy of the solar spectrum at the wavelengths 4330 and 8660 Å as 456 and 174, respectively (in the conventional units). In Wien's formula $c_2 = 1\cdot432\ \lambda$ and the letter E designates energy.

*982. For the determination of the solar constant a pyrheliometer was originally used, consisting of a cylindrical vessel, whose circular front was set up perpendicular to the Sun's rays, and covered with lamp black. The vessel was filled with water and a thermometer was placed in it.

Deduce the formula for the determination of the solar constant I, neglecting the absorption of sunlight by the atmosphere.

Note. The heated surface is p
The volume of water V;
of total thermal capacity c
The water heats up from t_1 to t_2 in time dt.
The cooling due to radiation from the surface of the box is P.
The loss of heat due to radiation for a unit of surface in 1 min was j. The heat absorbed by the thermometer itself may be neglected.

983. Taking the known value of the solar constant as $c = 1.94$ cal/cm² per minute, calculate the temperature of the Sun from the Stefan–Boltzmann Law ($E = \sigma T^4$).

You are given that the distance to the Sun is $R = 1.5 \times 10^8$ km, the radius of the Sun is $r = 6.9 \times 10^5$ km, the constant of Stefan's Law $\sigma = 5.73 \times 10^{-5}$, and the mechanical equivalent of heat $a = 4.18 \times 10^7$ erg.

984. By how much must the temperature of the surface of the Sun change in order to produce a change of 1 per cent in the solar constant?

985. Explain why various methods of determining the temperature of the Sun give slightly different results.

986. Calculate the temperature of an absolutely black body, located in the immediate vicinity of the Sun's photosphere.

*987. According to Helmholtz's theory, the energy of Solar radiation might be produced by a compression of the solar sphere at a rate of 35 m a year. At this speed of compression, when would the visible angular diameter of the Sun diminish by $0.1''$, a value within the measuring capacity of modern instruments?

*988. What is the work done by the force of gravity in compressing the Sun from infinitely great dimensions to its present size?

989. The Sun emits 2.2×10^{29} great calories of radiant energy per year. It has been suggested that this loss of energy is made up by the very large number of meteorites which fall on the surface of the Sun. Calculate by how much per year the mass of the Sun must increase if the meteorites fall from infinity, the constant of the force of gravity is $k = 6 \cdot 6 \times 10^{-8}$ in the cgs system, and the radius of the Sun, $R = 6 \cdot 9 \times 10^5$ km.

990. From the relationship between mass and energy, calculate by how much the mass of the Sun must diminish each year, if its annual output is $1 \cdot 2 \times 10^{41}$ erg.

991. It may be reckoned that one-third of the mass of the Sun $(2 \times 10^{33}$ g) consists of hydrogen. If the Sun loses $1 \cdot 2 \times 10^{41}$ ergs annually, how long will it keep burning at this rate if its source of energy is the conversion of hydrogen into helium?

Note. Due to the nuclear packing effect, the conversion of 1 g of hydrogen into helium releases $6 \cdot 6 \times 10^{18}$ ergs of energy.

CHAPTER XXIV

THE MOVEMENTS AND THE NATURE OF THE STARS

I

THE DISTANCE to a star, R, expressed in parsecs, is the reciprocal of the parallax of the star, π, expressed in seconds of arc. The path traversed by a ray of light in the course of a year is known as a light year. One parsec $= 3\cdot26$ light years $= 206,265$ astronomical units $= 3\cdot08 \times 10^{13}$ km.

The stellar magnitude, M, of a star, as it would be if it were situated at a distance of 10 parsecs from us, is called its absolute magnitude.

$$M = m+5+5 \log \pi$$

or

$$M = m+5-5 \log r,$$

where m is the apparent stellar magnitude of the light source, situated at a distance of r parsecs and having an annual parallax π. The absolute magnitude of the Sun is $+4\cdot85$, and its apparent magnitude is $-26\cdot84$. Given the absolute magnitude of stars we may compare their true brightnesses with each other.

The light from stars varies: the whiter the star, the higher is its temperature. The spectrum of a star also depends on its temperature, and stellar spectra are divided into various spectral classes, labelled O, B, A, F, G, K, M, in order of increasing redness of light and decreasing temperature.

The solar system as a whole moves through space in the direction of the constellations Lyra and Hercules with a velocity of $19\cdot5$ km/sec. In the part of the sky towards which we are moving (the apex), the stars in general are approaching us, and appear to disperse from the apex in a way similar to showering meteor trails. In the opposite hemisphere of the sky (the anti-apex) the stars in general appear to drift together, and recede from us. The coordinates of the apex of the motion of the solar system are $\alpha = 18$ hr 0 min, $\delta = +30°$.

II

The proper motion of a star μ is the name given to its angular displacement in the celestial sphere in the course of a year, caused by its movement in space relative to the Sun. In other words, μ is the projection on the celestial sphere of the displacement of the star in space relative to the Sun during a year.

The tangential velocity of a star, V_t (the velocity perpendicular to the line of sight), is expressed by the formula

$$V_t = 4·74 \frac{\mu}{\pi} \text{ km/sec,}$$

and the total velocity of a star in space is given by the formula

$$V = \sqrt{(V_t^2 + V_r^2)}$$

where V_r is the star's radial velocity. If the velocity V has an angle θ with the direction from us to the star, then we may write

$$V_r = V \cos \theta \quad \text{and} \quad V_t = V \sin \theta.$$

Some groups of stars move through space in parallel paths and from the Earth it appears that the direction of their proper motions converge on or diverge from a point known as the radiant. If we denote the angular distance from the radiant of some star of such a group (a moving cluster) by the letter θ, its proper motion by the letter μ, its parallax by π, its radial velocity by V_r, and its space velocity by V, then we can write

$$\pi = \frac{4·74\mu}{V \sin \theta} = \frac{4·74\mu}{V_r \tan \theta}$$

which allows us to determine the parallax of groups of this kind by means of their movement.

The proper motion of a star, μ, at an angle ϕ (anticlockwise) with the direction of the celestial North Pole may be resolved into two components: μ_α in Right Ascension and μ_δ in Declination

$$\mu^2 = \mu_\delta^2 + (15\mu_\alpha \cos \delta)^2,$$
$$\mu_\delta = \mu \cos \phi,$$
$$15\mu_\alpha \cos \delta = \mu \sin \phi,$$

where δ is the Declination of the star, μ_α is expressed in seconds of time and μ_δ in seconds of arc.

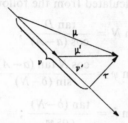

FIG. 37. Components of proper motion

The observed radial velocity V_r of a star is made up of its individual velocity, V_r' (the projection of its velocity on the line of vision) and of the velocity caused by the movement of the Sun relative to the surrounding stars, with a velocity V_0:

$$V_r' = V_r + V_0 \cos \lambda,$$

where λ is the angular distance of the star from the apex.

The effect of the Sun's motion on the proper motion of a star may be analysed as follows. We resolve it into two components: ν in the direction of the anti-apex (Fig. 37), and τ perpendicular to ν. Then

$$\mu^2 = \tau^2 + \nu^2.$$

The motion of the Sun has no effect on τ. If ν' is the true motion of the star in the direction indicated, and ν is the observed motion, then we may write:

$$\nu = \nu' + \frac{\pi V_0 \sin \lambda}{4 \cdot 74}.$$

Hence, we can determine the mean parallax π for a group of stars given ν and τ, as

$$\overline{\pi} = \frac{4 \cdot 74 \overline{\nu} \sin \lambda}{V_0 \overline{\sin^2 \lambda}}$$

$$\overline{\pi} = \frac{4 \cdot 74 \overline{\tau}}{V_r'}.$$

The stroke indicates that the corresponding value must be taken as a mean for the given group of stars.

The components ν and τ, and the angular distance of a star from the apex are calculated from the following formulae:

$$\tan N = \frac{\tan D}{\cos (a - A)} ;$$

$$\tan \psi = \frac{\cos N \tan (a - A)}{\sin (\delta - N)} ;$$

$$\tan \lambda = \frac{\tan (\delta - N)}{\cos \psi} ;$$

$$\nu = \mu \cos (\phi - \psi); \qquad \tau = \mu \sin (\phi - \psi),$$

N is the auxiliary angle, determined from the first formula $(0° < N < 180°)$, and ψ the positional angle of the parallactic displacement of the star.

One of the methods of determining the distances of stars is that of spectral parallax. From certain characteristic features in the spectrum it is possible to determine the absolute magnitude M of a star, whose visible magnitude m can be determined directly. A comparison of M and m gives the distance, or parallax of the star. In addition a relationship between the masses of most stars and their absolute magnitudes has been discovered. The luminosity of a star increases with its mass. Figure 38 shows empirically determined mass-luminosity relation from a number of stars.

The diameters of the largest stars can be measured by means of a special instrument – the stellar interferometer. The radius of the star in units of solar radii is given by the formula

$$\log R = \frac{5900}{T} - 0 \cdot 20 M - 0 \cdot 02$$

where M is the absolute magnitude of the star and T is its absolute temperature. The apparent angular diameter in seconds of arc may be found by the formula

$$\log d = \log \pi + \log R - 2\cdot030.$$

These formulae are derived on the assumption that stars are incandescent spheroids, whose brightness per unit surface area

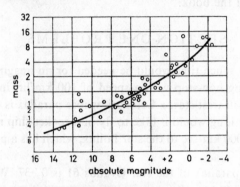

FIG. 38. The curve of the relationship between "mass and luminosity" of stars. Along the vertical the masses of the stars are given in a logarithmic scale in units of the mass of the Sun.

Vertical : Mass
Horizontal : Absolute magnitude

depends on the temperature T. The radiative output from a unit of surface expressed in erg/sec is determined by the Stefan–Boltzmann Law,

$$E = \sigma \times T^4.$$

If E is expressed in cal/cm²/min and T in thousands of degrees on the absolute scale, then $\sigma = 82$. This value, multiplied by the surface area of the star, determines the total energy output of the star, and corresponds to the bolometric luminosity. Our eyes are not sensitive to all the available energy, using only part of the light energy (from the red to the violet) so that the visual brightness of a star is related to T in a more complicated manner. Photographic plates have different colour sensitivity characteristics from the human eye (they are more sensitive towards the violet end of the spectrum). Thus, for instance, if white stars are reckoned to be equally bright for the human eye and photographic plates, then red stars will appear fainter on the plates than they do to the human eye. The difference in stellar magnitudes, determined photographically and visually for the same star, is known as its colour index (I). The empirical relationship between the colour index of a star and its spectral class is given in Table XIV at the end of the book.

SECTION ONE PROBLEMS

992. How much time would be needed for an imaginary journey, travelling non-stop with a speed of 100 km/hr, in order to arrive at the nearest star, α Centauri, whose parallax is $0''\cdot76$?

993. How long would it take to fly in a rocket-ship moving at a speed of 1000 km/sec to the star Pollux, which has a parallax of $0''\cdot10$?

994. The parallax of the star Cygnus 61 is $0''\cdot37$. What is its distance in light years?

995. The parallax of Sirius is $0''\cdot37$, and that of Spika is $0''\cdot01$. Express the distance to these stars in parsecs, in light years, in astronomical units and in kilometres.

996. The parallax of Altair is $0''\cdot20$, and the parallax of Vega is $0''\cdot12$. Express the distances to these stars in parsecs, in light years, in astronomical units, and in kilometres.

997. The parallax of Procyon (α Canis Minoris) is $0''\cdot312$. The probable error of this measurement is $\pm0''\cdot006$. What may one say about the distance of the star?

998. The parallax of Rigel is $0''\cdot006$ with a probable error $\pm0''\cdot006$. What may one say about the distance to the star?

999. The apparent stellar magnitude of Sirius is $-1\cdot58$, and that of its satellite $8\cdot44$. By how many times is the true brightness of Sirius greater than the true brightness of its satellite? Bear in mind that the distance between these stars is insignificantly small in comparison with the distance from the Earth to Sirius.

1000. Calculate the absolute stellar magnitude of Sirius, given that its parallax is $0''\cdot371$, and its apparent magnitude is $-1\cdot58$.

1001. Determine the absolute magnitude of Antares, given that its parallax is $0''\cdot009$, and its apparent magnitude is $+1\cdot22$.

1002. How many times is the Sun fainter than the star Proxima Centauri, for which $\pi = 0''\cdot76$; $m = 10\cdot5$.

1003. Which light source—the Sun or S Doradus (absolute magnitude $-9\cdot4$)—has the greater output of light, and by how many times?

1004. Calculate by how many times Rigel is brighter than the Sun, if its parallax is $0''\cdot0069$, and its apparent magnitude is $0\cdot34$.

1005. Determine the absolute magnitudes of the components of the star Kriuger 60, knowing that their apparent magnitudes are $9\cdot6$ and $11\cdot4$, and their parallax is $0''\cdot257$.

1006. Compare the luminosities of the components of the double star, Kriuger 60, with the Sun, given that their absolute magnitudes are $11\cdot6$ and $13\cdot4$, and the absolute magnitude of the Sun is $4\cdot85$.

1007. The stellar magnitude of Vega is $+0\cdot1$. What would its stellar magnitude be, if it were 1000 times farther from us? Would it then be visible to the naked eye?

1008. How many kilometres a year does the solar system move towards its apex of movement, if its velocity is $19\cdot5$ km/sec?

*1009. In which sectors of the sky do the angular distances between the stars continuously increase, and continuously decrease, due to the movement of the solar system through space.

SECTION TWO PROBLEMS

*1010. Plate XV shows spectrograms of various stars. Determine their spectral classes, using the appropriate tables and references. The upper six spectra were taken with a slit spectrograph, and the lower six with an objective prism camera.

1011. Prove that the change in apparent magnitude of a star for a change in its distance from the Sun is inversely proportional to its distance. (Parenago.)

*1012. A star approaches the solar system with a velocity V_r

km/sec. After how many years (y) will its apparent brightness increase n times, if the distance to the star is one light year, or R kilometres?

*1013. By the formula obtained in the preceding question, determine after how many years the apparent brightness of the star Altair will increase by an amount just distinguishable to the human eye (0·1 of a magnitude), if the distance to this star is 15·7 light years, and if we are moving towards it with a velocity of 26 km/sec.

*1014. The distance to Sirius is 2·70 parsecs, but because of its movement this diminishes by 8 km/sec. Calculate after how many years the apparent brightness of Sirius will be twice as great as it is at present.

*1015. If a star is situated on the ecliptic, then what difference will there be between measurements of its radial velocity on the 9th September, 1949, and 7th March, 1950?

*1016. Derive a formula giving the correction to radial velocity observations due to the orbital motion of the Earth for a case where the star is situated at the pole of the ecliptic.

*1017. Derive a formula giving the radial velocity correction for the orbital motion of the Earth for observations on a star lying in the plane of the ecliptic.

Assume the star to be situated at the point of the Vernal Equinox, and the orbit of the Earth to be circular; that is, its velocity V_0 may be taken to be constant at 29·5 km/sec.

1018. Is it possible, by observing over a very long period of time, to determine by purely geometrical methods the radial velocity of a star by measurements of its parallax?

*1019. A star with coordinates $\alpha = 11$ hr 36·8 min, $\delta = +27°20'$ has components of proper motion $\mu_\alpha = 0·0465$ sec, $\mu_\delta = -0''·795$. Determine the total proper motion μ and its positional angle ψ.

*1020. A star with the coordinates $\alpha = 22$ hr 28·0 min, $\delta = +8°52'$ has the components of proper motion $\mu_\alpha = +0·036$ sec, $\mu_\delta = +0''·152$. Determine the total proper motion μ and its positional angle ψ.

*1021. A star has a proper motion $\mu = 1''·24$ in a direction with position angle $\psi = 165°$. Determine the component μ_δ of proper motion.

*1022. A star ($\alpha = 15$ hr 58·5 min, $\delta = 20°56'$) has a proper motion of $\mu = 1''·59$ in a direction with positional angle $\psi = 218°$. Determine the two components μ_α and μ_δ of proper motion.

1023. Barnard's star has an annual proper motion of $10''·25$ and a parallax of $0''·546$. What is its tangential velocity?

1024. What is the tangential velocity of Sirius, if its parallax is $0''·371$ and its annual proper motion 1·315?

*1025. The radial velocity of Vega is -14 km/sec, its proper motion is $0''·348$ a year, and its parallax is $0''·124$. Determine its total velocity through space relative to the Sun.

*1026. The radial velocity of Aldebaran is $+54$ km/sec, and its tangential velocity 18 km/sec. Find its actual velocity relative to the Sun.

1027. The coordinates of Sirius are: $\alpha = 6$ hr 41 min, $\delta = -16°35'$. Its proper motion in Right Ascension is $-0''·0374$, and in Declination $-1''·209$ per year. Its radial velocity is $-7·5$ km/sec, and its parallax is $0''·38$. Determine the space velocity of Sirius relative to the Sun, and the angle between the direction of movement and the line of sight.

*1028. The radial velocity of Arcturus is -22 km/sec and its tangential velocity is 23 km/sec. Find the angle subtended by its direction of movement and the line of sight.

*1029. The radial velocity of the star Betelgeuse is $+21$ km/sec. Its proper motion is $0''·032$ a year, and its parallax is $0''·012$. Determine its velocity relative to the Sun, and the angle subtended by the direction of movement of the star through space and the line of sight.

*1030. The net velocity of the star β Crucis is 21 km/sec and its radial velocity $+13$ km/sec. Determine the tangential velocity.

*1031. The velocity of the star Canopus is 23 km/sec and its course subtends an angle of 37° with the line of sight. Determine the radial and tangential velocities.

*1032. The direction of movement of the star Capella has an angle of 48·2° with the line of sight. Its total velocity is 45 km/sec.

Determine the annual proper motion of the star if its parallax is
0″·063.

1033. You are given the velocity through space of a star S
subtending an angle of θ with the line of sight (Fig. 39), its radial
and tangential velocities V_r and V_t, its parallex π, proper motion
μ, and apparent magnitude m. At what time t is the star at its
shortest distance from the Sun O at the point M. What are then
the values of π, μ, m, V_r, V_t?

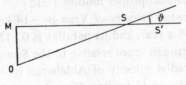

FIG. 39.

1034. From the formulae obtained in the preceding example,
determine the year when the Sun and α Centauri will be closest
together. Give the values of the parallax, proper motion, and
apparent stellar magnitude of the star at that moment if, at the
present time,

$$V_r = -22 \text{ km/sec,}$$
$$V_t = 23 \text{ km/sec,}$$
$$m = 0·06,$$
$$\mu = 3''·68,$$
$$\pi = 0''·758.$$

1035. Determine the date of the closest approach of Barnard's
star to the Sun, if the current data for it are

$$m = 9·57,$$
$$\mu = 10''·25,$$
$$\pi = 0''·546,$$
$$V_r = 117 \text{ km/sec,}$$
$$V_t = 90 \text{ km/sec.}$$

1036. What will the parallax and proper motion of Barnard's
star be in 2000 yr?

1037. Determine the apex of the movement of the solar system and its velocity from the following Table. It gives mean radial velocities of stars within quadrants of the celestial sphere of side of 40°, and centres with the given coordinates.

α	0 hr	12 hr	6 hr	18 hr	—	—
δ	0°	0°	0°	0°	+90°	−90°
No. of stars	32	27	33	26	24	43
Mean radial velocity	+4·4	+0·8	+23·7	−15·1	−8·2	+9·3

*1038. Is it possible in principle to determine a curvilinear movement of the solar system in space by means of systematic measurements of the radial velocities?

1039. Determine the Declination of the apex of the movement of the solar system, making use of the data and examples given below.

From Boss's star catalogue the stars which show proper motion of positive and negative sign, may be divided into 3 hourly sectors in Right Ascension as follows:

α	0 hr	3 hr	6 hr	9 hr	12 hr	15 hr	18 hr	21 hr
Positive	132	152	107	39	46	47	101	143
Negative	68	48	93	161	154	153	99	57

Draw a circle with the hours of Right Ascension marked round it, and mark in as vectors the predominant motions of stars at each 3-hr interval.

Interpolating in the diagram we see that the positive and negative movements cancel in the directions of 6 hr 20 min and 18 hr 0 min Right Ascension. In fact, the Right Ascension of the apex is taken to be 18 hr 10 min. (Russell, Dugan, Stewart.)

Find in a similar way the Declination of the apex, knowing that along the belt between 17 hr and 18 hr 30 min and 5 hr 30 min and 6 hr 30 min of Right Ascension the number of stars with positive and negative proper motion are as follows:

δ		$90°$ to $60°$	$60°$ to $30°$	$30°$ to $0°$	$0°$ to $-30°$	$-30°$ to $-60°$	$-60°$ to $-90°$
$\alpha = 6$ hr	$+$ve	3	9	22	29	31	16
	$-$ve	10	35	72	40	32	3
$\alpha = 18$ hr	$+$ve	10	25	22	8	6	4
	$-$ve	7	13	38	59	46	9

*1040. Suppose that the solar system moves towards the constellation Lyra among stars motionless relative to each other, and situated at equal distances from the Sun. How will the values of the observed radial velocity and the proper motion of the stars depend on their angular distance λ from the apex?

*1041. Would it be possible in principle to determine the direction of movement of the solar system in space solely by photometric observations of stars?

*1042. Our solar system approaches Vega ($\pi = 0''\cdot12$) at a rate of 14 km/sec. After how many years will the apparent brightness of Vega increase by $0\cdot1$ m?

*1043. Taking the coordinates of the apex of the Sun to be $\alpha = 18$ hr 0 min, $\delta = +30°$, and its velocity V_0 to be 19·5 km/sec, calculate by means of the formula $V_r' = V_r + V_0 \cos \lambda$ the observed radial velocity of the star R Scuti whose velocity, uncorrected for the motion of the Sun, is $+38\cdot3$ km/sec, and whose coordinates are

$$\alpha = 280\tfrac{1}{2}°,$$
$$\delta = -6°.$$

In the formula given, λ denotes the distance of the star from the apex.

*1044. Taking for the apex of the Sun a "standard" value (see the previous exercise), calculate the radial velocity of the star U Monocerotis, for which the uncorrected velocity relative to the Sun is $+34\cdot6$ km/sec, and the coordinates are

$$\alpha = 111\tfrac{1}{2}°,$$
$$\delta = -10°.$$

*1045. Resolve into its v and τ components the proper motion of AG Aurigae ($\alpha = 6$ hr 20·1 min, $\delta = 47°5'$), $\mu_\alpha = +0·0076$ sec, $\mu_\delta = -0''·054$. The elements of the movement of the Sun may be taken to be the usual ones.

*1046. Resolve into the v and τ components the movement of the star R Scuti ($\alpha = 18$ hr 42·1 min, $\delta = -5°49'$) which has a proper motion $\mu_\alpha = 0·0039$ sec, $\mu_\delta = -0''·030$.

*1047. A certain star has a parallax of $0''·0015$ and components of proper motion $v = 0''·015$, $\tau = 0''·064$. It is situated at $\lambda = 125°$ from the apex of the Sun. Calculate the component of its peculiar proper motion v' and τ'.

1048. The annual proper motion of a star, with coordinates $\alpha = 3$ hr 0 min and $\delta = +10°$, is $0''·1$. Assuming that its proper motion is completely parallactic, that is, due to the movement of the solar system, determine the parallax of the star, if the Sun moves towards a point with the coordinates $\alpha = 18$ hr 0 min, $\delta = +30°$ with a speed of 19·5 km/sec.

*1049. Determine the mean absolute velocity of variable stars of the type RV Tauri, if for eight of them $\tau = 0''·0165$, $\overline{V} = 33·4$ km/sec, and the mean apparent stellar magnitude is 8·5 m.

*1050. For a group of stars with the same physical properties the mean value of the τ-component of their proper motions is $0''·0150$, and the mean radial velocity $V' = 10$ km/sec. Determine the mean parallax of these stars.

*1051. For eleven variable stars of the RV Tauri type, P. P. Parenago originally found $\overline{v \sin \lambda} = -0''·0022$, $\overline{\sin^2 \lambda} = 0·366$, and a mean apparent stellar magnitude of 8·7 m. Taking the speed of the solar system to be 19·5 km/sec determine the mean parallax of this group of stars, and the mean absolute stellar magnitude.

*1052. For nineteen hot stars of spectral classes 08–09 the components of the proper motion were found to be

$$\bar{\tau} = 0''·0054, \qquad \frac{\overline{v \sin \lambda}}{\sin^2 \lambda} = 0''·082.$$

The mean apparent magnitude of these nineteen stars is 6·04 m. Find their mean parallax, and mean absolute magnitude.

1053. The angular distance θ of a star from the radiant of a moving stellar cluster is 30°, its radial velocity is +48 km/sec, and its proper motion is 0″18. Determine the parallax of the star cluster.

1054. Determine the velocity in space and the parallax of the moving cluster Hyades from the following data, for one star of the group.

$$\mu = 0''\!\cdot\!115, \quad V_r = +38\cdot6 \text{ km/sec}, \quad \theta = 29\cdot1.$$

1055. What is the distance to the Pole star in parsecs, if according to its spectrum its absolute magnitude is $-2\cdot4$, and its apparent magnitude is $+2\cdot1$. Find the same for the nova in Hercules if its absolute magnitude, determined spectrally, is $-7\cdot5$ and its apparent magnitude at maximum brightness was $+1\cdot2$.

---

*1056. The difference between the stellar magnitudes of an object, determined by photographic observation (m_p) and by visual observation (m_v) is called the colour index I. I measures the redness of a star. For blue stars the colour index is negative and connected to the absolute temperature, T, of the star by the relationship

$$I = m_p - m_v = \frac{7200}{T} - 0\cdot64.$$

At what temperature does the colour index of the star change most rapidly?

1057. The colour index of a star may be expressed by the formula

$$I = M_p - M_v = \frac{7200}{T} - 0\cdot64,$$

where M_v is the visual and M_p the photographic absolute magnitude of a star, and T is its temperature. Determine the upper limit of the negative value of the colour index.

*1058. The photographic and visual magnitudes of bright stars are set out below. Arrange them in order of colour — white, yellow, orange and red.

Star	Magnitude	
	Photographic	Visual
Spika	0·94	1·21
Antares	2·95	1·22
Altair	1·05	0·89
Capella	0·88	0·21
Arcturus	1·36	0·24
Rigel	0·30	0·34
α Centauri	0·63	0·06

1059. Making use of the Table of colour indices of stars (p. 312) determine the photographic magnitude of the components of the double star γ Andromedae, if their spectral classes are K0 and B9, and their visual magnitudes are 2·28 and 5·08, respectively.

*1060. Compare the photograph and the map (Plates XVI and XVII) in the area of the constellation Centaurus, the Southern Cross, and the Fly and find the yellow and red stars amongst those marked, arranging them in order of increasing colour index.

*1061. What must the separation D_0 of the mirrors of a stellar interferometer be, to measure the angular diameter β of a nova with a maximum brightness of $m_v = 1\cdot0$, $\pi = 0\cdot002$ min, $T = 10,000°$. The effective wavelength λ emitted by the nova is 5000 Å, and the formula for the calculation of angular diameter in seconds of arc is

$$\beta'' = \frac{1\cdot22\lambda}{D_0} \times 206,265.$$

*1062. Making use of the formula $d = 11''\cdot6/D$, for the resolving power of a telescope, where D is the diameter of its objective in centimetres, determine what size of telescope would be necessary to observe directly the disc of the giant star Betelgeuse, whose angular diameter is $0''\cdot04$.

*1063. Compare the diameter of the star α Scorpii with that of "Barnard's star" given that their absolute magnitudes are −4·0 and +13·4, and their temperatures, and consequently their surface brightnesses, are the same.

*1064. Determine the radius of β Centauri, if its temperature $T = 21,000°$, and its absolute visual magnitude is $M_v = -3\cdot8$.

*1065. Determine the radius of Antares, given that its temperature $T = 3100°$, and its absolute stellar magnitude $M_v = -4\cdot0$.

*1066. Determine the radius of the companion of Sirius, given that its $T = 7500°$ and $M_v = 11\cdot2$.

*1067. Determine the radius of Aldebaran and calculate its apparent angular diameter, given that the parallax of Aldebaran $\pi = 0''\cdot057$, $T = 3300°$, and $M_v = -0\cdot1$.

*1068. What would the diameter of the companion of Sirius be, if its absolute magnitude were 10 m fainter than that of Sirius, the distance between these stars were $20\cdot4$ astronomical units, and if it were illuminated by light from Sirius, like a planet. The absolute magnitude of Sirius is $+1\cdot3$.

Note. The reflecting power of the companion may be taken to be the same as that for the planet Jupiter, which is $5\cdot2$ astronomical units from the Sun, and has a stellar magnitude $-2\cdot2$ in opposition; the absolute magnitude of the Sun is $+4\cdot9$, and its apparent magnitude is $-26\cdot7$.

*1069. The temperature of a star may be determined from its colour index, by the formula

$$T = \frac{7200}{I+0\cdot64}.$$

Determine the mean temperature of stars of the spectral classes B0, A0 and G0, given that their mean colour indices are $-0\cdot33$, and $0\cdot00$ and $0\cdot57$, respectively.

*1070. Determine from their colour indices (given in brackets) the temperatures of the following stars:

$$\delta \text{ Eridani} \quad (1\cdot12),$$
$$\varepsilon \text{ Geminorum} \quad (0\cdot92),$$
$$\text{Procyon} \quad (0\cdot47),$$
$$\tau \text{ Scorpii} \quad (-0\cdot33).$$

*1071. The heat index is the name given to the difference between the stellar magnitude of an object determined visually (m_v), and that determined with the help of a radiometer or thermo-couple (m_r). This value is connected to the temperature of the star by the relationship

$$m_v - m_r = 10 \log T + \frac{29,500}{T} - 42 \cdot 1.$$

Within what limits do the temperatures of variable stars with long periods vary, if their mean heat indices are $+4 \cdot 3$ at maximum brightness, and $+7 \cdot 8$ at minimum brightness?

*1072. Calculate the mean temperature of a giant star of spectral class K0, given that its mean heat index is $+1 \cdot 2$.

*1073. The star α Orionis radiates heat to the Earth at the rate of $7 \cdot 7 \times 10^{-11}$ cal/cm²/min. How much heat could be collected from this star in a year, by the mirror of a telescope of diameter $2 \cdot 5$ m?

*1074. Determine what quantity of ice it would be possible to melt in the course of a year, using the heat radiated to the Earth by the star Sirius, and collected by a mirror of 1 m diameter if $5 \cdot 8 \times 10^{-11}$ calories of energy per cm² fall on the Earth from Sirius.

*1075. The star α Bootes radiates 64×10^{-12} cal/min/cm² on the surface of the Earth, perpendicular to its rays. The parallax of the star is $0'' \cdot 08$ and its radius is twenty-six times greater than that of the Sun. Determine the temperature of α Bootes.

*1076. The star α Orionis radiates energy at the rate of $7 \cdot 7 \times 10^{-11}$ cal/cm²/min at the surface of the Earth. Calculate from this the temperature of the star, given that its parallax is $0'' \cdot 011$ and its angular diameter, measured with an interferometer, is $0'' \cdot 047$.

*1077. Calculate the temperature of Arcturus, given that the amount of energy it radiates to the Earth is $6 \cdot 4 \times 10^{-11}$ cal/min/cm² perpendicular to its rays, that its parallax is $0'' \cdot 080$, and its angular diameter, measured with an interferometer, is $0'' \cdot 020$.

*1078. Calculate the temperature of Aldebaran, given that its apparent visual magnitude is $1 \cdot 1$ and its angular diameter is $0'' \cdot 020$.

*1079. From the mass-luminosity curve (Fig. 38) find the mass of the Pole star, if its absolute magnitude is −2·4.

*1080. From the mass-luminosity curve determine the mass of the star 70 Ophiuchi, if its parallax is 0″·19 and its visual magnitude is 4·3.

*1081. Determine the mean density of the star Capella, using the mass-luminosity relationship. The absolute magnitude of the Sun is +4·9 and that of Capella is −0·3. The temperature of the Sun is 6000°.

*1082. Calculate in cm³ the mean density of the star 40 Eridani from the following data. The mass of the star is 0·44 of the mass of the Sun.

$$T = 11,000°,$$
$$M_v = 11·2.$$

*1083. Determine the mean density of a white dwarf star, which is the companion of another star, from the following data. The spectra of the principal star, and of the companion, are the same. The mean density of the principal star is 0·2 g/cm³. The difference between the apparent magnitudes of the principal star and the companion is 10, and the ratio of their masses is 2 : 1.

*1084. Hot and massive stars (spectral class B) have, on the average, a mass of about 20×10^{33} g and a velocity of about 15×10^5 cm/sec. Stars of the same type as the Sun have masses of about $1·2 \times 10^{33}$ g and velocities of about 78×10^5 cm/sec. Bearing in mind the differences in the masses and velocities of the stars, compare their kinetic energies.

CHAPTER XXV

DOUBLE STARS

II

DOUBLE stars are called visual when their binary nature can be observed directly with a telescope, and spectroscopic when their binary nature is observable by the periodic bifurcation, or shifting, of the spectral lines. Visual double stars may be divided into optical pairs, when the apparent juxtaposition of the stars is due to perspective, and physical pairs, when the stars are really close together, and revolve about a mutual centre of gravity, according to Kepler's laws. Usually, the orbit of a companion is observed relative to the principal star. As a rule it is visible on the celestial sphere in projection, as it subtends an angle with the line of sight, which differs from the perpendicular by i, the inclination of the orbit.

The position of the companion relative to the principal star is characterized by its angular separation ϱ, and its position angle θ, which is the angle its direction forms with the direction of the North celestial Pole. This angle is reckoned anticlockwise. The principal star is usually not at the focus of the apparent ellipse, because of the projection effect, but is naturally located at the focus of the true ellipse of the orbit. In projection on the celestial sphere, the semi-major axis of the true orbit passes through the centre of the apparent orbit, and through the principal star. If α is the semi-major axis of the orbit, expressed in seconds of arc, A its size in kilometres, and π the parallax, then

$$A = a/\pi.$$

Because of this, the combined mass of a double star, $m_1 + m_2$ may be expressed by the following formula, from Kepler's Third Law:

$$m_1 + m_2 = \frac{A^3}{P^2} = \frac{a^3}{\pi^3 p^2}.$$

m_1 and m_2 are expressed in solar masses, and P is the period of revolution in years.

The so-called dynamical parallax of a double star is given by the formula

$$\pi = \frac{a}{\sqrt[3]{\{P^2(m_1 + m_2)\}}}.$$

If $(m_1 + m_2)$ is not known then the value of, say, 1 solar mass will give an approximate parallax. This may then be improved by successive approximations as follows. Having found the parallax, we determine the absolute magnitude of the components, and by the mass-luminosity law we determine the mass of each component separately, and redetermine the parallax from the formula. Repeating this procedure a few times, we obtain a more exact parallax.

If the observed shift of the lines in the spectrum of a spectral binary star is drawn on a graph as a function of time, a sinusoidally varying line is obtained. If a straight line is drawn parallel to the axis of the abscissa, and intersecting this curve of velocity so that the areas of the curve above and below it are the same, then the ordinate of this straight line represents the velocity of the centre of gravity of the system. For a spectroscopic binary star, the angle of inclination i remains unknown. The value of w, the distance of the periastra from the node, is determined from the radial velocity curve. If the line of sight is in the plane of the orbits of a binary system, the stars eclipse each other periodically. These are called eclipsing binaries of the Algol type.

SECTION TWO PROBLEMS

1085. What is the minimum distance between the components of a double star which can be resolved by a refractor which has an objective diameter of 76 cm (30 inches)?

1086. What is the stellar magnitude of a double star, whose components have magnitudes of 1·0 and 2·0?

1087. The double star Castor (α Geminorum) consists of two stars whose magnitudes are 2·0 and 2·8. What is the combined brightness of the stars in stellar magnitudes?

*1088. Prove that if a double star is optical — that is, if the components are not physically related, but simply located almost on the same line of vision — their relative motion is rectilinear and caused by their proper motions, and the following relationships hold:

$$\varrho^2 = a^2 + (t-T)^2 m^2 \quad \text{and} \quad \tan(\theta - \theta_0) = \frac{m}{a}(t-T),$$

    a is the perpendicular produced from one star to the line of relative motion of the companion;

    θ_0 is the position angle of this perpendicular;

    t is the time which corresponds to the distance ϱ between the stars at the position angle θ;

    T is the moment when the component is situated at the base of this perpendicular; and

    m is its annual movement.

If observation agrees with these formulae, then the pair is optical.

1089. Calculate the sum of the masses of the double star Capella if the semi-major axes of their orbits are equal to 0·85 astronomical units, and the period of revolution is 0·285 of a year.

1090. Determine the sum of the masses of the double star Procyon, if the period of rotation of the companion about the principal star is 39 yr, and the semi-major axis of the orbit is 13·0 astronomical units.

*1091. The semi-major axis of the orbit of the double star α Centauri subtends an angle of 17″·65. How many times is this distance greater than the distance between the Sun and the Earth? The parallax of the star is 0″·75.

1092. Calculate the mass of the double star α Centauri, for which

$$\pi = 0''\cdot75, \quad P = 79 \text{ yr}, \quad \alpha = 17''\cdot6.$$

1093. The double star ε Hydrae has a period of revolution of 15·3 yr, a parallax of 0″·020 and the angular measure of the semi-major axis of its orbit is 0″·23. Determine the linear dimensions of the semi-major axis of the orbit and the sum of the masses of the components.

1094. The double star α Geminorum has a parallax of 0″·076. The length of the semi-major axis of the orbit is 6″·06 and the period of revolution is 306 yr. Determine the combined mass of the components.

*1095. The parallax of the double star $\varkappa$ Pegasi is determined as 0″·026, with a probable error of ±0″·005. What is the probable error in the mass of the stars? The semi-major axis of the orbit is 0″·29.

1096. Suppose that the apparent distance between two stars must be at least 0″·2 for them to be visible as two separate stars in the most powerful telescopes. The distance to a double star is 500 parsecs. What must the distance between the components be in astronomical units in order for them to be distinguished as separate stars?

If the mass of each star is equal to the mass of the Sun, what will their period of revolution be? If their dimensions and surface brightnesses are the same as those of the Sun, then what will their separate and combined stellar magnitudes be?

*1097. The parallax of the visual double star Castor is 0″·076, its proper motion 0″·20, the radial velocity of the system +3 km/sec, the apparent magnitude of the components 2·0 and 2·8, the semi-major axis of the orbit 6″·06, and the period of revolution 306 yr. Determine the semi-major axis of the orbit in kilometres, the luminosity of the components in comparison with the Sun, the relative orbital velocity of the companion in kilometres per second, the masses of both stars, the ratio of their radii (assuming the temperatures of the stars to be the same) and the velocity of the system as a whole.

*1098. Suppose that the densities of the components of a double star are the same as that of the Sun, and that the two components (which may be considered to be spherical) are in contact. What is their period of revolution if the mass of each of them is 1/10 of the mass of the Sun? What will their relative velocity be, in kilometres per second?

1099. Determine the dynamical parallax of the components of the double star α Centauri, taking the sum of the masses of its components to be equal to twice the mass of the Sun. The period of revolution of the pair is 78·8 yr, and the semi-major axis of the orbit is 17"·65.

1100. Calculate the dynamical parallax of the double star β 7642 for which $a = 2"·87$ and the period $P = 317·5$ yr. The trigonometrical parallax of the star is 0"·088. How would you explain the difference in the parallaxes obtained?

*1101. Determine by means of successive approximations, using the mass-luminosity curve (Fig. 38), the dynamical parallax of the double star ϰ Pegasi, from the following data:

$$\text{the semi-major axis } a = 0"·29,$$
$$\text{the period } P = 11·35 \text{ yr,}$$

the apparent stellar magnitudes of the components are 4·8 and 5·5.

*1102. Using the mass-luminosity relation in Fig. 38, determine by the method of successive approximations the dynamical parallax of the double star ζ Herculis

$$P = 34·5 \text{ yr,}$$
$$a = 1"·35$$

the apparent stellar magnitudes are 3·0 and 6·5.

*1103. One turn of a micrometer screw corresponds to 8"·14. The distance along the line joining two stars corresponds to 0·34 turns of the screw. What is the distance between the components of the double star?

*1104. What is the angular separation α of the components of a close binary star, if a stellar interferometer registers the first fringes at a separation of $D_0 = 206$ cm? The formula is $\alpha = 206365 \lambda/2D_0$. The effective wavelength λ of the star may be taken to be 5500 Å.

*1105. The distance ϱ of a faint star from a bright one does not exceed 1" and varies in time as

$$\varrho = 1"·0 \sin \left(\frac{2\pi}{T} t + t_0\right)$$

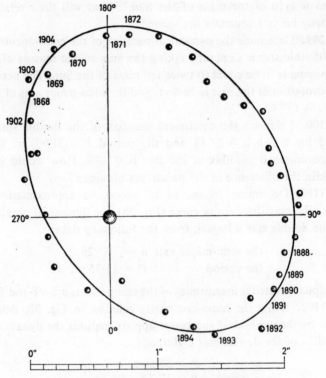

FIG. 40. The apparent orbit of a double star.

where T is the period, and t_0 is the moment from which time is reckoned. What can one say about these stars?

1106. Taking the ratio of the masses of the two components of a visual double system to be 4 : 3, the orbit to be circular, and its inclination to be 60°, draw the apparent orbits of both components, and the true orbit of one relative to the other.

*1107. Figure 40 shows the observed orbit of a companion about a bright star, and the position of the circle of Declination passing through the principal star. Determine graphically the position angle of the projection of the semi-major axis of the orbit on the celestial sphere.

*1108. In Fig. 41 the apparent orbit of the companion relative to the main component of a double star is plotted. By means of measurements on the plan determine the eccentricity of the true orbit.

*1109. In Fig. 41 we have plotted observed positions of the satellite relative to the principal star in the system ζ Herculis, covering an interval of 200 years. From these points construct the ellipse representing the complete orbit.

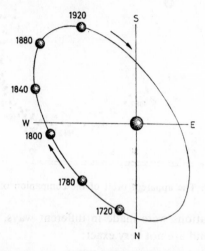

FIG. 41. The apparent orbit of the companion of ζ Herculis.

Given that the inclination of the orbit is 48°, draw the ellipse of the real orbit of the companion relative to the principal star. Determine the period of revolution, the eccentricity, and the semi-major axis of the orbit. Determine the moment of the passage of the satellite through the periast and the total mass of the system (parallax 0″·11).

Carry out the same exercise for the double star Sirius (Fig. 42), for which the inclination of the orbit $i = 43°$ and the parallax 0″·37.

1110. Construct the apparent orbit of the visual double star β Delphini; estimate the period of revolution, the semi-major axis of its apparent orbit, and the eccentricity, from the following observations.

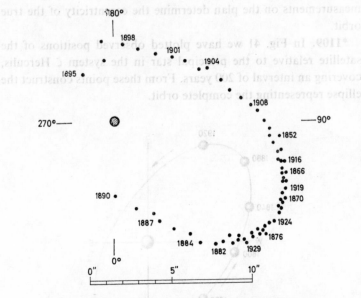

FIG. 42. The apparent orbit of the companion of Sirius.

The observations were made in different ways, with different instruments, and are not very exact:

t	θ	d	t	θ	d
1873·6	355°	0″·7	1877·8	48·8°	0″·32
1874·7	15·6	0 ·65	1878·6	53·7	0 ·24
1874·7	13·6	0 ·49	1878·7	59·2	—
1874·7	6·5	0 ·66	1880·7	133·6	0 ·26
1875·6	20·1	0 ·54	1881·5	149·2	0 ·26
1875·9	15·1	0 ·42	1882·6	167·5	0 ·26
1876·7	25·8	0 ·48	1883·6	182·5	0 ·23
1877·7	29·7	0 ·51			

1111. In the spectrum of Mizar the Hγ line of hydrogen is periodically bifurcated, to a maximum separation of 0·5 Å. What is the relative orbital velocity of the components in projection along the line of sight, if the wavelength of Hγ is 4341 Å?

1112. What are the velocities of the centres of gravity of the spectroscopic binary systems β Capricorni, ϱ Velorum and α Aurigae? (Fig. 43.)

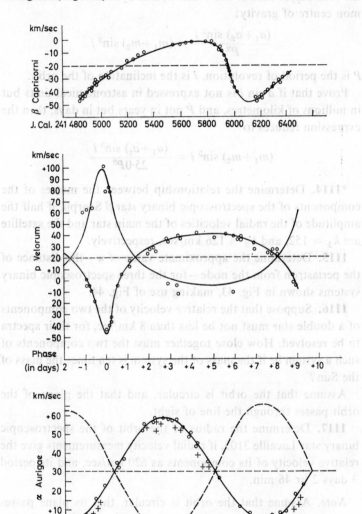

FIG. 43. The curves of the radial velocities of spectroscopic binary stars.

*1113. For spectroscopic binary stars the following relationship exists between the masses of the components m_1 and m_2 and the semi-major axes of the orbits a_1 and a_2 relative to their common centre of gravity:

$$\frac{(a_1+a_2)\sin^3 i}{P^2} = (m_1+m_2)\sin^3 i$$

P is the period of revolution, i is the inclination of the orbit.

Prove that if $a \sin i$ is not expressed in astronomical units but in millions of kilometres, and P not in years but in days, then the expression reduces to

$$(m_1+m_2)\sin^3 i = \frac{(a_1+a_2)\sin^3 i}{25{\cdot}0 P^2}$$

*1114. Determine the relationship between the masses of the components of the spectroscopic binary star β Scorpii, if half the amplitude of the radial velocities of the main star and the satellite are $k_1 = 152$, and $k_2 = 126$ km/sec, respectively.

1115. Determine the approximate value of w—the distance of the periastron from the node—for the three spectroscopic binary systems shown in Fig. 43, making use of Fig. 44.

1116. Suppose that the relative velocity of the two components of a double star must not be less than 8 km/sec, for their spectra to be resolved. How close together must the two components of such a system be if the mass of the system is ten times the mass of the Sun?

Assume that the orbit is circular, and that the plane of the orbit passes through the line of sight.

1117. Determine the radius of the orbit of the spectroscopic binary star Lacaille 3105, if radial velocity measurements give the relative velocity of its components as 620 km/sec, and its period 3 days 2 hr 46 min.

Note. Assume that the orbit is circular, that its plane passes through the Sun, and that the masses of both components are the same.

1118. Determine the radius of the orbit described by Spica, a component of a spectroscopic binary system, having a relative

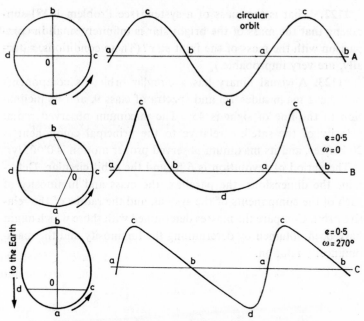

FIG. 44. The curves of the radial velocities for various orbits of
spectroscopic binary stars.

orbital velocity of 91 km/sec and a period of 4 days 0 hr 19 min.
The orbit may be taken to be circular, and the Sun to be in the
plane of the orbit.

1119. Determine the mass of the spectroscopic binary system
whose observed radius of orbit is the true one, if the stars are
twins, the period is 3 days 2 hr 46 min and the radius of the apparent orbit is 26,600,000 km.

1120. What is the mass of the system if the companion star
of the binary dealt with in Problem 1118 is equal in mass to the
bright star? In this case the radius of the relative orbit is the same
as the diameter of the orbit of Spica.

1121. What is the mass of a system (see Problem 1118) if the
dark star has a mass one-quarter of that of the bright star? In this
case the orbit of the dark star has a radius four times greater than
the radius of Spica, and the radius of the relative orbits is five
times greater than the radius of the relative orbit of Spica.

1122. What is the mass of a system (see Problem 1118) supposing that the mass of the bright star is infinitely small in comparison with the mass of the faint star? (These conditions, naturally, are very improbable.)

*1123. A visual binary has a circular orbit; its components both have magnitudes 7·3 and spectra of class 9, and its inclination to the line of sight is 45°. The maximum observed radial velocity of the satellite relative to the principal component is 20 km/sec, and its maximum observed proper motion is 0″·05/yr.

The period of revolution is 6 hr and the orbit circular. Determine the dimensions, the parallax, the mass and luminosity of each of the components of the system, and the radius of the relative orbit. Compare the masses determined with those which might have been obtained by determining the luminosity and the mass-luminosity relation.

CHAPTER XXVI

VARIABLE STARS AND NOVAE

VARIABLE stars are those whose brightness is not constant over normal periods of observation. They are classified as periodic or irregular—the former type repeating a cycle of variation in an accurately repeated period P, and with a fixed amplitude in brightness. The time at which a given brightness is repeated is given by $M = M_0 + PE$, where M_0 is a time at which the given brightness occurred, and E is an integer. For calculations of this type it is convenient to express the times in Julian days, which may be found in the *Astronomical Ephemeris*. It is most convenient to express minutes and seconds in fractions of a day, and Table III at the end of the book is supplied for this purpose.

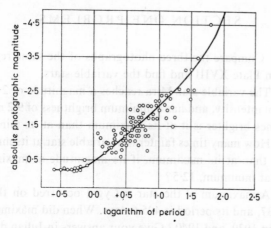

FIG. 45. The "period–absolute magnitude" curve for cepheids. Along the axis of the abscissa is given the logarithms of the period, expressed in days.

Periodic variable stars are classified according to the curves of their intensities and periods into Algols (eclipsing binaries), Cepheids (with periods varying from a few hours to a few days) and long period variables. The reasons for the changes in the brightness of Algols are given in Chapter XXV. Their light curves are characterized by prolonged periods of constant brightness and comparatively short periods of rapid intensity changes, which occur during the eclipse of one star by the other. The light curve of the Cepheids is characterized by continuous variation in which the rise in brightness usually proceeds faster than the fall. Their variability is explained by periodic pulsations of the surface — i.e. periodic changes in the dimensions of the star — accompanied by change in temperature. The notable property of Cepheids is that their pulsation period is related to their absolute magnitude. This relationship is illustrated in Fig. 45 in the form of a period-absolute magnitude curve.

The light curves of stars with long periods resemble those of the Cepheids, but they vary slightly from time to time and their periods are greater than 90 days. The causes of their changes in intensity are apparently the same as those for Cepheids

SECTION ONE PROBLEMS

*1124. Compare the three photographs of the same region of the sky in Plate XVIII and find the variable stars.

1125. The variable star Mira reaches a magnitude of 2·5 at its maximum intensity, and has a minimum brightness of 9·2 m. How many times brighter is it at its maximum than at its minimum?

1126. How many times fainter is a variable star at its minimum intensity than at its maximum, if its magnitude at maximum is 9·5, and at minimum, 12·5?

1127. A maximum of the star $\varkappa$ Cygni occurred on the 20th May, 1937, and its period is 405·6 days. When did maxima occur in 1938, in 1939, and 1940? Give your answers in Julian days.

1128. One of the minima of Algol occurred at 13 hr 55 min universal time on the 3rd January, 1938. If the length of its period is 2·8673 days, calculate the moment of the nearest minimum in that month and year.

Note. Make use of the Table for the conversion of fractions of days into hours and minutes.

*1129. By how many times does the radius of a cepheid change, if the amplitude of its variation is 1·5 stellar magnitudes and we suppose that its surface brightness remains constant?

1130. Determine the mean period and amplitude of the light-variation of $\varkappa$ Cygni from Fig. 46.

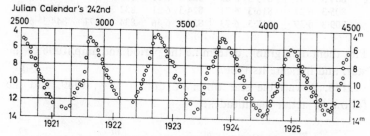

FIG. 46. The light curve of $\varkappa$ Cygni. Above, the number of Julian days; below, the number of years.

1132. Determine the period of light-variation of the eclipsing binary (Algol type) RV Ophiuchi, if some of its minima were observed at the following times, expressed in Julian days:

2416604·701	2418112·729
6641·572	8138·548
7334·753	8477·784

Determine the period to an accuracy of five places of decimals.

*1133. Draw the light curve of a variable star from the table below. The stellar magnitudes are given for times in days from an arbitrary zero point.

0·01	7·36	0·21	7·60	0·53	7·72
0·03	7·28	0·26	7·68	0·55	7·64
0·06	7·28	0·34	7·74	0·56	7·49
0·09	7·36	0·38	7·76	0·58	7·36
0·12	7·42	0·44	7·77	0·60	7·28
0·17	7·52	0·49	7·78	0·62	7·28

Determine the amplitude and the period. How would you classify variable stars with light curves of this form?

*1134. You are given the following data from observations of a variable star. The dates are in Julian days.

	m		m		m		m		m
2425799·3	6·63	810·3	6·51	818·3	6·77	826·4	6·40	835·4	6·68
800·3	6·64	811·3	6·51	819·3	6·77	827·3	6·49	836·4	6·64
801·3	6·61	812·3	6·57	820·3	6·57	828·3	6·57	837·3	6·30
802·3	6·57	813·3	6·57	821·3	6·31	829·3	6·64	838·3	6·24
803·3	6·53	814·3	6·58	822·3	6·27	830·3	6·75	839·3	6·20
804·3	6·31	815·3	6·63	823·3	6·31	831·3	6·80	840·3	6·33
805·3	6·27	816·3	6·71	824·3	6·31	832·3	6·81	841·3	6·33
809·3	6·39	817·3	6·73	825·3	6·36	834·4	6·71	844·3	6·64

Plot them on a graph, determine the period and amplitude of the star, and indicate its type.

1135. A variable star observed during May, 1949, had the following stellar magnitudes:

	m		m		m		m
May 4·5	4·00	May 14·5	4·13	May 21·5	3·72	May 25·5	4·16
May 6·5	3·87	May 16·5	3·70	May 22·5	3·84	May 28·5	3·93
May 7·5	3·91	May 17·5	3·90	May 23·5	3·97	May 29·5	4·10
May 13·5	4·05	May 19·5	4·11	May 24·5	4·12	May 31·5	4·08

Plot these observations on a graph, and establish the probable type of this star, and its approximate period and amplitude.

*1136. Plot the observations of a variable star set out below on a graph:

	m		m		m		m		m
2426423	6·98	461	6·96	480	7·52	498	7·44	539	7·53
436	7·17	462	6·95	482	7·65	513	7·59	540	7·60
440	7·34	464	6·86	484	7·69	514	7·65	545	7·45
448	7·36	467	6·88	486	7·57	515	7·61	555	7·34
454	7·23	472	6·99	488	7·23	516	7·77	557	7·35
457	6·90	473	7·06	492	7·49	526	7·44	560	7·05

What can be said about this variable star?

SECTION TWO PROBLEMS

1137. Why cannot the changes in brightness, and the other characteristics of Cepheids, be explained by eclipses?

1138. Using the period–absolute magnitude curve for Cepheids (Fig. 45), determine the distance to the Cepheid ζ Geminorum, having a period of 10 days, and a mean photographic stellar magnitude 4·8.

1139. The variable star δ Cephei has a period of 5 days, and a mean apparent photographic magnitude of 4·4. What is its distance from us in parsecs?

Make use of Fig. 45.

1140. Determine the ratio between the surface brightnesses of the components of the double star Algol, if their total intensities have a ratio of 0·93 : 0·07, and their radii are 0·21 and 0·24 solar radii, respectively.

*1141. If the amplitude of the light curve of a Cepheid in bolometric stellar magnitudes is 2·0 and if the changes in its intensity are explained by pulsation, what is the change in its radius? At maximum the temperature of the star $T_1 = 9000°$, and at the minimum $T_2 = 7000°$.

---

*1142. Determine the ratio of the radii (r/R) of the faint and bright stars in an eclipsing binary system of the Algol type, if the brightness of the system varies by a factor k from minimum to maximum.

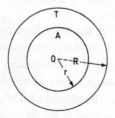

FIG. 47.

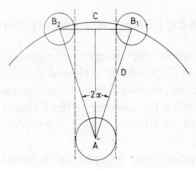

FIG. 48.

Note. Make use of Fig. 47, representing the moment of central eclipse of a bright star T by a less bright star A.

Assume that the brightness of a star at eclipse is proportional to the uncovered surface, and that the satellite A is completely dark.

*1143. Determine the radius D of the relative orbit of a faint companion of an eclipsing binary system of the Algol type, in units of R, the radius of the bright star, assuming the orbit to be circular and given the ratio of the radii of the stars r/R, the period P of the system, and the duration p of the eclipse.

Note. Use Fig. 48, in which A is the principal star, and B_1 and B_2 are the positions of the companion at the beginning and the end of the eclipse.

*1144. Use the formula obtained in Problem 1142 to determine the ratio of the radius of a dark companion to the radius of the principal star of the system RZ Cassiopeiae, an Algol type system, if the range of the light curve obtained from observation is 6·4 to 7·7 stellar magnitudes.

*1145. Determine from the formula obtained in Problem 1142, the ratio of the radii of the dark companion and the bright star in the Algol type system TW Andromedae, and also the radius of the orbit of the satellite in terms of the radius of the principal star. From observation, the period of TW Andromedae is 4·1227 days, the length of the eclipse is 8·8 hr, and the range of intensity variation 8·6 to 11·5 stellar magnitudes.

1146. Does the curve of an Algol type system change, and if so in what way, if the satellite is not completely dark, but only a few times fainter than the bright star?

*1147. From the curves for binary eclipsing stars, set out in Fig. 49, determine the qualitative elements of the eclipse; i.e. the duration, whether the eclipse is complete, partial or annular, whether the intensity of the satellite is a significant fraction of the intensity of the principal star, and how great are the dimensions of both stars in comparison with the radii of their relative orbits.

On which curves does the phase effect appear, i.e. the influence on the illumination of a dimmer star by a brighter one?

*1148. The density of a bright star in an eclipsing binary system can be determined without knowledge of its true dimensions. The theory leads to the approximate formula, giving the density of a star in fractions of the density of the Sun:

$$\varrho = \frac{1}{74 \cdot 4 P^2 r^3}$$

in which P is the period of revolution in days, and r is the radius of the bright star in fractions of the radius of its orbit (determined from photographic observation).

Estimate, by means of this formula, the density of the star RZ Cassiopeiae, for which

$$r = 0 \cdot 28,$$
$$P = 1 \cdot 20 \text{ days.}$$

*1149. The true period of the light variation of an eclipsing variable is 3 days, and its radial velocity is $+30$ km/sec. How long is the observed period of this star?

Hint. Take into account the speed of propagation of light.

1150. A variable star has the ecliptical coordinates λ and β. Prove that if T is the moment of its maximum observed from the Earth, and T_0 is the moment of the same phenomenon for an observer on the Sun, then the following relationship holds:

$$T_0 = T - \frac{a}{c} \cos \beta \cos (\lambda - \odot)$$

in which a is the radius of the Earth's orbit in kilometres, c is the velocity of light in kilometres/sec, and ⊙ is the longitude of the Sun.

1151. A nova in Perseus increased in brightness in two days from 12th to 2nd magnitude. By how many times on the average did it brighten per day?

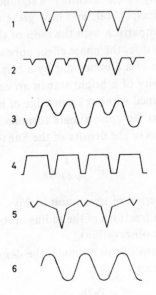

FIG. 49. Light curves of Algols.

1152. A nova in the constellation of Aquila in 1918 had an absolute magnitude $M = -8\cdot8$ at its maximum. How many times was its luminosity greater than that of the Sun? How far away is it if its apparent magnitude was $m = -1\cdot1$? At what distance would it appear as bright as the full Moon? The apparent stellar magnitude of the full Moon is $-12\cdot5$.

*1153. In 1934 a nova exploded in the constellation Hercules. It increased in brightness by 5 stellar magnitudes in the course of a day. The distance to the star, measured immediately after it exploded, was 1800 light years. On the principle that there is no velocity greater than that of light, show that the phenomenon mentioned could not be explained by a sudden approach of the star towards the Earth.

*1154. It is possible to explain by a change in temperature the bolometric amplitude of the light curve of novae amounting to 13 stellar magnitudes? In fact, this is disproved by spectral data.

Hint. Assume the surface temperature before explosion to be about 10,000°.

CHAPTER XXVII

THE STRUCTURE OF THE UNIVERSE

ALMOST all the stars observable through existing telescopes belong to a large stellar system called the Galaxy. The Galaxy is roughly lens-shaped, with stellar density increasing towards the plane of symmetry and towards the centre. The solar system is situated almost in the plane of symmetry of the Galaxy, and rather a long way from its centre. Because of this, we see more stars along the plane of the Galaxy than elsewhere in the sky. Very distant stars in the plane of the Galaxy appear to merge and appear in the sky as a circular bright belt, known as the Milky Way. The number of visible stars increases rapidly towards the mid-line of the Milky Way, though the effect is more marked for faint than for bright stars. The central portion of the Galaxy is surrounded by a number of dense star clusters, known as globular clusters. Outside the Galaxy, vast numbers of diffuse objects, extragalactic nebulae, lie at enormous distances. Some of these have spiral structures similar to the Galaxy.

The distances to the farthest globular star clusters and extragalactic nebulae can be most exactly determined in cases where variable stars can be observed in them. These stars are the Cepheids, whose absolute magnitudes depend in a well-known way on the period of their cycle (Fig. 45). The period and the apparent stellar magnitude of a Cepheid are found from observation, and the parallax of the Cepheid is then determined from the formula

$$\log \pi = -1 - 0 \cdot 2(m - M).$$

As the dimensions of the stellar systems containing Cepheids are small in comparison with their distances from us, the parallax determined is practically that of the stellar system as a whole.

The space between the stars near the plane of the Galaxy is filled with an extremely diffuse medium (interstellar dust). When a ray of light travels a great distance through this medium, it is almost completely absorbed so that, in general, very distant stars appear much fainter than they would through completely transparent space.

SECTION ONE PROBLEMS

1155. A planetary nebula in the constellation Lyra has an angular diameter of 83″ and is 660 parsecs from us. What are its linear dimensions in astronomical units?

1156. In the globular star cluster NGC 5694 the apparent stellar magnitudes of the stars are 18 magnitudes greater than their absolute magnitudes. What is the distance to this cluster?

1157. The angular diameter of the globular star cluster NGC 5694 is 3′ and the distance to it is 40,000 parsecs. What are the linear dimensions of the cluster?

1158. The apparent magnitude of a cepheid in the star cluster in Hercules is $m = 15 \cdot 1$. It is known from the length of its period that its absolute magnitude $M = 0 \cdot 0$.

Determine the distance to the cluster in Hercules.

1159. The star cluster in Hercules is 10·5 thousand parsecs from us, its angular diameter is 12′ and its integrated magnitude is 5·9 m. Calculate the actual diameter of the cluster and its absolute stellar magnitude.

1160. Using the period–absolute magnitude curve for Cepheids (see Fig. 45) determine the distance in light years and the linear diameter, of the spiral nebula in the constellation Triangulum if its angular diameter is 1° and the period of the Cepheids observed in it is 13 days for an apparent stellar magnitude of 19·6.

1161. The mean apparent photographic magnitude of the short-period Cepheids (mean periods of 0·54 days), found in the globular star cluster Messier 3, is 15·50.

Using the period–absolute magnitude curve (Fig. 45) determine the distance to this globular cluster.

*1162. Fig. 50 represents parts of the sky showing stars of magnitudes up to 8. Count the number of stars between 40° and 50° of Declination, and between the circles of Right Ascension 3 hr 0 min and 3 hr 20 min. The Milky Way passes through this sector. Count the number of stars in the section between the same

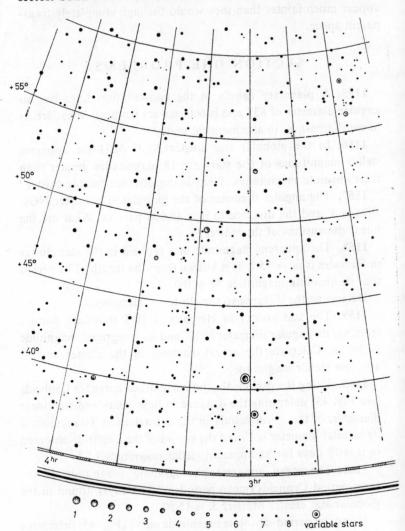

FIG. 50. A chart of the sky in the vicinity of the constellation Perseus.

limits of Declination, but between the circles of Right Ascension 3 hr 20 min and 3 hr 40 min.

This region lies just outside the belt of the Milky Way. Compare the results obtained with each other.

*1163. Using Fig. 50 determine, by counting, the number of stars brighter than the 4th, the 6th, and the 8th magnitudes on the same areas of the sky as in the preceding exercise and determine the relationship of the numbers obtained with each other.

SECTION TWO PROBLEMS

*1164. Deduce an expression for the number of stars within a sphere centred on the Sun, if the stars surrounding it are situated in plane-parallel layers.

1165. What is the ratio of the populations of stars of apparent magnitudes m and $(m+2)$, if the distribution of stars in space is uniform, and the intrinsic luminosity of all stars is the same?

*1166. Two novae, one very bright, the other very faint, are found at the same angular distance from the line of the Milky Way (that is, they have the same galactic latitudes). Are these stars at the same linear distance from the plane of the Milky Way?

Note. The absolute magnitudes of all novae at their maximum are almost the same.

1167. The line of the Milky Way does not form a great circle in the sky, but lies on a small circle close to a great circle. Show by means of a diagram how this is evidence that the Sun does not lie in the galactic plane.

*1168. What would the appearance of the Milky Way be for an observer located in its plane of symmetry, but very far away from its centre? How would it appear to an observer outside its plane of symmetry? Ignore the absorption of light in space.

*1169. The observed radial velocities of stars in their rotation about the centre of the Galaxy are given approximately by the formula

$$\Delta V = A_r \sin 2(l - l_0)$$

where l is the galactic latitude of the star, $l_0 = 325°$ is the galactic latitude of the direction to the centre of the Galaxy, r is the distance of the star in parsecs.

The constant $A = 0{\cdot}020$ km/sec/parsec, for a group of stars located on a small section of the sky with a galactic longitude $l = 345°$.

The mean radial velocity corrected for all known effects is 30 km/sec.

What is its distance from the Sun if this radial velocity is caused entirely by its galactic rotation?

1170. Prove that the absorption capacity of a given mass of dust is generally proportional to the radius of the particles into which it is divided.

*1171. The distances to a number of spiral nebulae were determined by the Cepheid method. It later became clear that interstellar space slightly absorbs light passing through it. How did this discovery effect the calculated diameters of the spiral nebulae?

*1172. If one supposes that the linear diameters and absolute integrated magnitudes of all globular clusters are the same, then what formulae connect their integrated apparent magnitudes m and their apparent angular diameters d, for different distances?

1173. How would the relation between the angular diameters and the integrated apparent magnitudes of the globular star clusters change (see preceding exercise) if light is noticeably absorbed in interstellar space?

*1174. In a spiral nebula 7·5 million light years away from us two Cepheids of the same period were observed, one of which was situated on the edge of the nebula nearest to us, and the other 20,000 light years farther off.

What is the difference in apparent magnitude of these stars, if we assume that their absolute magnitudes are exactly the same?

1175. If the mean absolute photographic magnitudes of extragalactic nebulae are $-13{\cdot}8$, and the limiting apparent photographic magnitude for a 2·5 m reflector is 20·2 then what is the penetration power of the telescope expressed in light years?

*1176. What mathematical spiral most closely approaches the form of the spiral nebula in the constellation Canis Venaticus? (See Plate XIX.)

Hint. Follow the spiral arms of the Galaxy by plotting their polar coordinates, r and ϕ.

MISCELLANEOUS PROBLEMS

THIS SECTION contains problems which do not readily fit into any of the preceding Chapters, or require the use of information contained in other sections of the book.

SECTION ONE PROBLEMS

1177. *A Chinese Problem*

"When, in the evenings, the tail of the Great Bear is turned towards the East", wrote the Chinese Sage, Go Koan Tse, in the fourth century B.C., "it is Spring in the World. When it is turned towards the mid-day Sun, it is Summer. When it is turned to the West, it is Autumn, and when it faces to the North, then it is Winter."

Is this also true for England? (Kamenschikov.)

1178. *Virgil's Problem*

Virgil, a Roman poet in the first century B.C., said that the soil should be ploughed at that season when Arcturus shines in the sky ...

"When, however, it will not bear fruit, it should be ploughed lightly under Arcturus."
When will this be? (Kamenschikov.)

1179. *The Osiris Sage*

In the sacred books of Egypt the constellation Orion is called "The Osiris Sage"—"The lord of all the movements of the Heavens".

According to tradition, the "Osiris Sage" revealed the source of the Nile, and indicated the path to the Sun. When does Orion rise together with the Sun? (Kamenschikov.)

1180. Sirius is sometimes called "The Ripener" by the peasants in Russia — "The Ripener ripens the corn — the corn is ripe, and she is gone."

When does Sirius begin to rise before the Sun rises? (Kamenschikov.)

1181. *The Meeting of V. G. Korelenko and the Wandering Pilgrim*
In the story *The Little Falcon*, V. G. Korelenko writes:

"We both went outdoors. The frost and the mist had dispersed. The Wanderer glanced at the sky. 'The Watchmen have climbed high,' he said, 'it is past mid-night.' "[†]

What was the time of the year? "The Watchmen" are the Pleiades. (Kamenschikov.)

1182. *Oblonskii and Levin's Hunt*

"It began to get dark. The tender beams of silver Venus already shone low in the west from the birch grove, and high in the east appeared the scarlet fires of sombre Arcturus. Above Levin's head, the stars of the Little Bear appeared and were lost again."[‡]

These lines are taken from the description of Levin and Oblonskii's hunt. On the basis of the data given by L. N. Tolstoy determine, from a map of the heavens, at what time of year, and in what month the hunt took place. (Kamenschikov.)

1183. *The Voyage of the "Nautilus"*

"When the 'Nautilus' was still at the South Pole, the constellations shone with incredible brightness. In the zenith burned the Southern Cross — the Pole Star of Antarctic countries."[§]

[†] V. G. Korelenko, *The Little Falcon*, Chapter VI.
[‡] L. N. Tolstoy, *Anna Karenina*, Book 2, Chapter XV.
[§] Jules Verne, *20,000 Leagues under the Sea*.

(1) Is it possible that the Southern Cross stood at the zenith at the South Pole?

(2) If not, then at what latitude was the "Nautilus"?

(3) Does the Southern Cross appear as "The Pole Star of Antarctic countries"?

(Kamenschikov.)

1184. The Voyage of Odysseus

In the description of the voyage of Odysseus, from the nymph Calypso to the island of Skeria, it is said:

"Odysseus hoisted the sail with joy, and with a favourable wind behind him, set sail. Sitting at the stern, and with his mighty hand guiding the rudder, he kept watch. No sleep could close his eyes as he kept his gaze upon the Pleiades. Boötes[†] slowly sank into the seas, and the Bear, as yet known as The Chariot, near to Orion, most sacred of old, kept his course, never bathing himself in the waves of the ocean. The noble goddess, Calypso, had bade him keep the Bear forever as he sailed, to leftward."[‡]

Determine, from this description of the sky, at what time of year, in which direction, and in what month Odysseus undertook his voyage. (Kamenschikov.)

SECTION TWO PROBLEMS

*1185. In the newspaper *Izvestia*, E. K. Feodorov, the astronomer of the drifting scientific station "North Pole", wrote on the 4th May, 1937:

"We will be able to determine the coordinates of the camp, in the main, by astronomical methods.... It should be mentioned that astronomical determinations made during the day by means of the Sun, are possible only to an accuracy of about 0·5 km. At night, by the stars, the determinations will be more accurate, with a probable error of only 200–300 m."

† Constellation of Boötes (the ox-driver or wagonner).
‡ Homer's *Odyssey*, Book X, lines 269 – 277.

Explain why observations at night give more accurate results than those made during the day. With what accuracy did E. K. Feodorov determine the zenith distance of the Sun, and the local time on the floating ice at latitude $+89°$? What would the error in longitude be in kilometres in the determination of the position of a ship sailing along the equator, if the navigator determines the local time with the same accuracy as E. K. Feodorov determined his, from the Sun?

*1186. In the newspaper *Red Star* for the 23rd May, 1937, the flag captain of the Soviet Expedition to the North Pole, I. T. Spirin, wrote about Arctic flights:

"Astronomy plays a very significant role in flights of this kind.... At about the 84th Parallel the altitude of the Sun is equal to its Declination, and the hour angle of the Sun is equal to its azimuth. On this basis special tables are constructed, which make calculations very simple."

Explain how and why the conditions of visibility of the Sun in the polar regions are as described by I. T. Spirin. Why does the circumstance indicated make the calculations necessary for establishing the course of a plane, and its coordinates, so much simpler?

*1187. In the limits of the Soviet sector of the Arctic lies the Island of Rudolph. Situated between $81°41'$ and $81°50'$ latitude north, and $57°50'$ and $59°0'$ longitude east, its shape is almost square. What is the area of the Island? When, on this island, does the polar day begin? When does it end? How many kilometres from the North Pole is the island? At what hour, by local time, does a person wintering on this island hear the broadcast chimes of the clock on the Kremlin tower? For how long a period may the planet Saturn not be visible on that island?

*1188. The Soviet aeronauts, M. Gromov, A. B. Iumashev and S. A. Danilin, left Moscow on a non-stop flight to North America at 3 hr 31 min on the 12th July, 1937 (by conventional time, reckoned at Moscow). They landed at San Jacinto, in California, 62 hr 17 min after they started. The geographical coordinates of San Jacinto are $\phi = 33°$, $\lambda = 120°$ to the west of Greenwich.

At what hour, by local time, and on what day of the month (by the local reckoning at San Jacinto) did the Soviet airmen touch American soil? What was the position of the Sun at that moment, relative to the horizon at San Jacinto?

*1189. The height of the lower edge of the Sun, measured from a ship at midday, was $62°24'45''$; the Declination of the centre of the Sun was $20°55'10''$, and half its diameter was $15'47''$.

At the given altitude the diurnal parallax of the Sun was $5''$, and the refraction was normal as tabulated (the pressure being 760 mm of mercury, and the temperature $10°C$).

The observer is at a height of 4·95 m above sea-level. Determine the geographical latitude of the position of the ship.

1190. Find the latitude of a place (taking refraction into account) given that the lower edge of the Moon at the meridian had an altitude of $49°37'$ (south of the zenith), the Declination of the Moon was $+3°13'$, its radius was $15'·0$ and its horizontal parallax $55'·2$.

The eyes of the observer were 12 m above sea level.

1191. Prove, using the lines of position, that a considerable error in calculated latitude does not affect the longitude, calculated by observation of the Sun at the prime vertical.

1192. On 10th January, 1919, the altitude of the Moon was measured with a sextant from an aeroplane at 8 hr 37 min 33 sec G.M.T. and found to be $38°55'$.

The altitude of the Sun at 8 hr 43 min 58 sec appeared to be $12°59'$.

These observations were corrected for refraction and for instrumental error. It is known that at this time the coordinates of the aeroplane were

$$\phi = 37·4°; \quad \lambda = 76°24' \text{ W}.$$

The altitude of the Sun, calculated for the moment of observations, was $12°55'$; the azimuth was S. $39°$ W.; while for the Moon the same calculated values were $39°4'$ and S. $81°$ E., allowing for parallax.

Draw the lines of position, and find the error in the position of the aeroplane determined from observations.

*1193. On the longest day of the year at Dneipopetrovsk, the Sun reaches an altitude of $\alpha = 65°$. What, at this time, is the length of the shadow of a man who is 1·80 m tall?

1194. A telegraph pole 9 m high is illuminated by the Sun. Rays of light from the upper edge of the Sun touching the top of the pole intersect the horizontal plane at an angle $\beta = 42°17'$.

What is the length of the penumbra of the pole's shadow, if the apparent diameter of the Sun is $\alpha = 32'$?

1195. A vertical wall h high runs in a direction θ west of south. Prove that on the days of the equinoxes the wall does not cast a shadow when the hour angle of the Sun, t, is determined by the formula

$$\tan t = \sin \phi \tan \theta$$

and show that at true midday the width of the shadow is

$$h \tan \phi \sin \theta.$$

1196. What is the central angle α of a spherical segment of the Earth, illuminated by the Moon when it is full? If the radius of the Earth is r the radius of the Moon is $0·273r$, and its distance from the Earth is $60r$.

*1197. Enumerate all the known phenomena affecting the determination of the coordinates of a star from observation, and which must be accounted for in determining the proper motion of the star.

This involves comparing coordinates of the star determined at intervals of at least 10 years. Do not take instrumental error into account.

1198. How would the dates change for the passengers of an aeroplane which takes off from Leningrad (Zone II) at midday on 1st July and circles the Earth along the parallel in 12 hr? (M. Borchev.)

1199. Which heavenly body do observers, on the average, see for longer over the horizon; the Sun or the Moon?

1200. What is the time between the conjunction and the opposition of a planet, if its brightness increases by $0·85$ magnitudes during this period? The orbit of the planet may be considered to be circular, and to lie on the plane of the ecliptic. (M. Borchev.)

PROBLEMS OF ARTIFICIAL CELESTIAL BODIES

Some problems concerning the motion of artificial celestial bodies were given in Section XVII: "Gravitation". Here follow some additional simple problems.

1201. Calculate the circular velocities for the Earth's artificial satellites which move at altitudes of 100, 500 and 1000 km.

1202. Calculate the period of revolution of an artificial satellite moving about the Earth at an altitude of 250 km in a circular orbit

1203. An artificial satellite moves in a circular orbit in the plane of the equator in the direction of the Earth's rotation at a speed of 6·9 km/sec. How often will it transit the zenith of a certain place on the Earth equator?

1204. An artificial satellite moves in a polar orbit at an altitude of 250 km. By how many kilometers will the projection on the Earth of its orbit move towards the West in one revolution at the latitude 57°37′?

1205. What must the velocity be of a satellite of the Moon, to revolve at an altitude of 50 km from the lunar surface?

1206. Calculate the distance from the Earth of a satellite, which will appear to be stationary in the sky at any point of the Earth surface.

1207. Calculate the velocity necessary for a rocket to leave the Martian surface.

1208. How long will you travel to Mars in a spacecraft which has its perihelion near the Earth's orbit and its aphelion near the Mars orbit?

1209. Find the velocity of a spacecraft in perihelion and aphelion, if the perihelion altitude is 227 km from the Earth's surface and the semi-major axis of its orbit is 6958 km.

1210. A spacecraft put in a circular orbit at an altitude 250 km, spends 5 min attaining this trajectory. Calculate the mean acceleration of the ship and the mean overload experienced by the cosmonaut during the launching.

1211. Calculate according to the formula given by Ciolkovski $M_o/M_f = e^{v/C_p}$ the change of the mass of the spacecraft if it moves first in a circular orbit with velocity 5 km/sec and then passes to a parabolic orbit. (M_o and M_f are the initial and the final masses of the ship, $e = 2\cdot72$, v is the difference of velocities, and C_p the velocity of the gaseous stream, $2\cdot8$ km/sec.

1212. After the cabin separates from the rocket, the latter moves in the wake of the cabin but later overtakes it. What is the reason for this effect?

ANSWERS AND SOLUTIONS

Chapter I

Interpolation

1. In the given case the change of equation of time per hour for neighbouring days is almost the same, and it is sufficient for the equation of time for midnight to add its hour change multiplied by 6. That is,

1 min 4·06 sec + (0·546 sec) × 6 = 1 min 7·34 sec.

2. Interpolating to the second differences, we obtain:

$$\delta = +23°15'52'''·3.$$

3. 6 hr 59 min 27·58 sec.   **4.** 7 hr 25 min 18·50 sec.

5. +22°18'33'''·8.   **6.** +3 min 37·43 sec.

7. We find the precession:

for $\alpha = 1\cdot8$ hr and $\delta = 60°$ it is equal to $+4\cdot1$ sec;

for $\alpha = 1\cdot8$ hr and $\delta = 70°$ it is equal to $4\cdot7$ sec

(differences greater than the first may be entirely neglected in the present case). Between the two values obtained we interpolate for $\delta = 63°$ and obtain $+4\cdot3$ sec. (If there were a column in the Table for $\delta = 80°$, it would have been better to obtain the second difference in a horizontal direction.)

8. +4·4 sec; +4''.   **9.** +1·0 sec; −0·5''.

10. +4·1 sec; −6''.

Chapter II

The Celestial Sphere

11. 1.9 m.   **12.** 3 km.

18. At 8 o'clock in the evening.

22. 34°15'.   **23.** 55°.

25. Either the observer is situated at one of the Earth's poles or else the body is situated at one of the celestial poles.

26. The ecliptic, the prime vertical, the equinoctial, and the solstitial.

27. As a great circle inclined to the horizon at an angle of 23°27'.

28. (90° − 55°45') ± 23°27'. The greatest angle is 57°42', the least is 10°48'.

29. On the polar circles: at the north, at the moment of the rising of the point of the Vernal Equinox; at the south polar circle at the moment of its setting.

30. See the answer to the preceding question.

31. $84\frac{1}{2}°$.   **32.** $11\frac{1}{2}°$; $58\frac{1}{2}°$; $0°$; $47°$.

33. $\sqrt{(r_1^2 + r_2^2 - 2r_1r_2 \cos \theta)}$.

Chapter III

Systems of Celestial Coordinates

I

34. The South Pole.   **35.** $89°2'^{\circ}$.

36. $180°$; $0°$; $270°$; $90°$.   **37.** $+42$.

38. $A = 180°$, $h = 23°27'$.

39. 0 hr indeterminate.   **40.** 6 hr, 18 hr, or $-$ 6 hr.

41. $\alpha = \delta = 0$.   **42.** For the point of the Vernal

Equinox. For it $\lambda = \beta = 0$.

43. $+66\frac{1}{2}°$. $90°$.   **44.** 18 hr 0 min $+66\frac{1}{2}$.

45. $\beta = 90°$, λ is indeterminate.

46. $45°$.   **47.** In the constellation Gemini.

49. Because this reckoning corresponds to the diurnal revolution of the celestial sphere.

50. Because in this case the moments of culmination of the stars are arranged in order of Right Ascensions.

51. For the first 18 hr 47 min 13 sec.

52. For the first $49°17'15''$.

53. $5°$.   **54.** To the south-west.

55. In the eastern sector.   **56.** 6 hr.

57. 2 hr 39 min.   **58.** $\alpha - 12 \text{ hr} < S < \alpha$.

59. $t = 6$ hr 44 min.   **60.** $S = 3$ hr 24 min.

61. 14 hr 36 min 36 sec.   **62.** Low in the south in both cases.

63. In the zenith.

64. In the west (5 hr 26 min) and in the east (18 hr 50 min); in the east (17 hr 26 min) and in the west (6 hr 50 min).

65. 1 hr 24 min.   **66.** 13 hr 24 min, 1 hr 24 min.

67. $0°$.

68. For an observer situated on the equator of the earth, observing an equatorial star.

69. On the north polar circle at the moment of the rising of the point of the Vernal Equinox.

70. The solstitial colure (excepting the arcs from the pole of the ecliptic to the celestial poles nearest to it).

71. The great circle passing midway between the equator and the ecliptic, and subtending angles of $78°16'·5$ with them.

72. The equinoctial points.   **73.** $\delta = 28°$, $\alpha = 12$ hr 40 min.

74. Culminating to the north of the zenith (and rising north of the point of east, if the intersection with the prime vertical recurring beneath the horizon, is not counted).

II

75. $83°46'32''$, $57°40'45''$ and $72°49'50''$.

76. $\cos l = \sin \delta_1 \sin \delta_2 + \cos \delta_1 \cos \delta_2 \cos (\alpha_2 - \alpha_1)$.

77. $l = 5°23'$. $\alpha_2 - \alpha_1$ is small, so it is possible to adopt it equal to zero within an accuracy of $1'$.

78. The length of the path is $71°18'10''$, the angles are $40'13'48''$ and $69°14'45''$.

79. After the reduction to the logarithmic form $\cos \delta \sin t = \sin z \sin A$, $\cos \delta \cos t = n \cos (\phi - N)$, $\sin \delta = n \sin (\phi - N)$, where

$$n \sin N = \sin z \cos A \quad \text{and} \quad n \cos N = \cos z \, (n > 0).$$

80. $\cos \beta \cos \lambda = \cos \delta \cos \alpha$,
$\cos \beta \sin \lambda = \sin \varepsilon \sin \delta + \cos \varepsilon \cos \delta \sin \alpha$,
$\sin \beta \quad = \cos \varepsilon \sin \delta - \sin \varepsilon \cos \delta \sin \alpha$.
For the sum: $\cos \lambda = \cos \delta \sin \alpha$.

81. $\cos \delta \cos \alpha = \lambda$, $\cos \delta \sin \alpha = \sin \lambda \cos \varepsilon$, $\sin \delta = \sin \lambda \sin \varepsilon$.

82. $\cos \beta \cos \lambda = \cos \delta \cos \alpha$, $\cos \beta \sin \lambda = n \cos (N - \varepsilon)$, $\sin \beta = n \sin (N - \varepsilon)$, where

$$n \sin N = \sin \delta \quad \text{and} \quad n \cos N = \cos \delta \sin \alpha \, (n > 0).$$

83. $\cos x'$, $\cos (y' - \theta') = \cos x \, (y - \theta)$,
$\cos x'$, $\sin (y' - \theta) = -\sin x \sin i + \cos x \cos i \, (y - \theta)$,
$\sin x' = \sin x \cos i - \cos x \sin i \sin (y - \theta)$.

85. $A = 279°33'$; $Z = 68°36'$.

86. $Z = 32°45'\cdot0$; $A = 343°42'\cdot9$.

87. $\alpha = 14$ hr 11 min 35 sec; $\delta = 19°38'\cdot7$.

88. $\lambda = 85°45'\cdot0$; $\beta = +45°7'\cdot8$.

89. $\lambda = 87°10'$; $\beta = 16°2'$.   **90.** $\delta = +17°11'\cdot5$.

91. $\alpha = 4$ hr 38 min 5 sec; $\delta = +22°8'\cdot0$.

92. $\alpha = 2$ hr 44 min 24 sec; $\delta = +15°\cdot9$; $\alpha = 9$ hr 43 min 36 sec; $\delta = +13°\cdot7$.

93. $281°\cdot3$, $102°\cdot7$.   **94.** $\delta = 15°20'\cdot3$. $A = 70°37'\cdot5$.

95. 4 hr 10·2 min.

96. $\sin z \sin p = \cos \phi \sin (s - \alpha)$,
$\sin z \cos p = m \cos (M - \delta)$,
$\cos z = m \cos (M - \delta)$,
where $m \sin M = \sin \phi$ and
$m \cos M = \cos \phi \cos (s - \alpha)$ $(m > 0)$.

97. The angle α between the plane of the horizon and the plane of the ecliptic is equal to the angle between the zenith and the pole of the ecliptic, and it follows that in the spherical triangle pole–zenith–pole of the ecliptic it is measured by the side from the pole of the ecliptic–zenith.

The other sides are equal to ε and $90 - \phi$ and the angle opposite to the side x is equal to $90° + s$. Employing the formula for the cosine of the side we have

$$\cos x = \cos \varepsilon \sin \phi - \sin \varepsilon \cos \phi \sin s.$$

The maximum at $s = 6$ hr, the minimum at $s = 18$ hr.

98. The formulae given are formulae for the transformation of spatial coordinates in the case where the Ox axis maintains its direction, and the axes Oy and Ox rotate by the angle ε.

99. The formulae given are the formulae for the transformation of spatial coordinates in cases of the parallel shifting of the axes by X_0, Y_0 and Z_0.

The left-hand sides are the main rectangular equatorial geocentric coordinates.

Chapter IV

Culmination, Determination of Geographical Latitude and Coordinates of Celestial Bodies

I

101. $0°$, if $\delta < \phi$ and $180°$.

102. For bodies culminating to the north of the zenith ($\delta < \phi$).

104. $47°$.

105. The altitudes differ by $30°$, and the azimuths are either equal, or differ by $180°$, if $-(\phi + 30°) < \delta < -\phi$ (this case corresponds to a few stars which never rise).

107. $17°3'$.   **108.** $14°3'$; $4°36'$.

109. Always.   **110.** This cannot occur anywhere.

111. $51°2'$.

112. Not always in Odessa and Tbilisi. Always in Moscow and Kiev.

113. No.   **114.** Beginning from lat. $35°$.

115. No.   **116.** $35°$.

117. $35°28'$.   **118.** $-16°36'$.

119. $\delta = 90° - \phi$.   **120.** $\delta = \phi$.

121. So that $\delta > 90° - \phi$; so that $\delta < -(90° - \phi)$.

122. $55°45'$; $50°27'$; $41°43'$.

123. to $-30°3'$;   to $-48°42'$.

124. On about 11th June, or on about 3rd July.

125. With an accuracy of $8''$.   **126.** $41°42'$.

127. $44°06'$.   **128.** $60°$.

129. Closer to the zenith. There the error in the correction for refraction is less, and the images of the stars in the telescope are more stable.

130. The stick was not perpendicular to the shadow.

131. $24°2'$.   **132.** $40°20'$.

133. $+40°51'13''$.   **134.** $+72°3'$.

135. The problem has two solutions:

(1) The star passes through upper culmination to the south of the zenith. In this case we have two equations:

$$\delta = \phi - 40° \quad \text{and} \quad \delta = 110° - \phi, \text{ whence we obtain}$$

$$\delta = 35°; \qquad \phi = 75°.$$

(2) The star passes through upper culmination to the north of the zenith; in this case we have the two equations

$$\delta = 40° + \phi \quad \text{and} \quad \delta = 110° - \phi,$$

from which we obtain $\delta = 75°$, $\phi = 35°$.

136. 54°12 .   **137.** On the equator.

138. 4 hr.   **139.** At 22 hr 33 min 48 sec.

140. 8 hr 48 min.

141. After 5 hr 2 min; after 18 hr 58 min sidereal time.

142. Approximately at 7 hr 20 min in the evening.

143. At 4 hr 42 min in the morning.

144. At about 5·30 in the evening.

145. At about 8 o'clock in the evening.

147. Those which have a Right Ascension of about 18 hr 30 min, for example, α and ε Ayrae.

149. In January.   **150.** At the beginning of a new year.

151. About 22nd August.   **152.** At midnight.

153. On about 22nd December, $\alpha = 5\frac{1}{2}$ hr.

154. 7 hr 35 min; 15°45' and 19 hr 35 min; 84°15'.

155. 5°48'; 10 hr 49 min 37 sec.

156. $\alpha = 15$ hr 15 min 10 sec; $\delta = 46°35'$.

157. $\alpha = 7$ hr 35 min 48·8 sec; $\delta = 12°5'$.

158. $\alpha = 0$ hr 16 min 45 sec; $\delta = -0°6'·2$.

159. $\alpha = 19$ hr 9 min 13 sec; $\delta = -18°10'18''$.

II

160. The maximum in the eastern and western parts of the sky (at the prime vertical), the minimum at the meridian.

161. Fastest at the meridian, and slowest in the east and the west (at the prime vertical).

162. The second is more exact.

163. See the answer to problems 160–161.

164. An equatorial star (Declination zero) observed from the Earth's equator.

165. Taking $t = 0$ we find $z = \mp(\phi - \delta)$.

166. 52°30'.

167. $\tan \phi = \tan \dfrac{\sin t_1 + \sin t_2}{\sin (t_1 + t_2)}$.

168. See Professor S. A. Kazakovs' book *A Course in Spherical Astronomy*, 2nd edition, 1940, p. 93, formula (49).

Chapter V

Refraction

II

170. On both, with the exception of the hour angle and the Right Ascension at culmination.

171. On both, and always.   **172.** 5°44′11″.

173. +7°44′28″.   **174.** 88°3′32″.

175. $\phi = 51°32′09″$; $\delta = +74°34′41″$.

176. To the pole from the north or the south polar circle in the summer. The possible error might be as large as 8–9 hr.

177. For 5 min.

178. Possible owing to the effect of atmospheric refraction.

179. Yes. Owing to the noticeable difference in refraction for the upper and lower edges of the discs of the Sun and Moon, their diameters appear shorter in a vertical direction.

180. No, it diminishes.   **181.** It does not change.

182. No, because for them the differences in refraction are insignificantly small.

183. No, because refraction does not alter the azimuth of a heavenly body.

184. $\delta = 74°34′43″$; $\phi = 40°22′10″$.

185. $\alpha = 5$ hr 14 min 55 sec; $\delta = -9°22′7″$.

186. By 3 days.   **187.** $Z = 53°49′52″{\cdot}3$.

188. The solution is: $z' = z+r$. By the law of refraction,

$$\frac{n}{1} = \frac{\sin z'}{\sin z} = \frac{\sin (z+r)}{\sin z} ,$$

or

$$n \sin z = \sin z \cos r + \cos z \sin r.$$

As r is very small, we take $\cos r = 1$, and $\sin r = r \sin 1″$. Then

$$(n-1) \sin z = r \sin 1″ \cos z$$

and

$$r = \frac{n-1}{\sin 1″} \tan z = 58″{\cdot}3 \tan z.$$

Chapter VI

The Apparent Motion of the Sun

190. For approximately 12 hr.   **191.** 90° and 0°;   270° and 0°.

192. 180°, 188°, 280°.   **194.** 0 hr and 0°, 12 hr and 0°.

195. 6 hr, +23°27′;   18 hr, −23°27′.

196. 90° and 0°;   180° and 0°.

197. About the 22nd of every month.

198. 57°42′.   **199.** 2°0′.

200. 53°30′; 72°0′; 90°; 45°54′; 43°06′; 0°.
the Tropic of Cancer; the north polar circle.

202. 66°33′. **203.** By 2°.

204. 23°27′. **205.** 43°49′; 22°44′.

206. 36°10′. **207.** On 3rd May or 11th August.

208. 12 hr, 115°.

209. At midday on about 22nd December.

210. The latitude is +34°47′, the obliquity 23°54′.

211. α — near the Earth is at perihelion (at the beginning of January); near the moment of equinox.

212. About 282°; about 101°.

213. It oscillates between the 20th to 21st March following the leap-year period; see the answer to the following question.

214. The ephemeris, calculated for midday of every day of a given year, will not be true for another year, because of the non-coincidence of the tropical year with the calendar. The greatest difference in the ephemeris is reached in a leap year, and the year preceding a leap year. The error may reach $1\frac{3}{4}$ times the diurnal displacement of the Sun, when a leap year is omitted by the Gregorian calendar (for example, in 1900).

215. In a triangle, formed by the equator, the ecliptic and the circle of Declination of the Sun, the angle opposite the side L is a right angle, and the formula takes on the form

$$\cos L = \cos \alpha \cos \delta.$$

By the sine theorem:

$$\sin \delta = \sin \varepsilon \sin L.$$

216. The formula is obtained from the answer to Problem 81.

217. On 9th June: $\alpha = 86°{\cdot}7$; $\delta = +23°{\cdot}4$; or $\lambda = 87°{\cdot}0$; $\beta = 0°$.
On 19th December: $\alpha = 266°{\cdot}7$; $\delta = -23°{\cdot}4$; or $\lambda = 267°{\cdot}0$; $\beta = 0°$

Chapter VII

The Determination of Time and Longitude

219. The solar days would be shorter than the sidereal.

220. No difference. **221.** 32°20′ = 2 hr 9 min 20 sec.

222. 0 hr 39 min 12 sec. **223.** 2 hr 30 min 17 sec east.

224. −3 hr 6 min 27 sec. **225.** 3 hr 16 min east.

226. 8 hr 45 min east. **227.** 6°26′.

228. 0 hr 22 min. **229.** 2 hr 14 min to the east of Pultov.

230. 9 hr 18 min east. **231.** 7 hr 47 min east.

232. 1 hr 22 min east.

233. On 3rd April at 0 hr 3 min, on 3rd April at 1 hr 3 min, on 2nd April at 23 hr 40 min.

234. 9 hr 28·6 min in the evening, 22°·13.

235. $\lambda = 2$ hr 57 min to the west of Greenwich, $\phi = 40°27′$.

237. (1) Observing the same star at the same altitude before and after its upper culmination, establish the midday line and the meridian.

(2) Find the time of the star across the meridian to establish the sidereal time, and correct the chronometer by it.

(3) At the same moment, read the graduated circle, to establish the latitude by the meridianal altitudes.

(4) Observe the moments of the eclipses of the satellites of Jupiter by the same chronometer. Transform the sidereal time into mean time, and by comparison with the tables, determine the longitude.

238. 20 km at this latitude indicates a difference in longitude of

$$360 \times \frac{20}{2\pi R \cos \phi} = 0°\cdot 32 = 1 \text{ min } 17 \text{ sec.}$$

This is the difference at the moment of midday.

239. -26 min $35\cdot07$ sec, and -26 min $34\cdot27$ sec.

240. 9 hr 16 min $18\cdot2$ sec.

241. $+6$ min 36 sec; $+5$ min 41 sec.

242. $+7\cdot4$ sec.

243. -2 min 35 sec; -2 min $38\cdot5$ sec; -3 min 03 sec.

244. A pendulum at the equator completes

$$n = 86,400 \sqrt{(g_0/g)} = 86,247 \quad \text{oscillations per day;}$$

that is, 153 less than at Moscow. The clock would be 2 min 33 sec per day slow.

245. In 1 min $43\cdot5$ sec.
246. 23 hr 56 min $4\cdot09$ sec.
247. 15 hr 9 min $21\cdot4$ sec.
250. 2 hr 23 min $48\cdot48$ sec.
251. 1461.
252. Ist July, 5 hr 28 min.
253. 14 hr 32 min and 19 hr 44 min, reckoning the first time from 23rd March, and the second time from 23rd June, when the sidereal time at midnight is about 18 hr.

254. 3 hr 0 min
255. 21 hr 20 min.
256. 13 hr 10 min.
257. 17 hr 59 min 39 sec.
258. 9 hr 10 min 30 sec
259. 23 hr 46 min 23 sec in Omsk and 4 hr 46 min 23 sec in Yakutsk.
263. At 11 hr 41 min 0 sec.
264. 4 hr 6 min; 11 hr 37 min.
265. 13 hr 4 min $15\cdot5$ sec.
266. 3 hr 18 min.
267. 6 min after true midday.
268. The clocks are fast by 1 hr 6 min.
269. -18 min 44 sec.
270. $+16$ sec, 10 hr 57 min 18 sec.
271. $+15$ min.
272. -9 min.
273. 32 min.
274. About 11 hr 48 min.
275. Yes.
276. Ten, for the crew of a ship cruising between Siberia and Alaska during a leap year, and leaving Siberia on Sunday, 1st February, under the conditions that one passage takes exactly a week.

277. 18 days.
278. On Saturday, 29th October.
279. By $8\cdot18$ sec.
280. 3 min 3 sec.

281. 236 times.   **282.** +1 min 6·91 sec.
283. By 6 min 6 sec.
284. The Right Ascension of the centre of the mean Sun at midday $= s$.
The Right Ascension of the true Sun at midday $= s + \varepsilon$. The Right Ascension
of the true Sun at the moment t is equal to

$$\alpha + t = s + \varepsilon \quad \text{or} \quad s - \alpha + \varepsilon - t = 0.$$

285. 20 hr 53 min 57·63 sec.   **287.** −29 min.
288. 12 hr 4 min 29·51 sec.   **289.** −1 min 18 sec.
290. +47 sec.
291. −57 min 29 sec;   −58 min 48 sec;   +1 min 12 sec.
292. −35 sec, 1 min 36 sec.
293. For local time, −57 min 48·3 sec.
294. 21st March, 23 hr 45 min.
295. Because the equation of time on these days increases faster than the
setting of the Sun advances due to its change in Declination.
296. It would be increased. It would become zero.
297. Significantly greater.   **298.** Mean time on Mars is necessary.

Chapter VIII

The Calendar

I

304. 252 days.   **305.** No.
306. Because there is not a whole number of days in the true year.
307. At 0 hr 47 min on 22nd March. At 6 hr 36 min on 22nd March.
On 21st March at 12 hr 24 min. On 21st March at 18 hr 13 min. On 22nd
March at 0 hr 2 min.
308. 5 hr 48 min 48 sec a year. On 15th April. After 730 years.
309. 27th February; 9th March; 18th March.
312. 16th March, 2445.   **313.** After 10,400 yr.
314. 365·2425 days; 0·0003 days, or 26 sec in a year.
315. 43 min 3½ hr; 7 hr on March 22nd, as it is now.
316. Then there would be 31 leap and 97 ordinary years in every 128
years, and the duration of a single year would be 365·24219 mean days.
This leads to an error of one day only in 10,000 yr, as the tropical year
equals 365·24220 mean days.
317. 0·013 days every 30 yr, or a day every 3000 yr.
318. In this case there would be 25 ordinary years of 365 days, and 8 leap
years of 366 days every 33 yr. The mean duration of the year would accordingly be 365·2424 mean days, i.e. greater than the real figure by only 0·0002
mean days, which is only one day in 5000 yr.
319. 19 yr = 235 months.   **320.** The forty-second year.
322. It was in 1880.   **323.** A.D. 1388.
324. In 22749 yr.

Chapter IX

The Rising and the Setting of a Heavenly Body

I

326. It is possible. It is not possible.
330. At 10 o'clock in the evening.
332. For all latitudes north of 72°.
333. To the south of 48°·5.   **334.** 60°·5.

II

337. In Irkutsk.   **338.** Earlier in London.

339. Anywhere on the earth the hour angle of its rising and setting are equal to 18 hr and 6 hr, and the azimuths of rising and setting are equal to 270° and 90°, because the star lies almost on the equator.

340. From formula (2) in Chapter IX we find the hour angles of rising and setting t:

$$
\begin{aligned}
\log (-\tan \phi) \qquad & 0 \cdot 1669_n, \\
\log \tan \delta \qquad & 9 \cdot 6726, \\
\hline
\log \cos t \qquad & 9 \cdot 8395_n,
\end{aligned}
$$

$$t = \pm 133°43';$$

that is
$$t_R = 15 \text{ hr } 5 \cdot 1 \text{ min}$$
$$t_s = 8 \text{ hr } 54 \cdot 9 \text{ min as the sidereal time,}$$
$$s = t + \alpha;$$

then
$$s_R = 21 \text{ hr } 44 \cdot 8 \text{ min,}$$
$$s_s = 15 \text{ hr } 34 \cdot 6 \text{ min.}$$

The azimuths of the points of rising and setting by formula (4) are given in this section:

$$
\begin{aligned}
\log (-\sin \delta) \qquad & 9 \cdot 6292_n \\
\partial \log \cos \phi \qquad & 0 \cdot 2496 \\
\hline
\log \cos A \qquad & 9 \cdot 8788_n
\end{aligned}
$$

$$A \pm 139°9',$$

in other terms
$$A_R = 220°51',$$
$$A_S = 139°9'.$$

341. By calculation we find log cos $t = 0 \cdot 1398$ and log cos $A = 0 \cdot 0944$, which is impossible. It follows that in Pulkov, Vega is a star that never sets.

342. 23 hr 54 min; That is 11 hr 54 min in the evening.

343. It rises at 6 hr 56 min 28 sec, and sets at 14 hr 12 min 30 sec; by mean time: 0 hr 11 min 7 sec and 13 hr 24 min 59 sec.

344. $t = \pm 7$ hr 27 min 56 sec; $A = \pm 115°2' \cdot 7$; 14 hr 53 min mean time. Rising at 12 hr 50 min 28 sec, setting at 3 hr 43 min 53 sec.

345. $\delta = -18°·8$; $A = 55°·1$.
346. $\delta = -32°·5$; 4 hr 48 min; $h = 5°·8$.

347. The angle ψ is equal to the third angle in the triangle (pole–zenith–body) and is called the parallax angle p. The other two angles are t and $180° - A$. Making use of the formulae of spherical trigonometry we obtain

$$\cos \delta \cos \psi = \sin z \sin \phi + \cos z \cos \phi \cos A.$$

For rising, $z = 90°$, giving the required formula.

349. $\phi = -64°48'$.

350. The calculation can be carried out by formula (5) given in Chapter IX.

log $0\cdot0145 \times 2\cdot1703$			
∂ log cos ϕ $\ 0\cdot1608$		log tan ϕ	$0\cdot0337$
∂ log cos δ $\ 0\cdot0287$		log tan δ	$9\cdot5755$
log total I $\ \ 2\cdot3670$		log total II	$9\cdot6092$
		total I	$0\cdot0233$
		total II	$0\cdot4066$
		cos t	$-0\cdot4299$ $t = \pm 7$ hr $41\cdot9$ min
		log cos t	$9\cdot6334$ $t_s = 4$ hr $18\cdot1$ min.
			$t + 115°28'$ $t_R = 19$ hr $41\cdot9$ min.

The duration of the day is 15 hr 21 min. The mean time of rising and setting is equal to the time angle of the true Sun plus the equation of time; that is, rising at 4 hr 14·7 min; setting at 19 hr 38·5 min.

351. The shortest day in Leningrad is 5 hr 31 min;

Samarkand 9 hr 18 min.

The sum of the length of the shortest day and the longest day is 24 hr.

353. $\phi = 52°30'\cdot2$.

354. After 1 hr 12 min; 1 hr 44 min; 2 hr 33 min.

355. 2 hr 30 min.   **356.** 77°·7.

357. $\cos A = -\dfrac{\sin \delta}{\cos \phi} = \dfrac{\sin \delta}{\sin \varepsilon}$.

For the sun $\sin \delta = \sin \varepsilon \sin l$ and it follows that $\cos A = -\sin l$.

Denoting the azimuth of the point of setting by A_S, we obtain

$$A_S = 90° + l$$

in the period 22nd December to 22nd June and

$$A_S = 270° - l$$

in the period 22nd June to 22nd December.

That is, the absolute value of the diurnal variation in A_S is equal to the diurnal change in l.

358. On any diametrically opposite points of the globe

359. On the north polar circle the plane of the ecliptic coincides once a day (at 18 hr sidereal time) with the plane of the horizon and it follows that at that moment the Sun rises or sets. Due to the increase in the longitude of the Sun from 90° to 270° (which corresponds to the half year from 22nd June to the 22nd December) its azimuth diminishes from 180° to 0° at 18 hr sidereal time and this is the moment of sunset.

In the period from 22nd December to 22nd June, the Sun rises at 18 hr sidereal time.

The change from the constant sidereal time of setting to the constant time of rising on the same scale occurs on the 22nd June when points of rising and setting of the Sun coincide with the point of its lowest culmination.

360. Let $t_{-90°}$ and t_3 be the hour angles of the passage through azimuth $-90°$ and of setting. Then

$$\cos t_{-90°} = \frac{\tan \delta}{\tan \phi}; \qquad \cos t_R = -\tan \phi \tan \delta.$$

At

$$\phi = 45°; \qquad \cos t_{-90°} = -\cos t_R,$$

whence

$$t_R - t_{-90°} = 12 \text{ hr and does not depend on } \delta.$$

361. Expressing dt in seconds of time, and dz in seconds of arc

$$dt = \frac{dz}{15 \cos \phi \cos \delta \sin t}$$

362. $\cos Z = \dfrac{\sin \delta}{\sin \phi}; \qquad \cos t = \dfrac{\tan \delta}{\tan \phi}.$

363. $h = 54°58'; \quad s = 0$ hr 16·8 min and 17 hr   2·2 min.
$h = 22°53'; \quad s = 8$ hr 44·8 min and 18 hr 58·0 min.
$h = 41°18'; \quad s = 0$ hr 37·8 min and   9 hr   7·2 min.

Chapter X

Precession

II

364. In 360 yr.
365. No, because now the solstices do not occur in these constellations.
366. In the constellation Virgo.
367. That the Earth had the form of a perfect sphere, or that its equator, the plane of the lunar orbit, and the ecliptic coincided.
368. Orion in upper culmination will touch the horizon with its lower section. The Southern Cross will rise above the horizon almost as high as Orion does now.
371. Faster in the first two cases; slower in the second two cases.
373. Yes. The distance from the Sun at a given time of the year drifts due to the ellipticity of the Earth's orbit.

374. $\lambda = 359°09'22''; \qquad \beta = -17°35'37'';$
$\lambda = 357°54'00''; \qquad \beta = -17°35'37'';$
$\lambda =   0°41'28''; \qquad \beta = -17°35'37''.$

375. All Right Ascensions increase continuously, except in a circular region with diameter equal to the distance from the celestial pole to the pole of the ecliptic, where they diminish. Declinations increase or decrease, depending on the Right Ascension.
376. For those about the poles.
377. 22 hr 4 min 56 sec; $+27°40'·5;$
22 hr 9 min   4 sec; $+28°   6'·9.$

378. 10 hr 58 min 17 sec; $-2°5'·6$;
3 hr 42 min 9 sec; $+23°44'·1$;
22 hr 26 min 34 sec; $+58°3'·4$;
2 hr 15 min 48 sec; $-3°17'·7$.

380. The longitude of perihelion increases by $0°·33$ in a century.

Chapter XII

Planetary Movement

I

381. About 6600 yr. **382.** In $12\frac{1}{2}$ min.
383. 0·7 yr. **384.** No. Yes. No.
385. No. **386.** The Upper.

387. Mars in opposition to the Sun, that is, in Libra. Venus approximately $45°$ to the east of the Sun, that is, in Pisces.

388. In spring, when the ecliptic subtends the greatest angle with the eastern horizon in the evening.

389. The one whose trace is longest is closest both to the Earth and to the Sun.

390. By $\dfrac{360°}{365·25} - \dfrac{360°}{687} = 0°·461$.

391. No. **392.** 688 days.
393. $\frac{3}{4}$, or $1\frac{1}{2}$ yr. **394.** $\frac{4}{3}$ or $\frac{4}{5}$ of a year.
396. 2 yr. **396.** 18th August, 1938.
397. 1320 days. **398.** 12th September, 1938.

400. First we find the sinodic period of Mercury, which is 87·97 days. Then the mean diurnal motion of Mercury is $4°5'30''$.

401. The period of these phenomena is 780 days, the same as the sinodic period of Mars.

402. $41°$. **403.** About $17'$.

404. From the relationship $\sin x = \dfrac{1}{5·2}$ we get $x = 11°$.

405. Suppose that an opposition of this sort occurs. The next one will occur in the same point of space after an interval of time including a whole number of revolutions of the Earth (x) and a whole number of revolutions of Mars (y).
It follows that

$$\frac{x}{y} = 1·88 = \frac{47}{25} = 1 + \cfrac{1}{1 + \cfrac{1}{7 + \cfrac{1}{3 + \ldots}}}$$

limiting ourselves to the first three links we have $\dfrac{x}{y} = \dfrac{15}{8}$, that is, the opposition occurs every 15 yr (after every eight complete revolutions of Mars).

406. We denote by x the number of days from the beginning of 1938 of the closest opposition of Jupiter to the Sun, and form an equation, given that at the moment of opposition the difference of the heliocentric longitudes of the Earth and of the planet is $0°$ or $360°$; in general $2n\ 180°$, where n is a whole number. The mean diurnal motion of the planet is given in the introduction to the section. Then we obtain the following equation:

$$(99°55' + 59''\ x) - (306°55' + 5'\ x) = 0,$$

which gives $54'\ x = 207°$　or　$x = \dfrac{207 \times 60}{54} \approx 230.$

Hence, the nearest opposition of Jupiter in 1938 was 230 days after 1st January, or on 19th August, 1938.

407. 31st January, 1938 and 7th March, 1939.

408. 21st November, 1938.　　　　**409.** 12th September, 1938.

410. 29th January, 1939.

411. 1st May, 1937, Mars was a few degrees from α Scorpio, which because of its brightness and red light emulates Mars, and for this reason is called Antares (Antares in Greek means "like Mars"). On 1st May, 1939, Mars was in the constellation of the Archer, between the stars λ and π.

412. In the constellation of the Archer, near the star π.

413. Yes.

414. Least in conjunctions and oppositions and greatest in quadrature and in maximum elongations.

415. In conjunctions $48'\cdot16$ per day. In oppositions $-21'\cdot52$ per day.

416. $53''\cdot68$ an hour, or $21'28''$ a day.

417. The length of transit is

$$\frac{277}{723} \times \frac{1}{675} \times 584 = 0\cdot332 \text{ days} = 7 \text{ hr } 58 \text{ min.}$$

The angular apparent velocity is $241''$ an hour.

418. $R = \sin 47° = 0\cdot73.$

419. $0\cdot39$ astronomical units $= 58 \times 10^6$ km.

420. If we denote the distance from Jupiter to the Sun, measured in astronomical units, by x and the angle at the Sun between the radius-vectors of the Earth and Jupiter by t, then obviously, we may write the relation:

$$\frac{x}{\sin \Delta l} = \frac{1}{\sin (180° - \Delta l - t)}$$

from which we obtain $x = 5.$

422. 1000 yr.　　　　　　　　　**423.** 4·62 yr.

424. 4 astronomical units.　　　**425.** 2·362 times further.

426. 74 yr;　at a distance of 0·0009 astronomical units.

427. 1·70.　　　　　　　　　　**428.** 0·63 astronomical units.

429. 0·763 and 1588 astronomical units.

430. 0·153.　　　　　　　　　　**431.** 11 hr 57 min;　739 days.

432. 0°.　　　　　　　　　　　　**433.** 4 astronomical units.

II

434. This cannot be a planet.

435. ε is the obliquity of the ecliptic, and φ is the latitude, then the greatest distance of the pole of the ecliptic from the zenith is $90° - \phi + \varepsilon$. The sine of the greatest altitude of Venus according to this will be $0.72 \cos (\phi - \varepsilon)$, occurring at the moment of the Vernal Equinox.

436. As can be seen from the formula of sinodic motion, the limiting sinodic period is equal to a sidereal year.

437. $\varrho^2 = a^2 + 1 - 2a \cos \phi$.

438. About $1'\cdot 5$ per day.

439. $\dfrac{P}{2\tau} - 1$ where 2τ is the duration of retrograde motion.

440. $\psi = 10°\cdot 6$.   **441.** $\omega = 3\pi a^{-3/2}$.

442. $v = 2\pi/\sqrt{a}$.   **443.** $33''\cdot 2$.

444. Denoting the unknown perihelion distance of the comet in millions of years by x, we have

$$\frac{2^2}{1^2} = \frac{(x + 820)^3}{2^3 \times 150^3},$$

whence we obtain $x = -343$, which is an impossible result. The data for the comet given by Jules Verne do not agree with each other.

445. By $3T\,\dfrac{\varDelta a}{2a}$ which is the differential form of Keplers' Third Law.

446. 10 and 190 astronomical units.

447. 222×10^6 and 102×10^6 km.

448. *Solution.* First we choose the unit of the scale. Take the distance from the Earth to the Sun as 5 cm. A circle of radius 5 cm (Fig. 51) represents the orbit of the Earth, as its eccentricity must in any case be neglected on this scale.

From the point S, representing the Sun, we draw arbitrarily the direction to the point of Vernal Equinox, γ. From the direction $S\gamma_0$ in an anti-clockwise direction, we measure the angle $= 30°$ and draw the dotted line of the notes NN'.

Let SN' be the direction to the ascending note. From this we measure anti-clockwise (as $i < 90°$; that is, the movement of the body is direct), and the angle $\omega = 45°$ and we draw as a dotted line the line of apsids KK'.

Perihelion is at a distance of $a(1-e) = 2(1-0.8) = 0.4$ astronomical units. From S in the direction of K' we measure off a distance $5 \times 0.4 = 2$ cm, and this will be the perihelion P.

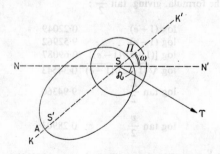

FIG. 51

The aphelion is at a distance of $a(1+e)$ from the Sun, or 18 cm on our scale. It will be at the point A. The second focus of the ellipse will be at the point S'. We insert a pair of pins at the points S and S', and tie a loop of thread so that its length is $2a = 20$ cm.

Using a sharp pencil so that it always stretches the thread, we draw the whole ellipse, establishing our orbit.

454. $E = 200°10'\cdot2$.   **456.** $E = 99°33'$.

457. $E = 5°40'\cdot3$.

458. By Kepler's Third Law the period $P = 4^{3/2} = 8$.

Consequently, a year after perihelion the mean anomaly M will be 45°, and Kepler's equation for this moment $45° = E - 0\cdot66144 \sin E$.

As the sine is tabulated for radians (or their logarithms), it must be multiplied by $57°\cdot2958$ (or the logarithm of $\sin E$ by $1\cdot57861$). Thus $45° = E° - 1°\cdot57861 \sin E$.

As the eccentricity is great, an approximate value of E may be found from Fig. 19; $E_1 = 82°30'$, and we can try to substitute it in the formula

log sin 82°30′	9·99627
log coefficient	1·57861
log $E°$	1·57488
$E°$	37°·573
$E_1°$	82°·500
Difference	44·927°

in place of the required 45°.

Obviously E must be slightly increased. We find finally that

$$E_2 = 82°\cdot58 = 82°34'\cdot8,$$

after substitution in Kepler's equation, satisfies it completely (within the limits of accuracy of our calculation — that is, to five-figure logarithms). If the second approximation did not immediately give a correct value for E, then it would have been necessary to change it again until substituting it in the equation satisfies the requirement that

$$E = e \sin E = 45°\cdot000,$$

v found from the formula, giving $\tan \dfrac{v}{2}$:

log $(1+e)$	0·22049
log $(1-e)$	9·52962
log $[(1+e)/(1-e)]$	0·69087
log $\sqrt{(1+e)/(1-e)}$	0·34543
log $\tan \dfrac{E}{2}$	9·94360
log $\tan \dfrac{v}{2}$	0·28903

$\dfrac{v}{2} = 62°47'\cdot8$,   whence $v = 125°35'\cdot6$.

r is found from the formula

$$r = a(1 - e \cos E)$$

log a	0·60206
log e	9·82049
log cos 82°34'·8	9·11106
log $ae \cos E$	9·53361
$ae \cos E =$	0·3417
$a =$	4·0000
$r =$	3·6483

459. $E = 122°06'·2$; $v = 151°57'·7$; $r = 5·4061$.
460. $E = 152°30'·0$; $v = 167°33'·6$; $r = 6·3468$.
461. $v = 62°54'·7$; log $r = 0·4504$.
462. The approximate value of E from the graph is 324°·25. After approximations $E = 324°16'·5$; $v = 315°1'·4$; $r = 2·112$.
463. log $M = 1·7354$; $v = 61°16'·0$; log $r = 0·1747$.
464. $v = -109°15'·9$; log $r = 9·9940$.
465.

Septem-ber	log r	log ϱ	α				δ
1·5	0·3270	0·0492	23 hr	15 min	46 sec		−4°44'·4
5·5	0·3292	0·0521	23	13	29		−5 33 ·5
9·5	0·3314	0·0564	23	11	11		−6 21 ·9

466.

June	log ϱ	α			δ
23·5	9·4802	5 hr	34 min	48 sec	+45° 3'·1
24·5	9·4948	5	38	33	+49 21 ·0
25·5	9·5115	5	42	44	+53 18 ·6

Chapter XIII

Parallax and Aberration

I

467. 8 min 18 sec.   **468.** 2"·38.
469. 23"·2.   **470.** 46"·4.
471. 0"·29. The concept of annual parallax is inapplicable to the planets.
472. 1"·47.   **473.** 71,800 km.

474. 12,600 km.

475. The distance is 60·3; the radius is 0·272; surface area 0·0740; volume 0·0201.

476. To an accuracy of 0·11 per cent 164,445 km.

477. 109 times; 1,391,000 km.   **478.** 0″·75. It is possible.

479. In practice it will not change at all.

480. The first question does not make sense. The distance in parsecs is equal to 1/206,265.

481. $57' \sin z = 46'·7$.   **482.** $49°17'·4$.

483. $65°13'20''$.

484. by 1/300 of the parallax in both cases.

485. $\phi > 16°$, which arises from the condition $\sin \phi > \frac{16}{57}$.

486. Yes, the nearer to us the Moon is, the greater, consequently, will be its parallax, and the greater its angular diameter.

487. $\dfrac{\sin \varrho'}{\sin \varrho} = \dfrac{\sin P'}{\sin P}$,   whence $\varrho' = 15'45''$.

489. About $0''·005$.

490. It is possible, but the accuracy of the result will be inversely proportional to the distance of the planet from the Sun.

491. 149·7 million km.

492. The parallax is $8''·805$.

493. The greatest difference in the radial velocities of the stars are observed at moments, separated by an interval of half a year (under the condition that the observations are carried out in the course of a whole year), and is obviously double the orbital velocity of the Earth.

494. If T is the number of seconds in a year, then $R = 30 \dfrac{T}{2\pi}$ km.

495. It can be seen from the map that the difference in the longitudes of the two points is almost 180°, and the difference in latitudes is almost 90°, that is, the base may be taken to be equal to the diameter of the Earth.

From the length of the chord passing through Venus, we find

$$D = 46'',$$

whence, $$p = 8''·8.$$

496. From observation of the transit of Mercury across the disc of the Sun the parallax would be determined by the formula

$$p = D \frac{92}{58} \frac{r}{d}.$$

For this reason in the calculation of the parallax of the Sun an error in the measurement of D in the case of observations of Mercury would increase by $\frac{92}{58}$ times, and in the case where it is based on the observations of Venus would diminish by $\frac{72}{28}$ times.

497. Taking the derivative of both sides of the formula we see that if the error $dM/M = 0·01$, then $dD/D = 0·003$, or 0·3 per cent.

498. $ESM = (FEM - MEN)/2 = 360° \times 0·6/(2 \times 29·5 \times 24) \simeq 0°·15$; $SE = ME/\sin 9' \simeq 386\ ME$. Aristarchus found $SE = 19\ ME$.

499. Put $KD/MK = n$. Then from Fig. 22 (p. 108) $(AD - GK)/(GK - QM) = n$. On the other hand, if ϱ is the radius of the Moon, then $AD = n\varrho$. It follows that, $(N - GK)/(GK - QM) = n$.

Thus $\varrho + QM = GK(1 + 1/n)$, that is, (the radius of the Moon) + (the radius of the shadow) = $(1 + 1/n)$(the radius of the Earth).

It follows from the conditions of the problem, that, (the radius of the shadow) = $15'/40'$ (the radius of the Moon), and consequently (the radius of the Moon) = $3/11 (1 + 1/n)$ (the radius of the Earth).

But as the angular radius of the Moon is $15'$, its distance is 220 times greater than its radius. It follows that in radii of the Earth (the distance of the Moon) = $60 (1 + 1/n)$, or, as $1/n = \frac{1}{390}$, (the distance of the Moon) $= 60(1 + \frac{1}{390})$.

The problem can be solved in another way.

"The radius of the Earth's shadow", β, is $40'$, and equal to $P + p - s$, where p and P are the parallaxes of the Sun and the Moon, and S is the angular diameter of the Moon and the Sun.

From the condition

$$\frac{P}{p} = n = 390,$$

$$P = \frac{(\beta + s)390}{391}$$

which gives the parallax of the Moon.

500. (1) By the western eclipses of the satellites of Jupiter.
    (2) By the radial velocity of the stars.
    (3) By the constant of annual aberration.

II

501. When the Earth moves directly towards a star, or directly away from it.

502. PR/RQ is equal to the ratio of the velocities of the Earth at perihelion and at aphelion, and the latter, (see Problem 713) are equal to $(1 + e)/(1 - e)$.

503. No.

504. $0'\cdot32$. At the pole the diurnal aberration is zero.

506. The ratio of the maximum velocity of the Earth to the velocity of light gives the "constant of diurnal aberration" $0''\cdot32$. For latitude ϕ we have, obviously, a diurnal aberration of $0''\cdot32 \cos \phi$. The maximum diurnal aberration, in Right Ascension, at the moments of culmination, increases it by

$$\Delta\alpha = 0\cdot32 \cos \phi \sec \delta,$$

where δ is the Declination of the star.

Chapter XIV

The Earth

II

507. About 30 km.

508. The length of the orbit would increase by $6\frac{1}{4}$ m and the year would increase by 1/5000 fraction of a second, which is quite imperceptible.

510. They would be of the same duration.

511. The distances of the Earth and the Sun in perihelion and sphelion would be related as 1:3, and, generally speaking, this cause would be more important than the inclination of the Earth's orbit.

Winter in the northern hemisphere would be very short and warm; summer would be longer, but colder.

The change in the days and nights in summer and in winter would remain the same as it is at present.

512. Everywhere, and at all times, the days would be equal in length to the nights, and the changes in the seasons of the year would cease.

513. At an inclination of 45°.   **514.** After 10,400 yr.

515. $\dfrac{2\pi R \cos \phi}{24 \times 60 \times 60} = 232$ m/sec.

516. (a) 464 m/sec.   (b) 308 m/sec.

517. (1) At latitude ϕ, where $\cos \phi = \dfrac{\cos 56°}{2}$, i.e. $= 73°\cdot 7$.

(2) At latitude $\phi = 44°\cdot 2$.

518. Faster.

519. Its distance from the axis is $R \cos \phi = 2$ light years. In a day it would complete a circumference of $2\pi \times 2 = 13$ light years or, in other words, would cover in an hour the distance which light takes half a year to cover. Its velocity would be 4320 times that of light.

520. At the equator.   **521.** 22 mm.

522. $7°\cdot 5$; $13°$; $10°\cdot 6$; $14°\cdot 5$; $15°$; $0°$.

523. The speeds of the ships are related as the radii of the parallels along which they sail. It thus follows that the speed of ship x is equal to

$$15 \frac{\cos 48°}{\cos 15°} = 10\cdot4 \text{ knots.}$$

524. No, because from it the radius of the horizon is 285 km.

525. 357 km.   **526.** 38 km.

527. 564 km.   About 5 km.   **528.** 57′.

529. By 12 min.

531. 1 nautical mile, equal to $1\cdot85$ km.

532. $R = 6341$ km.   **533.** 6336 km; 6374 km; 6414 km.

534. They are accumulating.   No.

535. With an accuracy to a few centimetres.

536. The polar diameter will be 1 cm shorter.

537. Degree measurements, and the determination of the force of gravity.

538. The train going westwards. Its weight is slightly reduced by centrifugal force, caused by the circular rotation about the Earth's axis as it is moving opposite to the movement of the Earth.

539. $a = R \left(\dfrac{2\pi}{T}\right)^2 = 0 \cdot 03391$ m/sec^2.

540. $g = \pi^2 l = 9 \cdot 781$ m/sec^2.

541. $g = 9 \cdot 809$ m/sec^2; $\quad l = g/\pi^2 = 993 \cdot 85$ mm.

543. The amount of heat received in the day would be greater. The diurnal and annual oscillations of temperature would be greater.

544. The same as in the preceding exercise.

545. $1 : 0 \cdot 9171 : 0 \cdot 3987$.

546. $\dfrac{\cos (\phi - 23\frac{1}{2}°)}{\cos (\phi + 23\frac{1}{2}°)} = \dfrac{0 \cdot 882}{0 \cdot 259} = 3 \cdot 4.$

547. $28 \cdot 6$; $\quad 2 \cdot 5$; $\quad 1 \cdot 5$; $\quad 1 \cdot 0$.

548. The effect of the inclination of the rays of light is greater than the effect of the distance to the Sun by

$$\frac{\cos (\phi - \varepsilon)}{\cos (\phi + \varepsilon)} \bigg/ \frac{(1+e)^2}{(1-e)^2} = 4 \cdot 42 / 1 \cdot 03 = 4 \cdot 29 \text{ times}$$

549. 0 hr.   **550.** Annual aberration.

551. As the apparent diameter of the Sun is inversely proportional to the distance from it, so

$$e = \frac{p-q}{p+q} = 0 \cdot 0168.$$

552. Because, due to the elliptical nature of the Earth's orbit, and the non-uniformity of its motion, the increase in the radius vector of the Earth during the first half of the year is greater in 6 hr than the radius of the Earth, the amount by which the distance to the Sun changes due to the diurnal rotation of the Earth.

In the second half of the year the Earth approaches the Sun, and the phenomenon is the reverse of that described above.

553. $\sin 23\frac{1}{2}° : (\sin 66\frac{1}{2}° - \sin 23\frac{1}{2}°) : (1 - \sin 66\frac{1}{2}°) = 0 \cdot 40 : 0 \cdot 52 : 0 \cdot 08.$

554. It has an effect.

555. The anomalistic year is equal to $365 \cdot 2596$ mean days. The period of revolution of the line of the apsid is 108,000 years.

556. The radius of the sphere is

$$r = \sqrt[3]{(3m/4\pi\delta)} = 0 \cdot 09267 \text{ m}.$$

If m is the mass of the sphere, M its moment of inertia relative to the axis of rotation, and l is the length of the pendulum, then

$$M = \tfrac{2}{3} mr^2 + mK^2;$$

$$l = M/Km$$

$$= \left(\tfrac{2}{3} r^2 / K\right) + K,$$

whence it can be seen, that the centre of oscillation is lower than the centre of gravity by

$$\tfrac{2}{5} r^2/K = 0.0648 \text{ mm.}$$

557. $AB = (R \cos 60°). \; 2\pi\frac{60}{360} = 3330$ km, along the parallel. The arc of the great circle AB corresponds to the central angle

$$AOB = 2(AOD).$$

The angle AOD is found from the relationship

$$\sin AOD = AD/AO = \frac{1}{2} AB/AO = \frac{R}{4} \Big/ R = 0.25,$$

and from the Table we obtain

$$AOD = 14°28'\cdot5, \quad \text{and}$$
$$AOB = 28°57'.$$

It follows that the arc

$$AB = \frac{28°57'}{360°} \times 2\pi R = 3210 \text{ km.}$$

That is 120 km shorter than the arc of parallel produced between the sam points.

558. The arc of the great circle $AB = 83°48'\cdot8$, or 9320 km.

559. At $\lambda = 23°54'$ at an angle of $72°24'\cdot7$. The length of the path is 4559 km or 8·5 days.

562. $\dfrac{1}{295 \cdot 9}$.

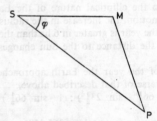

Fig. 52

563. The centrifugal acceleration at latitude ϕ is $a = a_0 \cos \phi$, where a_0 is the centrifugal acceleration at the equator.

565. The acceleration due to the attraction of the Earth on the equator is 289·4 times than the acceleration due to centrifugal force.

Thus, the Earth would have to rotate $\sqrt{289\cdot4} = 17\cdot01$ times faster.

566. Approximately $x = g \left(1 - \dfrac{2h}{R}\right)$.

567. To an accuracy of within $\tfrac{1}{2} \times 10^{-7}$ part of the acceleration itself.

569. The value of the astronomical latitude is always greater than the geocentric, except at the poles and the equator, where they coincide.

570. They are not the same. Geocentric degrees are longer at the equator.

571. We construct a triangle, setting the bob of the plumb-line at M, the vector MP representing the force of gravity applied to it, and the vector MS representing the centrifugal force $m\omega^2 r$. From Fig. 52 we see that

$$\frac{\sin MPS}{\sin \phi} = \frac{MS}{MP} = \frac{\omega^2 R \cos \phi}{g_0 \left(1 + \dfrac{\omega^2 R}{g_0} \sin^2 \phi\right)}$$

so that

$$MP = g_\phi = g_0 \left(1 + \frac{\omega^2 R}{g_0} \sin^2 \phi\right),$$

where $g_0 = 978$ cm/sec^2 is the acceleration due to gravity at the equator; ϕ is the latitude.

Neglecting the second term of the denominator, and replacing $\sin MPS$ by the arc $MPS = \varrho$, we have

$$P = \frac{\omega^2 R \cos \phi \sin \phi}{g_0}$$

$$= \frac{\omega^2 R \sin 2\phi}{2g_0}.$$

Obviously, the maximum of P will be at $\phi = 45°$. Substituting the numerical values, we find P maximum 0.00173 or $6'$.

572. $< OKC = \dfrac{180° - \alpha}{2}$

From the triangle KOC we have

$$\sin OKC = \frac{R}{R+h}$$

or

$$h = R \frac{1 - \cos \alpha/2}{\cos \alpha/2}.$$

Given that $R = 6371$ km we find $h = 80$ km. This layer of atmosphere is also noteworthy in many other connections.

573. The height of the layer is 10 km—this is approximately the border line between the troposphere and the stratosphere.

574. *Solution.* Taking the reflection of energy into account, an area of 1 cm^2 of the Earth receives $E' = 0.63 \times 1.94 \times q/60$ erg/sec, and on the whole illuminated hemisphere of the Earth falls $E'\pi R$ ergs/sec. It is completely radiated back into space by the whole of the Earth's surface. That is, every square centimetre radiates in 1 sec

$$E'\pi R^2/4\pi R^2 = 0.25 \ E'.$$

This energy is equal to σT^4. Comparing these values, and substituting numerical quantities, we find

$$T = 247°,$$
$$K = -26° \ C.$$

The difference obtained is explained by the incomplete radiation capacity of the Earth and by the fact that the atmosphere absorbs some of the radiation passing through it.

Chapter XV

The Movement and Phases of the Moon

I

575. $5\frac{1}{2}$ days.

578. It is not possible, because the dark parts of the Moon lie between the horns of the Moon illuminated by the Sun.

579. The direction away from the Sun.

580. Because the straight line through space joining the crescent of the Moon and the Sun, appears as an arc of a great circle upon the celestial sphere.

581. It is possible, in tropical countries.

582. Full Earth; New Earth; the phases of the Earth and the Moon would be opposite to each other.

583. The phase between the full Moon and the last quarter.

585. 49°42′; 68°35′; 77°15′.

587. From 241°25′ to 298°35′.

588. Because the Moon at that time will be in the same place on the ecliptic where the Sun is in summer.

589. The answer is analogous to the answer to Problem 588.

590. About 6·0 in the evening. **591.** About 6·0 p.m.

592. The first quarter; full Moon.

593. At midnight in winter, at 6·0 p.m. in spring; at 6·0 a.m. in the autumn; and in the spring.

594. In the winter; in the summer.

595. Between the pole and the polar circle; in winter.

596. Not visible.

597. In June, in the vicinity of the North Pole and in December in the vicinity of the South Pole.

598. No, because lunar days are longer than solar.

599. 24 hr 20·34 min.

601. $\dfrac{360°}{13°10'15''} = 27.3216$ days.

602. 71·7932 days.

603. At every point on the Earth the Moon would maintain an unchanging position above the horizon, and on one hemisphere of the Earth the Moon would not be visible at all.

In the second case, the Moon would rise in the west and set in the east.

604. $\dfrac{1}{P} = \dfrac{1}{S} + \dfrac{1}{T}$, where S is the sidereal month, and T is a year. The sinodic month would be 25·42 days.

II

605. If the Moon L is visible in the form of a crescent, then the angle α between the directions from it to the Sun S and the Earth T is less than 90°. Drawing a plan (Fig. 53) we see that the desired value

$$x = \frac{1}{2} - \frac{1}{2}\cos\alpha = \sin^2\frac{\alpha}{2},$$

if the diameter of the Moon is taken to be 1.

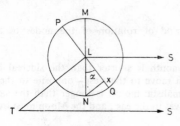

Fig. 53

606. As the Moon is a sphere, the true terminator is always a circle. In projection it changes, as is well known, to an ellipse.

607. (a) From 175° to 180°.   (b) From 0° to 5°.   (c) Exactly 90°.

608. The ellipticity of the lunar orbit and the uneven movement of the Moon along it. The maximum of this effect occurs when the Sun is situated on a line passing through the Moon and perpendicular to the semi-major axis of the lunar orbit.

609. At 9 hr 37 min. If the Declination of the Moon increases the rising will occur earlier.

610. The Moon must be simultaneously at the point of the Vernal Equinox, in the ascending node of its orbit and in apogee. Under these conditions its diurnal movement through the celestial sphere will be least and, consequently, the difference in the moments of its two successive risings will also be least.

612. $90° - (23°27' + 5°8') = 61°25'$.

613. At a latitude at a distance of about 5° from the polar circles. When the plane of the lunar orbit inclined by 5° to the ecliptic coincides with the horizon, the sidereal time of rising on adjacent days is the same.

615. This happens after 9 yr on account of the movement of the nodes of the Moon's orbit.

616. Because of this inclination the upper edge of the Moon in perigee has a latitude between the limits $\pm(5°20'6'' + 16'46'')$ where the second term is the maximum radius of the Moon.

The maximum horizontal parallax further increases this distance by $61'18''$. Because of the constant motion of the nodes of the Moon's orbit, the longitude of the Moon in this position can be anywhere, and consequently, within the belt indicated, the Moon can eclipse any star.

617. We denote the period of rotation of the perigee by R, and a sidereal month by S.
Then

$$\frac{1}{P} = \frac{1}{S} - \frac{1}{R},$$

whence

$$P = 27 \cdot 55 \text{ days}.$$

618. 57′ for both hemispheres of the Moon.

619. $\dfrac{1}{D} = \dfrac{1}{S} + \dfrac{1}{R},$

where R is the period of rotation of the nodes of the Moon's orbit.
$D = 27 \cdot 21$ days.

The Drakonitic month is shorter than the sidereal because the nodes of the Moon's orbit move to the west — opposite to the movement of the Moon, and the anomalistic month is longer than the sidereal because the line of the apsid moves to the east, and the Moon must overtake it.

Chapter XVI

Eclipses

I

623. The least curved inner part of the crescent, the rate of the change in phase, the time of observation and the reddish-brown light of the eclipsed part of the Moon.

624. It is not possible between the poles, and $\phi = \pm 61°$.

625. This is explained by refraction in the Earth's atmosphere.

626. It can occur.

627. 2 hr 13·6 min in the morning.

628. It can occur. It cannot occur, because the interval of time between the epochs of the eclipses is only a little shorter than half a year.

629. The Moon is in apogee. It is true that at this time the Moon traverses a smaller section of the cone of the Earth's shadow, but according to Kepler's Laws, it moves slower at this time; and this is the deciding factor.

630. It is possible. It is not possible.

632. It is possible, in the polar regions.

633. Because the spots of light in the shadows of leaves are images of the Sun, formed by the tiny holes between the leaves, in the same way as in a camera obscura.

634. The western.

635. It is possible. It is not possible.

636. By 5·4 times.

638. The eclipses would occur on the same day of the year, but not every year.

639. The eclipses are visible more often between the tropics.

641. In 1959. In 1923.

643. It was possible near the Earth's equator.

644. Yes, on the north polar circle, when the eclipse occurs near midnight in the course of the polar day.

645. If the first eclipse of a certain cycle occurred on the 1st January, there are 20 days in December of that year in which an eclipse of the third cycle could occur, but there can only be one new (or full) Moon during this period, and the following full (or new) Moon will fall on the 1st January or the 2nd.

($12\frac{1}{2}$ sinodic months are longer than a leap year.)

646. $l = \Delta \dfrac{r}{R-r} = \dfrac{1}{108\cdot5} \Delta = \dfrac{r}{\sin (S-p)}$.

647. (a) $x = Lr/(R-r) = 219r$,
where x is the length of the cone of the Earth's shadow.

(b) $y = (x-l)r/\surd(x^2-r^2) = 0\cdot726r$.

648. The diameter of

$$x = \frac{bR-al}{R-l} \approx 140 \text{ km}.$$

The area of the spot of shadow is $\pi x^2/4 = 15{,}400^2$ km.

649. $x < 0$. (The notation of Problem 648.) It is impossible. The eclipse will be annular.

650. No, because then the maximum visible diameter of the Moon, at present equal to $33'32''$ will become 10 per cent less, that is, will be $30'11''$, and will not then cover the visible diameter of the Sun ($31'32''$).

This result may also be obtained from a calculation of the length of the cone of the Moon's shadow, and a comparison of it with the radius of the Moon's orbit.

651. $M'ES = P-p$.

652. $\sin \beta = \tan MEC \cot i$, about $17\frac{1}{2}°$.

653. $MEN = P+p-S = 41'9''$, that is, this angle will be significantly less than the analogous angle for a solar eclipse, and consequently the conditions of the lunar eclipses are more strict, and they occur more rarely than solar eclipses.

654. From the spherical triangle, made up of the ecliptic, the projection of the lunar orbit on the celestial sphere, and the circle of latitude passing through the Moon, we obtain

$$\sin A = \frac{\sin (MEN+r)}{\sin i} \approx 10\frac{1}{2}°.$$

Chapter XVII

Gravitation

I

655. The acceleration caused by the Earth on the Moon is greater by 151,000 times.

656. On the line of the centres, at a distance of 4664 km from the centre of the Earth.

657. The desired point lies at a distance of B, equal to

$$r\{\sqrt{(mm')} - m\}/(m - m')$$

At a distance of 6 Earth radii from the centre of the Moon.

658. The movement of this comet may be compared with the movement of the given body, and be described by Kepler's Third Law

$$\left(\frac{T}{2t}\right)^2 = \left(\frac{a}{a/2}\right)^3,$$

where T is the period of rotation of the given body in days. Hence, we obtain

$$t = \frac{T}{4\sqrt{2}} = \frac{T}{5 \cdot 65}.$$

659. 64·6 days.   **660.** 4·8 days.

661. For 44 yr.

662. 17·1 times the mass of the Earth.

663. 14·7 times the mass of the Earth.

664. 0·10 of the mass of the Earth.

665. $\dfrac{1}{3,050,000}$ of the mass of the Sun.

666. 317 of the mass of the Earth.

667. $m_1 = 0\cdot0009$, of $\frac{1}{1100}$ solar masses. (The exact value is $\frac{1}{1047}$.)

668. $\dfrac{M}{m} = \left(\dfrac{149,500,000}{384,400}\right)^3 \times \left(\dfrac{27\cdot3217}{365256}\right)^2$, whence $\log \dfrac{M}{m} = 5\cdot51740$ or $M = 329,000\ m$.

669. The comparison of centrifugal force, and the acceleration due to the force of gravity gives

$$\omega^2 R = f\frac{M}{R^2},$$

so that $M = 1\cdot9 \times 10^{33}$ g.

670. It leads to the diminishing of the semi-major axis.

II

671. According to Kepler's Third Law

$$\frac{M'+m}{M+m} = \frac{(2r)^3}{T^2}\bigg/\frac{r^3}{T^2},$$

where r is the distance of the Moon from the Earth, T is the period of rotation of the Moon, m is the mass of the Moon, M is the true mass of the Earth, and M' is the desired mass of the Earth.

This gives $M' = 8M$, if the mass of the Moon is neglected.

672. 186·6 times greater than its true mass.

673. For any shortening greater than 50 per cent, which we obtain from the formula of parabolic velocity, comparing the latter with the observed velocity of the Moon, considering it to be circular.

674. It would increase by ten times—that is, to 420·9 km/sec.

675. No, as we find after calculation that the parabolic velocity at the distance of the Earth from the Sun in this case, would diminish, to the present orbital velocity of the Earth.

676. No.

677. 7·91 km/sec.

678. 1 hr 24·7 min.

679. 2·4 km/sec.

680. 617 km/sec.

681. 435·8 km/sec.

682. 2 hr 47·4 min.

683. Four times greater than the distance to the Moon.

684. 17,000 km.

685. 4·8 km/sec.

686. $g_1 = pqg$.

687. 0·01.

688. 10 sec.

689. The acceleration due to gravity on the surface of the Moon

$$g' = \frac{g \times 6370^2}{81 \times 1740^2} = 1\cdot6231 \text{ m/sec}^2.$$

$$l' = g'/\pi^2 = 0\cdot1645 \text{ m},$$
$$t' = \sqrt{g/g'} = 2\cdot458 \text{ sec}.$$

690. With exactly the same velocity, as the mass of the shell on the Moon would not change. Only its weight would change.

691. 364 km/sec.

692. By approximately 267 km/sec².

693. It would double.

694. $\frac{1}{1657}$ of the acceleration due to gravity on the Earth.

695. $g = g_0 \dfrac{m}{r^2} = 2\cdot62 \, g_0$ or 26 m/sec².

696. $g = nR \left(\dfrac{2\pi n}{t}\right)^2 = 24\cdot83$ m/sec².

697. The first is related to the second as 46,000:1.

698. 50,000 km; 65×10^{12} km³; 1·6 g/cm³ 11·0 m/sec².

II

699. 981 cm/sec² $= f \times 4r^3\pi \times \delta/3r^2$, whence $f = 6\cdot7 \times 10^{-8}$ cm³ g⁻¹ sec⁻².

700. $k = \dfrac{2\pi z^{3/2}}{P \sqrt{(M+m)}} = 0\cdot01720210$.

701. All the planets would disperse, as the present velocity of each of them is equal to the parabolic velocity for the diminished mass of the Sun.

702. It would immediately be transformed to an elongated ellipse, with its aphelion close to that point in space where the Earth was located at the moment of the imaginary change in the mass of the Sun.

703. $x^2/t^2 \frac{1049}{1048} = a^3/a^3 = 1$, from whence we obtain

$$x = t \left(\frac{1049}{1048}\right)^{1/2} = t \left(1 + \frac{1}{2} \times \frac{1}{1048} + \ldots\right);$$

$$x \approx t \left(1 + \frac{1}{2096}\right)$$

as $t = 4332\cdot6$, then $(x-t) \approx \dfrac{4332\cdot6}{2096} \approx 2\cdot067$ days.

704. By $\dfrac{1}{660,000}$ of a year, that is, by 47·8 sec.

705. The duration of the day would increase by the value

$$\frac{5}{3} \times \frac{m}{M} \times T = 0\cdot 0004 \text{ sec.}$$

706. v will be equal to the parabolic velocity at the distance of the Earth, that is $v_0\sqrt{2} = 42$ km/sec.

707. $v = 606$ km/sec. **708.** A straight line.

709. The parabolic velocity in a westerly direction will be 49·7 km/sec. Obviously the orbit is an ellipse, and the question is framed about Venus.

710. The velocity of the comet is equal to the parabolic velocity at that distance from the Sun, and accordingly the orbit is a parabola, and its eccentricity is 1.

711. $e = 0\cdot 99$; $a = 0\cdot 5025$; $T = 0\cdot 36$ yr; $q = 0\cdot 005025$.

714. In perihelion the linear velocity is three times, and the angular velocity ten times greater than at aphelion.

715. At perihelion the linear velocity is twice, and the angular velocity four times greater than in aphelion. In perihelion the linear velocity is 7 times, and the angular velocity is 49 times greater than in aphelion.

716. 0·6.

717. The velocity at the ends of the semi-minor axes is equal to the mean velocity.

718. At the ends of the semi-minor axes, because its distance from the focus of the ellipse (from the Sun) is equal to the mean distance, while the linear velocity depends on the distance from the Sun.

719. By the law of area, the angular velocity is proportional to r^{-2}. At the ends of the semi-minor axis $r = a$, but a^{-2} is not equal to the mean of all r^{-2}.

720. The velocity of a comet in perihelion is equal to $\sqrt{2}\times$(the velocity of the Earth in its orbit). The same relationship holds for their sectorial velocities. The sectorial velocity of the Earth, that is the area described by its radius vector, is equal to π "square astronomical units" in a year.

For the comet, the sectorial velocity will then be equal to $\pi\sqrt{2}$. From the properties of the parabola $SQ = 2PS$ and the area of the sector SPQ is equal to $\frac{2}{3}$ the area of the rectangle $PRQS$, that is $\frac{4}{3}$ a square astronomical unit.

Thus, we find the desired time equal to $4/(3\pi\sqrt{2})$ years, or approximately to 3/10 years (09·61 days).

722. $M_1 M_2 = \dfrac{R_1}{R_2} d.$ **723.** 384,000 km.

724. 7·9 km/sec.

725. $v_0^2 = \dfrac{2gR(d-R)}{d} \cdot \dfrac{\sqrt{(M/m)(d-R)} - R}{\sqrt{(M/m)(d-R)} + R} = 2gR\left(-1 - \dfrac{1}{60}\right)\dfrac{1-a}{1+a}$

where

$$a = \frac{1}{59\sqrt{80}};$$

$$v_0 = 10\cdot 8 \text{ km/sec.}$$

726. Taking $R = 150,000,000$ km and $S = 330,000\ E$ we find

$$\frac{R\sqrt{SE}}{S-E} = 262,000 \text{ km}; \qquad \frac{ER}{S-E} = 454 \text{ km}.$$

727.

$$\frac{D_S}{A_S} = \frac{r^2(R+\varrho)}{R^2} = 0.005,$$

$$\frac{D_S}{A_E} = \frac{Sr^3(R+\varrho)}{MR^2\varrho^2} = 0.011.$$

728.

$$\frac{D_S}{D_E} = \frac{S}{E}\frac{r^2}{\varrho^2}\frac{R^2-\varrho^2}{R^2-r^2} = \frac{S}{E}\frac{r^3}{\varrho^3}\frac{R+\varrho}{R+r} = 0.0114.$$

730.

$$\frac{P_{pol}}{P_{equ}} = 1 + \left(\frac{2\pi}{3600}\right)^2\frac{R^3}{fM} + \left(\frac{2\pi}{3600}\right)^4\frac{R^6}{f^2M^2} + \cdots$$

731. By 37 per cent. **732.** By $2\frac{1}{2}$ times.

733. Greatest in January, in perihelion. In July, when the Earth is in aphelion, it is least. The ratio of these forces is equal to 1·11.

Chapter XVIII

Astronomical Instruments and Methods

II

734. The image of the Moon would be a little less bright, but its form would not change.

735. It would not be seen, because the image of a finger at that distance in general would not be obtained in the focal plane of the objective of a telescope.

736. $1''\cdot5$;   12th stellar magnitude.

737. $0''\cdot19$.

738. $0''\cdot15$;   16·9 stellar magnitudes.

739. About 45 times.

740. 1500 times.

741. 250 times.

742. 65 mm;   19·5 mm;   6·5 mm.

743. $x = 2F\tan\dfrac{\beta}{2} = 3\cdot72$ m.

744. 23 mm.

745. 166·35 cm.

746. $2\frac{1}{4}$ mm.

747. 0·76 mm.

748. By 100 times.

749. By 100 million times.

750. By 630 times.

751. 11·0 stellar magnitudes.

752. 2·50.

753. By 1·11 stellar magnitudes brighter. It would be fainter by 0·73 stellar magnitudes.

754. 387 times.

755. The amplitude of the change of brightness corresponds to the change in the surface area, that is, to the change in the square of the radius, assuming the star to be a sphere. The brightness changes, consequently, by a factor of 4, and the amplitude is equal to 2·5 log 4 = 1·5 stellar magnitudes.

756. 100.   **757.** 35.

758. 7·75.   **759.** By 1·8 times.

760. The star moves towards us with a radial velocity 50 km/sec.

761. 7×10^{14}.   **762.** 3·16 Å.

763. $\lambda_2 = 665$ mμ; $\lambda_1 = 383$ mμ.

764. 700 km/sec.   **766.** 0·29 mm;   2·4 μ.

771. In seconds of arc $d = 15\ t \cos \delta$.

772. (3 min 4 sec) cos 86°36'·6 = 10·9 sec = 163''·5.

773. It does not depend on it.   **774.** 16''·0.

775. 5 sec.

776. The image of the Moon becomes only twice as dim. The diffraction discs about the stars, and the circles about them became half circles.

777. $d + 2b \tan \frac{1}{2} \alpha = 4\cdot3$ cm.

778. $\beta = 5°20'$, the length is 168 cm.

779. (a) At a distance of 45·07 cm from the concave mirror,

   (b) The image in the concave mirror will be 0·0012 of the size of the object,

   (c) The apparent diameter of the Moon will be increased by 9 times.

780. $F = \dfrac{F_1 F_2}{F_1 + F_2}$.   **781.** The mean.

782. 13×18 cm.

783. The first for purposes 1, 3 and 6. The second for purposes 2, 4, 5.

784. A unit, as the surface brightness does not depend on the distance.

785. 13·2 visually and 4·5 photographically.

786. 2·20.   **787.** 1·85.

788. 1·70.   **789.** At a distance of 27 km.

790. $+0\cdot8$; $-14\cdot2$.   **791.** 9·68;   9·50;   in the mean 9·59.

793. It would shorten.   **794.** $-20\cdot7$ km/sec.

795. About 4μ.   **796.** -30 km/sec.

797. The red end is the right. The upper star is whiter.

798. This is the Balmer series of hydrogen.

802. $\delta = 1°41'$. On the photograph of the spectrum this would be about 17 mm.

803. The deviation of the red rays is $\delta_R = 38°29'$ and of the violet $\delta_v = 41°46'$.

804. $\delta_v = 35°39'$, the dispersion is 1°20'.

805. $\gamma = 32°$; $\delta_G = 8\cdot512°$; $\delta_R = 8\cdot492°$.

Chapter XIX

The Moon

I

806. Approximately $12\frac{1}{2}$ revolutions.

807. 27·32 days are equal to a sidereal month. The day and the night are equal to half a sinodic month, or 14·76 mean solar Earth days.

808. For an observer on the Moon, the Earth does not rise or set.

809. The Earth will then be visible in the zenith and, because of libration, will oscillate a little about this position.

810. The Earth will rise and set very slowly, describing about the horizon complex curves a few degrees along and perpendicular to the line of the horizon.

812. It is possible, because, being situated near to the Sun the Earth or its atmosphere would theoretically appear as a very thin crescent, with its convex side to the Sun, and would be visible in a black sky.

813. 80 times brighter than the Moon.

814. 480,000 times.

815. The effect of shadows cast by irregularities on the soil of the Moon at the oblique illumination by the Sun.

816. No. From the Moon the atmosphere surrounding the Sun can be seen, which is visible from the Earth only during a total eclipse of the Sun.

817. No.

818. Never, because the polar aurora are electrical phenomena of the atmosphere, which does not exist on the Moon.

819. The force of gravity on the Moon is equal to 0·16 that of Earth.

820. By 3 m.

821. 9·6 kg; 60 kg, if the weights were made on Earth.

822. 75 km.

II

823. 750 m.

824. By measurement of the length of the shadow with a ruler, it is equal to $1 = 24''·8 = 46·3$ km (taking the shortening due to perspective, which is equal to 12/15, into account); $H = l \tan h = 578$ m.

825. Knowing the scale of the photograph, we find AK in seconds of arc, and then in kilometres. If O is the centre of the Moon, then $OK = R + h$ where R is the radius of the Moon, and h is the height of the mountains. From the triangle $AKO (R+h)^2 = R^2$, and $h = 0''·7$ or 1·3 km.

826. At the given conditions we find that the mean square velocity of a molecule of hydrogen is 2·2 k/sec. Thus, the overwhelming majority of the molecules would have a velocity greater than the parabolic velocity, and would leave the Moon.

Chapter XX

The Planets

I

828. 4''·2.

829. 62''·2; 62''·8; 17''·0.

831. $\dfrac{17·75}{8·80} \times 5·431 = 10·95.$

832. 6800 km.

833. 42,000,000 km.

834. By 41°; by 2°.

835. 54 km.   **839.** 90 times.

840. 6·25; 2·04; 1; 0·44; 0·037.

841. 1'; 900 times.   **842.** 0·84 cal/cm²/min.

843. By 1/5000 part or approximately by the same fraction of a stellar magnitude.

844. −19·3 stellar magnitudes,which is 12×10^6 times brighter than Sirius.

845. 58 times.

846. Approximately by $2^2 \times \left(\dfrac{9 \cdot 2}{4 \cdot 2}\right)^2$, that is, by 19 times.

847. Because Venus has phases. However, during the upper conjunction of Venus, it is brighter at the Earth than the Earth as seen from Venus, because, although the distances between the planets are the same, Venus is nearer to the Sun.

848. It is greater for Jupiter.

849. It would be stronger by as many times, as the surface which is reflecting the light of the Sun increases.

850. See the answer to Problem 606.

851. In quarters, when the Earth is seen, like the Moon in the first or the last quarter.

852. From the triangle STP $\sin P = \dfrac{ST}{SP} \times \sin T$. The greatest value of P occurs when $T = 90°$, that is, in quadrature. For Mars, $P = 41°1'$, for Jupiter $= 11°5'$, for Saturn $P = 6°1'$.

853. 108,540 km.

854. $\dfrac{1}{15 \cdot 6}$.

855. R^2, because the area of the sky, occupied by the Sun, from a given point, changes approximately proportionally to $R^{-\frac{1}{2}}$.

856. +172°C. We find this value comparing the energy illuminating this sphere, $4\pi a^2 \sigma T^4$, with the solar energy which is absorbed by it from the Sun, $b\pi a^2$, where a is the radius of the sphere, and b the solar constant for Mercury.

858. The apparent position of the centre of a planet changes due to diurnal parallax by only a fraction of a second of arc, while the planeto-centric coordinates of the details on the planet are in general determinable with an exactitude of less than 1°.
So the effect is practically negligible.

860. By 0·92 sec.   **861.** By 387 km/hr.

862. By a distance of 110 m.   **863.** −1·16.

864. $m = m_0 - 5 \log (a^2 - a) + 5 \log (\varrho r)$.

865. 14·4.

866. The sinodical period of revolution is $5\frac{1}{2}$ Earth days.

867. 82 times ($42\frac{1}{2}$)°.

868. 23 times. The brightness changes $2\frac{1}{2}$ times, or by a stellar magnitude.

869. In Martian days the period of revolution of Phobos is 7 hr 39 min, $24/24 \cdot 6 = 7 \cdot 5$ hr.
The diurnal apparent motion of Phobos among the stars is $\dfrac{360°}{7 \cdot 5/24} =$

1151°, and the interval of time, x, between culminations is found from the proportion $\dfrac{360° - 1151°}{360} = \dfrac{24 \text{ hr}}{x}$; $x = 10 \text{ hr } 55 \text{ min.}$

870. On the eastern edge.

871. The shadow follows the satellite.

872. The satellite moves slowly with respect to the horizon, but fast among the stars.

873. I and III in eclipse, II appears in front of the disc, or vice versa

874. The angular velocity of rotation w is constant, and $v = wr$. For this reason the Döppler displacement is proportional to the distance from the centre of the disc.

Chapter XXI

Comets

I

875. By its movement among the stars, which can be observed in a few hours, or even within a few score minutes.

876. The observation that they participate in the diurnal movement of the celestial sphere, and the measurement of their parallax.

877. It is not possible to be exact, because the tail gradually fades away to nothing.

879. It is not possible, because the gas, emitted on heating of the nucleus by the Sun, will gradually disperse.

880. 18·5 million years.

881. 0·34 and 4·10 astronomical units.

882. Either, because of the fact that the self-luminosity of comets would fade, or because of the fact that the surface of the comet reflecting the light of the Sun diminishes, or by the simultaneous operation of both factors.

883. These were appearances of Neujmin's comet; its period of rotation is 5 years and 5 months.

II

884. No. Because of perturbation by the planets.

885. At eccentricities close to 1, ellipses whose foci very closely coincide have very different semi-major axes.

886. 19·6 astronomical units.

887. $a = 84$ astronomical units; $e = 0·999907$. In perihelion the velocity is 476 km/sec; in aphelion 22 m/sec.

888. The period is 13·7 yr, $a = 5·72$ astronomical units. This is the periodic comet Tuttle.

889. It can also be so for those whose perihelion distance is less than 1.

890. On the true dimensions of the tail, the angle between the orbit and the line of sight, and the distance of the comet.

891. From the equation for semi-major axes it follows that

$$a = \frac{r}{2}\left(\frac{u^2}{u^2 - v^2}\right) ,$$

where u is the parabolic velocity at the distance r, v is the real velocity. Obviously for v close to u, a small change in v produces a large change in a.

892. About 0·13 km/sec.

893. For this component $a = (769)^{2/3} = 83·9$ astronomical units; by the equation of kinetic energy (the equation of orbital velocity)

$$v^2 = (29·76)^2 \times \left(\frac{2}{0·00775} - \frac{1}{83·9} \right),$$

so that we obtain $v = 29·76 \sqrt{257·99} = 477$ km/sec.

894. For this component $a = (875)^{2/3} = 91·4$. If the velocities of the first and second components are denoted by v_1 and v_2, then,

$$v_2^2 - v_1^2 = (29·76)^2 \times \left(\frac{1}{83·9} - \frac{1}{91·4} \right) = 0·86,$$

or

$$(v_1 + v_2)(v_2 - v_1) = 0·86;$$

$$v_1 + v_2 = 954;$$

$$v_2 - v_1 = 0·0009 \text{ km/sec} = 90 \text{ cm/sec}.$$

895. From aphelion to perihelion the distance between the components will increase, and vice versa.

895. The dimensions of comets will increase with their distance from the Sun.

897. It is possible.   **898.** A straight line.

899. An hyperbola, with its convex side to the Sun, which is its outer focus.

900. Almost a straight line, along the radius vector to the comet from the Sun.

901. An orbit with an eccentricity slightly greater than that of the comet.

902. One of the points of the projection of the radius vector (which must all lie on a straight line) $\alpha = 21$ hr 50 min, $\delta = 9°14'$. The upper tail is of type I, the middle tail is of type II, and the lower tail of type III.

903. 64 times.

904. 64 times, or by 4·5 stellar magnitudes.

905. 7·7 stellar magnitudes.

906. In no way, because this observed change in brightness follows the inverse square law of the distance from the Sun, which is the law for change in intensity of reflected light.

907. Because its brightness depends on its distance from the Sun.

908. The mass of the block is

$$m = \frac{4}{3} \pi R^3 \delta \approx 1·35 \times 10^{12} \text{ g}.$$

The parabolic velocity is

$$v_0 = \sqrt{\frac{fm^2}{r}} = 4·2 \text{ cm/sec}.$$

The mean square velocity of a molecule under the given conditions is

$$r = 111·4 \sqrt{\frac{T}{D}}$$

where $T = 273 + 200$, D (the molecular weight of cyanide) is equal to $12 + 14 = 26$. $v = 475$ m/sec, which is many times greater than the parabolic velocity, and molecules will leave the nucleus of the comet in large quantities.

909. Under the influence of the solar "tide" the clusters of meteoric particles would disperse.

910. 46·8 km/sec.

Chapter XXII

Meteors and Meteorites

I

912. It would be quite unnoticeable from the Moon.

913. In the morning.   **914.** 10·34 astronomical units.

915. Its width is not less than the length of a path which the Earth covers in that time, which is $30 \times 60 \times 60 \times 24 \times 37$ km $\approx 9{\cdot}6\ 10^7$ km.

917. Because of the non-parallelism of their paths through the atmosphere.

919. 2·2 m.

920. Because along this line the density of population is greater.

921. Those flying in the same direction as the Earth fall on it, as their relative velocity is low; meteorites coming from the opposite direction will escape from the Earth.

922. $1{\cdot}8 \times 10^5$ kg/m.   **923.** 11m/sec and 355 m/sec.

924. About 9 cm and 85 cm.

II

925. 34°.

927. It does not remain so, because of the tidal action of the Sun. The swarm will become more scattered after each approach to the Sun.

928. A ring.   **929.** 12·3 km/sec and 71·9 km/sec.

930. On the morning side of the Earth there fall both the meteors which it encounters, and also those which it overtakes, while on the evening side fall only those meteors which gain on the Earth.

931. It can only meet twice a year with streams of meteors which move almost exactly in the plane of its orbit, and there are practically no streams of this sort. The other condition for two meetings is also rarely satisfied – the distance of the perihelion from the node must be 90°.

932. In Fig. 54, O is the observer, OA is the direction to the radiant, and the rectilinear velocities of the meteors are $v = ML$.

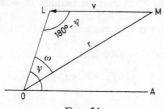

FIG. 54

From the triangle *OIM*

$$\frac{v}{\sin w} = \frac{r}{\sin \psi}$$

when *w* is small

$$v = \frac{r}{\sin \psi}\, w.$$

933. 8300.

934. About 1,300,000.

935. About 110 km.

936. About 250.

937. 78,700,000.

938. 100 km.

939. $a = 259°$; $b = 150$ km; $H = 105$ km (in the mean).

941. From the constellation Draco, near ϑ.

942. About 10^{-16}.

943. $\dfrac{10^9}{1\cdot8\times10^{12}}$ or $\dfrac{1}{18000}$. The remainder goes to warming of the air, its ionization, dissociation, on the production of waves in the air and so on.

944. The mean height is found by the formula $H = d \tan h$, which is 8·6 km.

Chapter XXIII

The Sun

I

945. The radius is 109 times that of the Earth. The surface is 11,900 times the surface of the Earth. The volume is 1,300,000 times that of the Earth.

946. $2\frac{1}{2}$ yr.

947. Many in 1950, few in 1954.

949. $17''\cdot6$, twice the parallax of the Sun.

950. 7 times greater than the diameter of the Earth.

951. 500 km.

953. Because in 1933 the number of sun spots, causing the auroral displays, increased all the time.

955. Moving farther away with a velocity of 137 km/sec.

956. By 2·22 Å.

957. A star of magnitude $+0·6$.

958. 38 g.

959. 13·6 g.

960. About 25 m.

II

961. $\beta = 82°49'5''$; $\lambda = 343°47'$.

962. 30·43 days.

966. About 9 m/sec.

967. On the equator 27·25 days, at latitude 30°—26·34 days, at latitude 45°—27·75 days.

968. 510 days, which is very much longer than the duration of the "life" of a sun-spot.

969. $bc = ac \cot AOa' = 8900$ km.

971. $(r+h)^2 = \left(\dfrac{AB}{2}\right)^2 + (SE)^2$, where $(SE) = (LE)-(LS)$; $(LS) = R-r$;

$(LE)^2 = R^2 - \left(\dfrac{AB}{2}\right)^2$.

972. $3 \cdot 02 \times 10^{27}$; 50,000 candles.

973. $3 \cdot 79 \times 10^{28}$ lumens; 624,000 lamberts.

974. 13·5 lamberts. **975.** 100 lumens or 8 candles/Watt.

976. $5 \cdot 18 \times 10^{23}$. **977.** 15·8 mm.

978. About a minute. **979.** About a million roubles.

980. 6130°.

981. Transforming the relationship between the energy in the two parts of the spectrum into logarithmic form, we find T from the formula

$$T = \frac{c_2 \left(\dfrac{1}{\lambda_1} - \dfrac{1}{\lambda_2} \right) \log e}{\log E_1 - \log E_2 + 5(\log \lambda_1 - \log \lambda_2)} = 6760°.$$

982. $cV \, dT = I p \, dt - jP(t_1 - t_2) \, dt.$

983. The total luminosity of the Sun is $\dfrac{4\pi R^2 ac}{60}$ ergs/sec. Consequently the output per unit surface of the Sun/sec is

$$\frac{4\pi R^2 ac}{60 \times 4\pi \times r^2} = \sigma T^4,$$

whence

$$T = 5750°.$$

984. From Boltzmann's Law, in its logarithmic form, we have

$$\frac{dt}{T} = \frac{1}{4} \frac{dE}{E},$$

giving the desired $dT = \frac{1}{4}$ per cent of 6000° or 15°.

985. One of the reasons is that the spectrum of the Sun is not that of an absolutely black body. The other reason is that various methods, strictly speaking, give the temperatures of different parts of the Sun's atmosphere.

986. $\dfrac{5750°}{\sqrt[4]{2}} = 4835°K.$ **987.** In 2000 yr.

988. For a sphere of mass M and radius R this energy

$$W = \frac{3}{5} K^2 \frac{M^2}{R} = 2 \cdot 27 \times 10^{48} \text{ ergs.}$$

989. 5×10^{24} g. **990.** $1 \cdot 3 \times 10^{20}$ g $= 1 \cdot 3 \times 10^{14}$ m.

991. 3×10^{10} yr.

Chapter XXIV

The Movement and the Nature of the Stars

I

992. About 46 million yr.

993. About 9800 yr. **994.** 8·8 light years.

995. 2·7 parsecs $= 8 \cdot 8$ light years $= 558,000$ astronomical units $= 8 \cdot 3 \times 10^{13}$ km; 100 parsecs $= 326$ light years $= 20 \cdot 6 \times 10^6$ astronomical units $= 3 \cdot 08 \times 10^{15}$ km.

996. 5 parsecs = 16·3 light years = $1·03 \times 10^6$ astronomical units = $15·4 \times 10^{13}$ km. 8·3 parsecs = 27·2 light years = $1·7 \times 10^6$ astronomical units = $2·56 \times 10^{14}$ km.

997. The parallax is within the limits 0·306″ and 0·318″, and consequently the distance is within the limits of 3·26 and 3·14 parsecs, which is an accuracy of a few per cent.

998. Taking probable errors into account the parallax of the latter will be within the limits of 0″·012 and 0″. That is, the distance to the star is within the limits 83 parsecs and infinity, or it is only possible to say that the distance to the star is not less than about 80 parsecs.

999. Sirius is 10,200 times brighter than its companion.

1000. +1·27.   **1001.** −4·0.

1002. 10,500 times.

1003. S Doradus is 500,000 times brighter.

1004. 14,000 times.   **1005.** 11·6 and 13·4.

1006. 0·0020 and 0·00038.

1007. The apparent stellar magnitude of Vega would be 15·1.

1008. 4·1 astronomical units.

1009. They would increase in the neighbourhood of the constellations Lyra and Hercules, and decrease in the opposite part of the sky.

II

1012. $y = \left(1 - \dfrac{1}{\sqrt{n}}\right) \dfrac{a \times c}{Vr}$ yr.

1013. About 8000 yr.   **1014.** After 97,000 yr.

1015. In relation to a particular star the velocity of the Earth will be reversed after 6 months. The difference in the observed radial velocities of the stars will be equal to twice the projection of the velocity of the Earth on the line of sight to the star at one of the given moments.

It follows that this difference must lie between 0 and 60 km/sec, depending on the longitude of the star.

1016. The correction to this is always equal to zero, as at any moment the velocity of the Earth in orbit is perpendicular to the radial velocity of the star (to the line of sight joining the star to the observer).

1017. On Fig. 55 let S be the Sun, T the Earth, TA the velocity of the Earth, and $T'A'$ its projection on the line of sight of the observer. The correction for the velocity of the Earth $T'A'$ is $TA \sin \alpha$ where α is

$$\frac{360}{365\frac{1}{4}} t$$

and t is the time between the moment of the Vernal Equinox and the moment of observation, expressed in days.

For $\alpha < 90°$ the speed of the Earth towards the star adds to the solar speed of approach to the star and the correction will have the form

$$V = 29·5 \sin \frac{360°}{365·25} t.$$

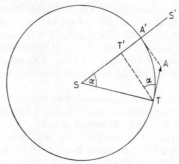

FIG. 55

1018. Yes, the observation of the systematical change in their parallaxes.

1019. $1''\cdot01$; $142°$.
1020. $0''\cdot55$; $74°$.
1021. $-1''\cdot20$.
1022. $+1125''$; $-0°\cdot07$.
1023. 90 km/sec.
1024. 17 km/sec.
1025. 19 km/sec.
1026. 57 km/sec.
1027. 18 km/sec; $114°$.
1028. $46°$.
1029. 25 km/sec at an angle of $31°$.
1030. 16 km/sec.
1031. $+18$ and 14 km/sec.
1032. $0''\cdot44$.

1033. $OM = OS \sin \vartheta = \dfrac{206,265}{\pi'}$ astronomical units. It follows that

$\pi' = \dfrac{\pi}{\sin \vartheta}$. If M is the absolute magnitude of the star, then $M = m+5+$

$5 \log \pi - 5 \log \pi' = m + 5 \log \sin \vartheta$. At the point M, $V_r' = 0$, $V_t' = \dfrac{4\cdot74\mu'}{\pi'}$,

from which we obtain

$$\mu' = \frac{V\pi'}{4\cdot74} = \left(\frac{1}{4\cdot74}\right) \times \left(\frac{V_t}{\sin \vartheta}\right) \times \left(\frac{\pi}{\sin \vartheta}\right) = \frac{\mu}{\sin^2 \vartheta}.$$

The velocity along MS is equal to $V/4\cdot74$ astronomical units per year. Consequently, the time t taken to traverse the path MS is

$$t = \frac{4\cdot74 \times MS}{V} = \frac{4\cdot74 \times 206,265 \cos \vartheta}{\pi V}$$

and as $V = V_t/\sin \vartheta = 4\cdot74\mu/\pi \sin \vartheta$; so:

$$t = \frac{206,265}{\mu} \sin \theta \cos \theta = \frac{206,265}{\mu} \frac{V_r V_t}{V_r^2 + V_t^2}.$$

Ir V_r is negative, then t is also negative and indicates that the closest appfoach to the Sun will be in the future.

1034. In the year A.D. 30050; $\pi = 7''\cdot11$; $m = -0\cdot69$.

1035. $\theta = 142°\cdot4$; $\pi = 0\cdot80$; $\mu = 22''\cdot5$; $m = 8\cdot9$; $t = -9800$; the date is the year A.D. 11700.

1036. $\mu = 11''\cdot56$; $\pi = 0''\cdot574$.

1037. From the two following tables it can be seen that the Sun approaches the North celestial Pole with a speed of 8·2 km/sec, and moves away from the southern pole with a speed of 9·3 km/sec; in the mean it has a velocity of 8·7 km/sec northwards. We also find that the Sun approaches a point lying on the equator, and having $\alpha = 18$ hr with a velocity of 19·4 km/sec (and with a speed of 1·8 km/sec to a point with the coordinates $\alpha = 12$ hr, $\delta = 0°$).

We find from these three components their resultant vector in the usual way, finding a movement with a velocity of 21·3 km/sec towards an apex with the coordinates $\alpha = 17$ hr 40 min, $\delta = +24°$.

1038. Yes, as movement in a curved line will cause the radial velocity of the star to undergo a slow systematic change. This change will be different for stars situated in different directions, as the direction of the vector of the velocity of the Sun will rotate with respect to the stars, and their velocity observed relative to the Sun is the resultant velocity of the Sun and the star through space.

1039. Draw a diagram analogous to the preceding, but marking degrees of Declination along the circle. We find the Declination of the apex about $+35°$, and that of the anti-apex about $-40°$, giving a mean Declination of the apex of $+37°$.

1040. The radial velocity will change proportionally to $\cos \lambda$, and the proper movement proportionally to $\sin \lambda$.

1041. It is possible, by the systematic increase in the apparent brightness of the stars close to the apex, and by the systematic decrease in the brightness of stars at the anti-apex.

1042. After 26,000 yr.   **1043.** $+53·8$ km/sec.

1044. $+17·6$ km/sec.

1045. $v = -0''·0460$; $\tau = -0''·0797$.

1046. $v = -0''·022$; $\tau = +0''·0628$.

1047. $v' = 0''·010$.   **1048.** $0''·028$.

1049. $\pi = 0''·0023$; $M = +0·3$.   **1050.** $0''·0071$.

1051. $0''·0015$; and $M = -0·4$.

1052. $\tau\pi = 0''·00129$; $\pi = 0''·00123$. $\pi = 0''·00126$; $M = -3·5$.

1053. $0''·031$.   **1054.** $V = 44·2$ km/sec; $\pi = 0''·25$.

1055. 79 parsecs;   550 parsecs.   **1056.** At the lower temperatures.

1057. $-0·64$ for $T = \infty$.

1059. The brighter component. $2·28 + 1·12 = 3·40$, the weaker component; $5·08 - 0·04 = 5·04$.

1061. 57 m.   **1062.** 3 m.

1063. The diameter of α Scorpio is 3000 times greater.

1064. 10·5 the radius of the Sun.

1065. 480 times the radius of the Sun.

1066. 0·034 of the radius of the Sun.

1067. 62 times the radius of the Sun. $0''·033$.

1068. In diameter 630 times greater than Jupiter, or 63 times greater than the Sun, which is 35 times greater than Sirius itself—an improbable value. From this we conclude that the companion is a selfluminous body.

1069. 23,000°;   11,200°;   6000°.

1070. 4100°;   4600°;   6500°;   23,000°.

1071. Between 2300° to 1650°.

1072. 4200°.   **1073.** 2 cal/yr.

1074. 3 mg.   **1075.** 4350°.

1076. 3100°.   **1077.** About 4000°.

1078. 4000°.   **1079.** 10 times the mass of the Sun.

1080. 0·9 times the mass of the Sun.

1081. 5×10^{-3} g/cm³.   **1082.** About 100 kg/cm³.

1083. 10^5 g/cm³.

1084. The kinetic energies are related as $2·2:4·1:3·6$. That is, in spite of the significant difference in masses and speeds, the kinetic energies differ very little, and indicate an even distribution of energy among the stars.

Chapter XXV

Double Stars

1085. $0''·16$.   **1086.** $0·64$.

1087. $1·6$.   **1089.** $7·5$ times the mass of the Sun.

1090. $1·5$ times the mass of the Sun.

1091. $23·5$ times.

1092. $m_1 + m_2 = 2·1$ the mass of the Sun.

1093. $11·5$ astronomical units, and $6·5$ times the mass of the Sun.

1094. $5·5$ times the mass of the Sun.

1095. $1·7$ times.

1096. 100 astronomical units. $P = 707$ yr; $m_1 = m_2 = 13·35$; combined magnitude $12·6$.

1097. $a = 12 \times 10^9$ km; the absolute magnitudes are $1·4$ and $2·2$, that is 24 and $11·5$ times brighter than the Sun: the masses are $2·4$ and $2·0$ times the mass of the Sun.

The velocity of the centre of gravity is 13 km/sec; the ratio of the radii of the stars are $1/1·45$ and the mean orbital velocity is $7·8$ km/sec.

1098. The period is $0·232$ days; the velocity is $20·2$ km/sec.

1099. $0''·76$.

1100. $0''·049$. The difference received is explained by the fact that the sum of masses of this pair is much smaller than two solid masses.

1101. $0''·040$.   **1102.** $0''·095$.

1103. $2''·77$.   **1104.** $0''·022$.

1105. This is a visual binary system with a circular orbit, lying in the plane passing through the line of sight.

1107. About 85°. Bear in mind that the semi-major axis of the true orbit passes through the principal star, and the centre of the apparent ellipse coincides with the centre of the true ellipse.

1108. $e = 0·46$. It is equal to the ratio of the apparent distance of the principal star from the centre of the ellipse, to the apparent diameter of the ellipse passing through the principal star (to the projection of the semi-major axis), since the distance of the focus from the centre, and the semi-major axis of the ellipse, are both distorted by projection, in the same ratio.

1109. The exact data for ζ Herculis are $-a = 12·2$ astronomical units, $P = 34·5$ yr, $e = 0·46$, $m_1 + m_2 = 1·6$.

For Sirius $a = 20\cdot4$ astronomical units, $e = 0\cdot60, P = 50\cdot0$ yr, $m_1 + m_2 = 3\cdot4$.

1110. $a = 0''\cdot54$, $e = 0\cdot36$, $P = 26$ yr.

1111. $34\cdot6$ km/sec.

1112. -19 km/sec; $+19$ km/sec; $+30$ km/sec.

1114. $\dfrac{m_1}{m_2} = \dfrac{k_2}{k_1} = 1\cdot20$.

1115. $90°$; $0°$; w is indeterminate.

1116. 138 astronomical units.   **1117.** 26,600,000 km.

1118. 5,020,000 km.

1119. About 80 times the mass of the Sun.

1120. $8 \times 0\cdot315 = 2\cdot5$ the mass of the Sun.

1121. $125 \times 0\cdot315 = 39$ the mass of the Sun. The mass of the bright star is $31\cdot50$, and of the faint, $7\cdot87$.

1122. $0\cdot315$ the mass of the Sun.

1123. $\pi = 0''\cdot0084$; the luminosity is 15 times greater than that of the Sun, and the semi-major axis $= 5\cdot7$ astronomical units, the mass is $2\cdot5$ times greater than the mass of the Sun.

By the mass absolute magnitude curve, the luminosity of the mass obtained would be about twice the mass of the Sun.

Chapter XXVI

Variable Stars and Novae

I

1125. 480 times.   **1126.** $15\cdot8$ times.

1127. On 30th June, 1938;   on 9th August, 1939;   on 17th September, 1940.

1129. Twice.

1130. The range is $5\frac{1}{2}$–$13\frac{1}{2}$ stellar magnitudes, the period is about 400 days.

1132. 3 days, 68713.

1133. The amplitude is $7\cdot27$–$7\cdot78$ stellar magnitudes; the period is $0\cdot567$ days—this is the short period Cepheid RR Lyrae.

1134. The period is $16\cdot5$ days, the range is $6\cdot25$–$6\cdot73$ stellar magnitudes. This is a long period Cepheid (X Cygni).

1135. The period is $5\cdot3$ days, the variability from $3\cdot69$ to $4\cdot13$ stellar magnitudes. This is the Cepheid δ Cephei.

1136. The star with the uneven oscillations of intensity (this is CH Cygni).

II

1137. The spectral observations of Cepheids contradict thi

1138. 240 parsecs.   **1139.** 166 parsecs.

1140. $17\cdot4$.

1141. $\dfrac{I_1}{I_2} = \left(\dfrac{T_1}{T_2}\right)^4 \times \left(\dfrac{R_1}{R_2}\right)^2$. From which we obtain

$$\left(\dfrac{R_1}{R_2}\right)^2 = 6 \cdot 3 \times \dfrac{1}{2 \cdot 7}$$

or

$$\dfrac{R_1}{R_2} = 1 \cdot 5$$

1142. $k = 1 - \dfrac{r^2}{R^2}$, from which we obtain

$$\dfrac{r}{R} = \sqrt{(1-k)}$$

1143. $2\alpha = 360° \dfrac{p}{P}$; $\dfrac{R+r}{D} = \sin \alpha$,

whence

$$\dfrac{D}{R} = \left(1 + \dfrac{r}{R}\right) \operatorname{cosec} \alpha.$$

1144. 0·836.

1145. $r/R = 0.965$;   the radius of the orbit is 7·13 times the radius of the orbit of the bright star.

1146. Midway between the main minima, a lesser, secondary minimum will be observed.

1147. (a) A partial eclipse, a faint component.

　　(b) Double eclipse, a bright component.

　　(c) Double eclipses of two bright stars of unequal luminosity almost adjacent.

　　(d) An annular eclipse, by a faint companion.

　　(e) The same as (b), only showing the phase effect.

　　(f) Double eclipses, of almost adjacent, almost identical stars.

1148. 0·42 times the density of the Sun.

1149. The observed period is greater than the true period by 1 part in 10,000, a difference of about 26 sec.

1151. 100 times.

1152. The answer to the last question; from a distance of 1·8 parsecs; that is, farther than the nearest star.

1154. In this case the ratio of the luminosities must be $16 \times 10^4 \ (T/T_1)^4$, which gives $T = 200,000°$, which is improbable.

Chapter XXVII

The Structure of the Universe

I

1155. 55,000 astronomical units.　　**1156.** 40,000 parsecs.

1157. 35 parsecs.　　　　　　　　　**1158.** 10,500 parsecs.

1159. 37 parsecs; −9·2 stellar magnitudes.

1160. 240,000 parsecs = 780,000 light years; the diameter is 13,500 light years.

1161. 14,000 parsecs.

II

1164. Proportionally to the square of the radius of the sphere.

1165. 15·86 times, as the corresponding number of stars is in the same ratio as volumes of spheres whose radii are in a ratio of 2·512:1.

1166. The faint star is farther away.

1169. 2400 parsecs.

1171. Taking into account the absorption of light the calculated linear diameters of the spiral nebulae became less than was previously the case.

1172. $m = a - 5 \log d$, where a is a certain constant.

1173. The relationship will be represented graphically not as the straight line $m = a - 5 \log d$, but as a line closer to the $\log d$ axis.

1174. 0·006 stellar magnitudes.

1175. 63 million parsecs, or about 200 million light years.

1176. A logarithmic spiral, $r = Ce^{\alpha\phi}$, where α and C are constants.

Chapter XXVIII

Miscellaneous Problems

I

1177. It would be correct.

1178. With the help of the star globe we find that this would be from April to September.

1179. Near the Summer Solstice.

1180. In the middle of August, that is, to the time when the corn began to ripen.

1181. This problem can be very simply solved with the help of the celestial globe. We set up the globe so that the North Pole is under the horizon at an altitude of $50° - 60°$, as if the observation was made in Siberia.

We turn the celestial globe about its axis, so that the "Watchmen" (the Pleiades) stand high above the horizon, approximately near the meridian of the place. From the words of the wanderer we know that "it is past midnight", or that the Sun is at about its lowest culmination below the horizon. From this it is easy to determine the position of the Sun on the ecliptic.

It is only necessary to look now at the stellar globe which we have set up as indicated above. It appears that at the given moment the Sun is about to enter the constellation Sagittarius, which gives the data as about 22nd November.

We may thus say that V.G. Korelenko met the Wanderer in November, between the 20th and 30th.

1182. It is possible to solve this problem with the help of the celestial globe, in the following way:

Set the axis of the world on the globe at an angle of $50°$ to the horizon, at about the latitude of Europe. Now turn the globe so that the stars of Ursa Major stand in the zenith, and Arcturus high in the east. (Arcturus is α Böotes.)

Further, from the story, we know the position of Venus in the sky. As we know that Venus cannot go far from the Sun, its maximum elongation being 48°, we can determine from this the position of the Sun on the ecliptic. Thus, we discover that the Sun, at that moment is entering the constellation Taurus so that the date is the end of April, and Oblonskii and Levin's hunt took place in the spring.

1183. (1) No.

(2) Knowing that "in the zenith burned the wonderful southern cross" it is simple to determine from the celestial globe that the Nautilus was then not at the South Pole, but between latitude 65° and 54° south.

(3) No. The Southern Cross is not a star, but a constellation, occupying in the sky the area between 55° and 64° of southern Declination. The south pole lies in the constellation Octantis, close to the 5th magnitude star σ Octantis.

σ Octantis is thus the southern polar star.

1184. With the help of the celestial globe, we find that at latitude 40° N. the constellations mentioned in these lines are located above the horizon; that at the moment of the rising of the Pleiades, Böotes sets, and the Great Bear is indeed a non-setting constellation — "never dipping herself in the waves of the Ocean".

Further, it is given that Odysseus did not turn his eyes from "Böotes descending late into the sea", meaning that this setting of Böotes was very much later than that of the Sun, or approximately at midnight. In other words, at the moment of the setting of Böotes, or at the rising of the Pleiades, the Sun is in lower culmination.

If we now look at the ecliptic for this setting of the celestial globe, we see that at that moment the constellation Leo is in lowest culmination, and it is here that the Sun is located in the month of July.

II

1185. 16″·2;   62 sec;   30 km.

1187. 300 km²;   12th April;   2nd September.   900 km to the pole.   The chimes of the clock are heard at 0 hr 54 min;   Saturn can be invisible for about 11 yr.

1188. 14th July at 6 hr 48 min local time, 2 hr after sunrise.

1189. $+48°19'03''$ if the Sun is located in the south.

1190. 42°50′.

1192. 9 nautical miles to the west, and 2 miles to the north of the true position.

1193. $1·8 \cot 65° = 0·84$ m.

1194. $x = h(\cot \beta - \cot(\beta+\alpha)) = 0·18$ m.

1195. (1) The azimuth of the Sun should be equal to θ. From formulae (5), (6), Chapter III, inserting $\delta = 0$ and $A = \theta$ we find the desired formula.

(2) $x = h \tan z \times \cos(90-\theta)$, but $z = \phi-\delta = \phi-0 = \phi$, consequently, $z = h \tan \phi \sin \theta$.

1196. $\cos \dfrac{\alpha}{2} = \dfrac{5 - 0 \cdot 273r}{60r}$; $a = 178°36'$.

1197. Refraction; aberration, annual and diurnal; precession; nutation; annual parallax.

1198. From the 1st to 2nd July on the crossing of the International Date Line, from the 2nd to 1st July on entry into the second zone, and from the 1st to 2nd July at the moment of landing.

1199. This duration depends on the value of the horizontal parallax; the Sun would be visible longer.

1200. About 200 days.

1201. 7·80, 7·58 and 7·32 km/sec.

1202. $T = \dfrac{2\pi(R+h)}{v}$ where $v = \sqrt{gM(R+h)}$, $T = 89 \cdot 3$ min.

1203. From the equation: $1/S_{\text{sat}} = 1/T_{\text{sat}} - 1/T_{\text{earth}}$, we obtain $S_{\text{sat}} = 139 \cdot 2$ min.

1204. 1329 km.

1205. 1·6 km/sec.

1206. 36340 km.

1207. 5 km/sec.

1208. 0·7 year.

1209. $V_p = 7 \cdot 98$ km/sec, $V_a = 6 \cdot 84$ km/sec.

1210. $a = 25 \cdot 7$ m/sec². Overloading is $(g_o + a)/g_o = 3 \cdot 7$.

1211. $M_o : M_f = 2 \cdot 1$, or 52·4 % of the initial mass is used.

1212. The rocket has a larger cross-section and it suffers a larger air resistance. Therefore its orbits become lower and lower and its velocity increases.

APPENDIX

TABLE I
MATHEMATICAL AND PHYSICAL CONSTANTS

Number	Logarithm	Number	Logarithm
π 3·1416	0·49715	4π12·5664	1·09221
2π 6·2832	0·79818	e 2·7183	0·43429

Number of degrees in a radian	57·2958	1·75812
Number of minutes in a radian	3437·75	3·53628
Number of seconds in a radian	206,265	5·31443
1′ in radians	0·000291	$3·46489 - 10$

$1 \text{ km} = 10^3 \text{ m} = 10^5 \text{ cm} \quad 10 \text{ mm} = 10^4 \mu = 10^7 \text{ m}\mu = 10^8 \text{ Å.}$

$1 \text{ Joule} = 10^7 \text{ ergs} = 0·101972 \text{ (kilogram metres).}$

Astronomical Constants

	Number	Logarithm	
The mechanical equivalent of heat (m. calories)	$4·185 \times 10^7$ ergs	7·62170	
Velocity of light in a vacuum	$2·998 \times 10^{10}$ cm/sec	10·47638	
Gaussian constant k	0·017202	$8·23558 - 10$	
Gravitational constant (cgs)	$6·673 \times 10^{-8}$	$2·82432 - 10$	(last 3
The constant of Stefan's Law σ (cgs)	$5·72 \times 10^{-}$	$5·75740 - 10$	in cgs system)
The constant of Wien's Law (cgs)	0·289	$9·46090 - 10$	
Number of seconds in a day	86400	4·93651	
Equatorial radius of the Earth	6378·24	3·80469	
Polar radius of the Earth	6356·86	3·80324	
Radius of a sphere of the same size as the Earth:	6371·23	3·80423	

A sidereal day is 23 hr 56 min 4·091 sec of mean solar time.
A mean solar day is 24 hr 3 min 56·555 sec of sidereal time.

TABLE I *(cont.)*

Duration of a year (in mean time):

    tropical   365·2422 days = 365 days 5 hr 48 min 47 sec.
    sidereal   365·2654 days = 365 days 6 hr 9 min 10 sec.
    anomalistic 365·2596 days = 365 days 6 hr 13 min 53 sec.

Duration of a month (in mean time):

    synodical   29·5306 days = 29 days 12 hr 44 min 3 sec.
    sidereal   27·3217 days = 27 days 7 hr 43 min 12 sec.
    draconitic 27·2122 days = 27 days 5 hr 5 min 36 sec.

	Number	*Logarithm*
Mass of the Earth	$5·974 \times 10^{27}$ g	27·77627
Mass of the Sun = 331,950		
the mass of the Earth	$1·983 \times 10^{33}$ g	33·29732
Radius of the Sun	$6·963 \times 10^{10}$ cm	10·84217
Absolute magnitude of the Sun	+4·85	
Volume of the Sun = 1,300,000		
the volume of the Earth		
Mean density of the Sun	1·41 g/cm^3	0·14922
Period of rotation of the Sun		
at the equator	24·65 days	
Force of gravity on the surface		
of the Sun = 27·89 Earth		
gravity	274 m/sec	2·43775
Parabolic velocity at the		
surface of the Sun	617·0 km/sec	2·79029
Parallax of the Sun	8″·80	
Astronomical unit	$1·495 \times 10^8$ km	8·17464
Light year = $6·33 \times 10^4$ astrono-		
mical units	$9·463 \times 10^{12}$ km	12·97603
Parsec = 3·26 light years =		
= 206,265 astronomical units	$3·084 \times 10^{13}$ km	13·4891

TABLE II

The Sun 1931 Mean Greenwich Midnight (0 hr Universal Time)

Date	Week-day	Time equation Mean−True	Time correction	Apparent Right Ascension	Apparent Declination	Hourly rate	Solar radius	Sidereal time
June 13	Sat.	−0 min 25·75 sec	0·514 sec	5 hr 20 min 56·47 sec	+23° 8′48″·9	9″·68	946″·39	17 hr 21 min 22·223 sec
14	Sun.	0 13·31	0·522	5 25 5·47	23 12 28·9	8 ·66	946 ·29	17 25 18·782
15	Mon.	−0 0·70	0·529	5 29 14·64	23 15 44·4	7 ·63	946 ·20	17 29 15·341
16	Tues.	+0 12·06	0·535	5 33 23·96	23 18 35·3	6 ·60	946 ·11	17 33 11·899
17	Wed.	0 24·95	0·539	5 37 33·40	23 21 1·5	5 ·57	946 ·03	17 37 8·458
18	Thurs.	0 37·93	0·542	5 41 42·94	23 23 2·9	4 ·54	945 ·96	17 41 5·017
19	Fri.	+0 50·97	0·545	5 45 52·55	+23 24 39·5	3 ·51	945 ·89	17 45 1·576
20	Sat.	1 4·06	0·546	5 50 2·19	23 25 51·3	2 ·47	945 ·83	17 48 58·134
21	Sun.	1 17·15	0·545	5 54 11·84	23 26 38·2	1 ·44	945 ·77	17 52 54·693
22	Mon.	1 30·23	0·544	5 58 21·48	23 27 0·3	0 ·40	945 ·72	17 56 51·252
23	Tues.	1 43·26	0·542	6 2 31·07	23 26 57·5	0 ·63	945 ·67	18 0 47·810
24	Wed.	1 56·23	0·539	6 6 40·60	23 26 30·0	1 ·66	945 ·63	18 4 44·369
25	Thurs.	+2 9·11	0·535	6 10 50·04	+23 25 37·7	2 ·70	945 ·59	18 8 40·928
26	Fri.	2 21·88	0·530	6 14 59·37	23 24 20·6	3 ·37	945 ·55	18 12 37·486
27	Sat.	2 34·52	0·524	6 19 8·57	23 22 38·9	4 ·75	945 ·52	18 16 34·045
28	Sun.	2 47·01	0·517	6 23 17·61	23 20 32·5	5 ·78	945 ·49	18 20 30·604
29	Mon.	2 59·33	0·510	6 27 26·49	23 18 1·6	6 ·80	945 ·47	18 24 27·162
30	Tues.	3 11·46	0·501	6 31 35·18	23 15 6·2	7 ·82	945 ·45	18 28 23·721

TABLE II (*cont.*)

Date	Week-day	Time equation Mean—True	Time correction	Apparent Right Ascension	Apparent Declination	Hourly rate	Solar radius	Sidereal time
July 1	Wed.	+3 min 23·39 sec	0·492 sec	6 hr 35 min 43·67 sec	+23°11′46″·4	+·3 8″·83	945″·43	18 hr 32 min 20 sec·280
2	Thurs.	3 35·10	0·483	6 39 51·93	23 8 2 ·3	9 ·84	945 ·41	18 36 16 ·838
3	Fri.	3 46·56	0·472	6 43 59·95	23 3 53 ·9	10 ·85	945 ·40	18 40 13 ·397
4	Sat.	3 57·76	0·461	6 48 7·72	22 59 21 ·4	11 ·86	945 ·39	18 44 9 ·955
5	Sun.	4 8·69	0·449	6 52 15·20	22 54 24 ·9	12 ·86	945 ·38	18 48 6 ·513
6	Mon.	4 19·32	0·437	6 56 22·39	22 49 4 ·4	13 ·85	945 ·38	18 52 3 ·072
7	Tues.	+4 29·64	0·423	7 0 29·26	+22 43 20 ·1	14 ·84	945 ·38	18 55 59 ·630
8	Wed.	4 39·62	0·409	7 4 35·80	22 37 12 ·1	15 ·82	945 ·39	18 59 56 ·188
9	Thurs.	4 49·25	0·394	7 8 41·99	22 30 40 ·5	16 ·80	945 ·40	19 3 52 ·747
10	Fri.	4 58·51	0·378	7 12 47·81	22 23 45 ·6	17 ·77	945 ·42	19 7 49 ·305
11	Sat.	5 7·38	0·361	7 16 53·24	22 16 27 ·4	18 ·74	945 ·44	19 11 45 ·863
12	Sun.	5 15·84	0·344	7 20 58·26	22 8 46 ·1	19 ·70	945 ·46	19 15 42 ·422
13	Mon.	+5 23·88	0·326	7 25 2·86	+22 0 41 ·9	20 ·65	945 ·49	19 19 38 ·980
14	Tues.	5 31·48	0·307	7 29 7·01	21 52 15 ·0	21 ·59	945 ·53	19 23 35 ·538
15	Wed.	5 38·61	0·287	7 33 10·70	21 43 25 ·6	22 ·53	945 ·57	19 27 32 ·096
16	Thurs.	5 45·25	0·267	7 37 13·91	21 34 13 ·8	23 ·45	945 ·62	19 31 28 ·654
17	Fri.	5 51·40	0·245	7 41 16·61	21 24 40 ·0	24 ·37	945 ·67	19 35 25 ·212
18	Sat.	5 57·03	0·223	7 45 18·79	21 14 44 ·3	25 ·27	945 ·73	19 39 21 ·770

TABLE III
HOURS, MINUTES AND SECONDS IN FRACTIONS OF A DAY

Hours in fractions of a day		Minutes in fractions of a day				Seconds in fractions of a day	
1	0·041667	1	0·000694	31	0·021528	1	0·000012
2	0·083333	2	0·001389	32	0·022222	2	0·000023
3	0·125000	3	0·002083	33	0·022917	3	0·000035
4	0·166667	4	0·002778	34	0·023611	4	0·000046
5	0·208333	5	0·003472	35	0·024305	5	0·000058
6	0·250000	6	0·004167	36	0·025000	6	0·000069
7	0·291667	7	0·004861	37	0·025694	7	0·000081
8	0·333333	8	0·005556	38	0·026389	8	0·000093
9	0·375000	9	0·006250	39	0·027083	9	0·000104
10	0·416667	10	0·006944	40	0·027778	10	0·000116
11	0·458333	11	0·007639	41	0·028472	11	0·000127
12	0·500000	12	0·008333	42	0·029167	12	0·000139
13	0·541667	13	0·009028	43	0·029861	13	0·000150
14	0·583333	14	0·009722	44	0·030556	14	0·000162
15	0·625000	15	0·010417	45	0·031250	15	0·000174
16	0·666667	16	0·011111	46	0·031944	16	0·000185
17	0·708333	17	0·011805	47	0·032639	17	0·000197
18	0·750000	18	0·012500	48	0·033333	18	0·000208
19	0·791667	19	0·013194	49	0·034028	19	0·000220
20	0·833333	20	0·013889	50	0·034722	20	0·000231
21	0·875000	21	0·014583	51	0·035417	30	0·000347
22	0·916667	22	0·015278	52	0·036111	40	0·000463
23	0·958333	23	0·015972	53	0·036805	50	0·000579
24	1·000000	24	0·016667	54	0·037500	60	0·000694
		25	0·017361	55	0·038194		
		26	0·018055	56	0·038889		
		27	0·018750	57	0·039583		
		28	0·019444	58	0·040278		
		29	0·020139	59	0·040972		
		30	0·020833	60	0·041667		

TABLE IV

THE EXPRESSION OF DEGREES IN HOURS, MINUTES AND SECONDS

Degrees in hr, min and sec				Minutes of arc in hr, min and sec				Seconds of arc in hr, min and sec			
1°	0 hr 4 min	120°	8 hr 0 min	1′	0 min 4 sec	31′	2 min 4 sec	1″	0·07 sec	31″	2·07 sec
2	0 0 8	130	8 40	2	8	32	8	2	0·13	32	2·13
3	0 0 12	140	9 20	3	12	33	12	3	0·20	33	2·20
4	0 0 16	150	10 0	4	16	34	16	4	0·27	34	2·27
5	0 0 20	160	10 40	5	20	35	20	5	0·33	35	2·33
6	0 0 24	170	11 20	6	24	36	24	6	0·40	36	2·40
7	0 0 28	180	12 0	7	28	37	28	7	0·47	37	2·47
8	0 0 32	190	12 40	8	32	38	32	8	0·53	38	2·53
9	0 0 36	200	13 20	9	36	39	36	9	0·60	39	2·60
10	0 0 40	210	14 0	10	40	40	40	10	0·67	40	2·67
11	0 0 44	220	14 40	11	44	41	44	11	0·73	41	2·73
12	0 0 48	230	15 20	12	48	42	48	12	0·80	42	2·80
13	0 0 52	240	16 0	13	52	43	52	13	0·87	43	2·87
14	0 0 56	250	16 40	14	56	44	2 56	14	0·93	44	2·93
15	0 1 0	260	17 20	15	1 0	45	3 0	15	1·00	45	3·00

3·07	46	1·07	16	4	46	4	16	
3·13	47	1·13	17	8	47	8	17	
3·20	48	1·20	18	12	48	12	18	
3·27	49	1·27	19	16	49	16	19	
3·33	50	1·33	20	20	50	20	20	
3·40	51	1·40	21	24	51	24	21	
3·47	52	1·47	22	28	52	28	22	
3·53	53	1·53	23	32	53	32	23	
3·60	54	1·60	24	36	54	36	24	
3·67	55	1·67	25	40	55	40	25	
3·73	56	1·73	26	44	56	44	26	
3·80	57	1·80	27	48	57	48	27	
3·87	58	1·87	28	52	58	52	28	
3·93	59	1·93	29	56 (3)	59	56 (1)	29	
4·00	60	2·00	30	0 (4)	60	0 (2)	30	

0	18	270	20
40	18	280	30
20	19	290	40
0	20	300	50
40	20	310	60
20	21	320	70
0	22	330	80
40	22	340	90
20	23	350	100
0	24	360	110

20	1
0	2
40	2
20	3
0	4
40	4
20	5
0	6
40	6
20	7

TABLE V

THE CONVERSION OF HOURS, MINUTES AND SECONDS INTO DEGREES

Hr		Min				Sec			
1 hr	15°	1 min	0°15′	31 min	7°45′	1 sec	0′15″	31 sec	7′45″
2	30	2	0 30	32	8 0	2	0 30	32	8 0
3	45	3	0 45	33	8 15	3	0 45	33	8 15
4	60	4	1 0	34	8 30	4	1 0	34	8 30
5	75	5	1 15	35	8 45	5	1 15	35	8 45
6	90	6	1 30	36	9 0	6	1 30	36	9 0
7	105	7	1 45	37	9 15	7	1 45	37	9 15
8	120	8	2 0	38	9 30	8	2 0	38	9 30
9	135	9	2 15	39	9 45	9	2 15	39	9 45
10	150	10	2 30	40	10 0	10	2 30	40	10 0
11	165	11	2 45	41	10 15	11	2 45	41	10 15
12	180	12	3 0	42	10 30	12	3 0	42	10 30
13	195	13	3 15	43	10 45	13	3 15	43	10 45
14	210	14	3 30	44	11 0	14	3 30	44	11 0
15	225	15	3 45	45	11 15	15	3 45	45	11 15
16	240	16	4 0	46	11 30	16	4 0	46	11 30
17	255	17	4 15	47	11 45	17	4 15	47	11 45
18	270	18	4 30	48	12 0	18	4 30	48	12 0
19	285	19	4 45	49	12 15	19	4 45	49	12 15
20	300	20	5 0	50	12 30	20	5 0	50	12 30
21	315	21	5 15	51	12 45	21	5 15	51	12 45
22	330	22	5 30	52	13 0	22	5 30	52	13 0
23	345	23	5 45	53	13 15	23	5 45	53	13 15
24	360	24	6 0	54	13 30	24	6 0	54	13 30
		25	6 15	55	13 45	25	6 15	55	13 45
		26	6 30	56	14 0	26	6 30	56	14 0
		27	6 45	57	14 15	27	6 45	57	14 15
		28	7 0	58	14 30	28	7 0	58	14 30
		29	7 15	59	14 45	29	7 15	59	14 45
		30	7 30	60	15 0	30	7 30	60	15 0

TABLE VI

The Conversion of Units of Mean Time into Sidereal Time

| Hours | | Minutes | | | | Seconds | |
Mean	Stellar	Mean	Stellar	Mean	Stellar	Mean	Stellar
1hr	1hr0' 9"·86	1'	1'0"·16	31'	31'5"·09	1"	1"·00
2	2 0 19 ·71	2	2 0 ·33	32	32 5 ·26	3	3 ·01
3	3 0 29 ·57	3	3 0 ·49	33	33 5 ·42	5	5 ·01
4	4 0 39 ·43	4	4 0 ·66	34	34 5 ·59	7	7 ·02
5	5 0 49 ·28	5	5 0 ·82	35	35 5 ·75	9	9 ·02
6	6 0 59 ·14	6	6 0 ·99	36	36 5 ·91	11	11 ·03
7	7 1 9 ·00	7	7 1 ·15	37	37 6 ·08	13	13 ·04
8	8 1 18 ·85	8	8 1 ·31	38	38 6 ·24	15	15 ·04
9	9 1 28 ·71	9	9 1 ·48	39	39 6 ·41	17	17 ·05
10	10 1 38 ·56	10	10 1 ·64	40	40 6 ·57	19	19 ·05
11	11 1 48 ·42	11	11 1 ·81	41	41 6 ·74	21	21 ·06
12	12 1 58 ·28	12	12 1 ·97	42	42 6 ·90	23	23 ·06
13	13 2 8 ·13	13	13 2 ·14	43	43 7 ·06	25	25 ·07
14	14 2 17 ·99	14	14 2 ·30	44	44 7 ·23	27	27 ·07
15	15 2 27 ·85	15	15 2 ·46	45	45 7 ·39	29	29 ·08
16	16 2 37 ·70	16	16 2 ·63	46	46 7 ·56	31	31 ·08
17	17 2 47 ·56	17	17 2 ·79	47	47 7 ·72	33	33 ·09
18	18 2 57 ·42	18	18 2 ·96	48	48 7 ·89	35	35 ·10
19	19 3 7 ·27	19	19 3 ·12	49	49 8 ·05	37	37 ·10
20	20 3 17 ·13	20	20 3 ·29	50	50 8 ·21	39	39 ·11
21	21 3 26 ·99	21	21 3 ·45	51	51 8 ·38	41	41 ·11
22	22 3 36 ·84	22	22 3 ·61	52	52 8 ·54	43	43 ·12
23	23 3 46 ·70	23	23 3 ·78	53	53 8 ·71	45	45 ·12
24	24 3 56 ·56	24	24 3 ·94	54	54 8 ·87	47	47 ·13
		25	25 4 ·11	55	55 9 ·04	49	49 ·13
		26	26 4 ·27	56	56 9 ·20	51	51 ·14
		27	27 4 ·44	57	57 9 ·36	53	53 ·15
		28	28 4 ·60	58	58 9 ·53	55	55 ·15
		29	29 4 ·76	59	59 9 ·69	57	57 ·16
		30	30 4 ·93	60	60 9 ·86	59	59 ·16

TABLE VII

THE CONVERSION OF UNITS OF STELLAR TIME INTO MEAN TIME

Hours		Minutes				Seconds	
Stellar	Mean	Stellar	Mean	Stellar	Mean	Stellar	Mean
1hr	0hr59′ 50″·17	1′	0′ 59″·84	31′	30′ 54″·92	1″	1″·00
2	1 59 40 ·34	2	1 59 ·67	32	31 54 ·76	3	2 ·99
3	2 59 30 ·51	3	2 59 ·51	33	32 54 ·59	5	4 ·99
4	3 59 20 ·68	4	3 59 ·34	34	33 54 ·43	7	6 ·98
5	4 59 10 ·85	5	4 59 ·18	35	34 54 ·27	9	8 ·98
6	5 59 1 ·02	6	5 59 ·02	36	35 54 ·10	11	10 ·97
7	6 58 51 ·19	7	6 58 ·85	37	36 53 ·94	13	12 ·96
8	7 58 41 ·36	8	7 58 ·69	38	37 53 ·77	15	14 ·96
9	8 58 31 ·53	9	8 58 ·53	39	38 53 ·61	17	16 ·95
10	9 58 21 ·70	10	9 58 ·36	40	39 53 ·45	19	18 ·95
11	10 58 11 ·87	11	10 58 ·20	41	40 53 ·28	21	20 ·94
12	11 58 2 ·05	12	11 58 ·03	42	41 53 ·12	23	22 ·94
13	12 57 52 ·22	13	12 57 ·87	43	42 52 ·96	25	24 ·93
14	13 57 42 ·39	14	13 57 ·71	44	43 52 ·79	27	26 ·93
15	14 57 32 ·56	15	14 57 ·54	45	44 52 ·63	29	28 ·92
16	15 57 22 ·73	16	15 57 ·38	46	45 52 ·46	31	30 ·92
17	16 57 12 ·90	17	16 57 ·22	47	46 52 ·30	33	32 ·91
18	17 57 3 ·07	18	17 57 ·05	48	47 52 ·14	35	34 ·90
19	18 56 53 ·24	19	18 56 ·89	49	48 51 ·97	37	36 ·90
20	19 56 43 ·41	20	19 56 ·72	50	49 51 ·81	39	38 ·89
21	20 56 33 ·58	21	20 56 ·56	51	50 51 ·64	41	40 ·89
22	21 56 23 ·75	22	21 56 ·40	52	51 51 ·48	43	42 ·88
23	22 56 13 ·92	23	22 56 ·23	53	52 51 ·32	45	44 ·88
24	23 56 4 ·09	24	23 56 ·07	54	53 51 ·15	47	46 ·87
		25	24 55 ·90	55	54 50 ·99	49	48 ·87
		26	25 55 ·74	56	55 50 ·83	51	50 ·86
		27	26 55 ·58	57	56 50 ·66	53	52 ·86
		28	27 55 ·41	58	57 50 ·50	55	54 ·85
		29	28 55 ·25	59	58 50 ·33	57	56 ·84
		30	29 55 ·09	60	59 50 ·17	59	58 ·84

TABLE VIII

MEAN DISPLACEMENT ACCORDING TO ZENITH DISTANCE

z	Refraction	z	Refraction	z	Refraction
0°	0' 0''·0	50° 0'	1' 8''·5	72°20'	2' 58''·8
1	1 ·0	30	9 ·9	40	3 2 ·4
2	2 ·0	51 0	11 ·0	73 0	6 ·1
3	3 ·0	30	12 ·3	20	10 ·0
4	4 ·0	52 0	13 ·6	40	3 13 ·9
5	5 ·0	30	14 ·9	74 0	18 ·1
6	6 ·0	53 0	16 ·3	10	20 ·5
7	7 ·1	30	17 ·6	20	22 ·4
8	8 ·1	54 0	19 ·1	30	24 ·6
9	9 ·1	30	20 ·6	40	26 ·9
10	10 ·1	55 0	22 ·1	50	29 ·2
11	11 ·2	30	23 ·6	75 0	31 ·5
12	12 ·2	56 0	25 ·2	10	34 ·0
13	13 ·3	30	26 ·8	20	36 ·5
14	14 ·4	57 0	28 ·4	30	39 ·0
15	15 ·4	30	30 ·1	40	41 ·6
16	16 ·5	58 0	31 ·9	50	44 ·2
17	17 ·6	30	33 ·7	76 0	46 ·9
18	18 ·7	59 0	35 ·5	10	49 ·6
19	19 ·8	30	37 ·4	20	52 ·5
20	20 ·9	60 0	39 ·4	30	55 ·3
21	22 ·1	30	41 ·4	40	58 ·2
22	23 ·3	61 0	43 ·5	50	4 1 ·2
23	24 ·4	30	45 ·6	77 0	4 ·3
24	25 ·6	62 0	47 ·8	10	7 ·5
25	26 ·8	30	50 ·2	20	10 ·7
26	28 ·1	63 0	52 ·6	30	14 ·0
27	29 ·3	30	55 ·0	40	17 ·3
28	30 ·6	64 0	57 ·5	50	20 ·8
29	31 ·9	30	2' 0 ·1	78 0	24 ·4
30	33 ·2	65 0	2 ·8	10	28 ·1
31	34 ·6	30	5 ·7	20	31 ·8
32	36 ·0	66 0	8 ·6	30	35 ·7
33	37 ·4	30	11 ·6	40	39 ·7
34	38 ·8	67 0	14 ·8	50	43 ·9
35	40 ·3	30	18 ·1	79 0	47 ·8

TABLE VIII *(cont.)*

z	Refraction	z	Refraction	z	Refraction
36	0′ 41″·8	68 0	2′ 21″·6	79°10	4′52″·1
37	43 ·4	30	25 ·1	20	56 ·6
38	45 ·0	69 0	28 ·9	30	5 1 ·1
39	46 ·6	30	32 ·8	40	5 ·8
40	48 ·3	70 0	36 ·9	50	10 ·6
41	50 ·0	30	41 ·3	80 0	15 ·5
42	51 ·8	71 0	45 ·7		
43	53 ·6	20	48 ·8		
44	55 ·5	40	52 ·0		
45	57 ·5	72 0	55 ·4		
46	59 ·6				
47	1′ 1 ·7				
48	1 3 ·8				
49	1 6 ·2				

(For Table IX sec pp. 308–9)

TABLE X

ELEMENTS OF PLANETARY ORBITS

Planets	Mean distance from Sun in astron. units	Mean distance in millions of km	Period of Rotation in stellar years	Eccentricity	Inclination of orbit to the ecliptic	Longitude of ascending node	Longitude of perihelion
Mercury	0·387099	57·85	0·2408	0·20562	7°00'12"	47°22'50"	76°12'39"
Venus	0·723331	108·10	0·6152	0·00681	3°23'38"	75°57'35"	130°26'44"
Earth	1·000000	149·45	1·0000	0·01674	0°00'00"	—	101°33'53"
Mars	1·523688	227·72	1·8808	0·09333	1°51'01"	48°56'25"	334°35'12"
Jupiter	5·202803	777·62	11·862	0·04837	1°18'28"	99°38'24"	13°02'01"
Saturn	9·538843	1425·6	29·457	0·05582	2°29'29"	112°57'29"	91°28'50"
Uranus	19·190978	2868·1	84·013	0·04710	0°46'22"	73°35'27"	169°22'07"
Neptune	30·070572	4494·1	164·783	0·00855	1°46'38"	130°53'56"	43°55'50"
Pluto	38·579436	5915·2	248·858	0·24720	17° 6'51"	109°13'15"	222°21'15"

Elements of orbits referred to beginning of 1920.

TABLE IX
ANNUAL PRECESSION

Precession according to Right Ascension

α \ δ	−40°	−30°	−20°	−10°	0°	+10°	+20°	+30°	+40°	+50°	+60°	+70°	Precession in declination
0hr	3·1 sec	3·1 sec	3·1 sec	3·1 sec	3·1 sec	3·1 sec	3·1 sec	3·1 sec	3·1 sec	3·1 sec	3·1 sec	3·1 sec	+20
1	2·8	2·9	3·0	3·0	3·1	3·1	3·2	3·3	3·4	3·5	3·7	4·0	+19
2	2·5	2·7	2·8	3·0	3·1	3·2	3·3	3·5	3·6	3·9	4·2	4·9	+17
3	2·3	2·5	2·7	2·9	3·1	3·2	3·4	3·6	3·9	4·2	4·7	5·7	+14
4	2·1	2·4	2·7	2·9	3·1	3·3	3·5	3·7	4·0	4·4	5·1	6·2	+10
5	2·0	2·3	2·6	2·8	3·1	3·3	3·5	3·8	4·2	4·6	5·3	6·6	+ 5
6	2·0	2·3	2·6	2·8	3·1	3·3	3·6	3·8	4·2	4·7	5·4	6·7	0
7	2·0	2·3	2·6	2·8	3·1	3·3	3·5	3·8	4·2	4·6	5·3	6·6	− 5
8	2·1	2·4	2·7	2·9	3·1	3·3	3·5	3·7	4·0	4·4	5·1	6·2	−10
9	2·3	2·5	2·7	2·9	3·1	3·2	3·4	3·6	3·9	4·2	4·7	5·7	−14
10	2·5	2·7	2·8	3·0	3·1	3·2	3·3	3·5	3·6	3·9	4·2	4·9	−17
11	2·8	2·9	3·0	3·0	3·1	3·1	3·2	3·3	3·4	3·5	3·7	4·0	−19
12	3·1	3·1	3·1	3·1	3·1	3·1	3·1	3·1	3·1	3·1	3·1	3·1	−20
13	3·4	3·3	3·2	3·1	3·1	3·0	3·0	2·9	2·8	2·7	2·5	2·1	−19
14	3·6	3·5	3·3	3·2	3·1	3·0	2·8	2·7	2·5	2·3	1·9	1·2	−17

15	3·9	3·6	3·4	3·2	3·1	2·9	2·7	2·5	2·3	2·0	1·4	0·5	−14
16	4·0	3·7	3·5	3·3	3·1	2·9	2·7	2·4	2·1	1·7	1·1	0·1	−10
17	4·2	3·8	3·5	3·3	3·1	2·8	2·6	2·3	2·0	1·5	0·8	0·5	− 5
18	4·2	3·8	3·6	3·3	3·1	2·8	2·6	2·3	2·0	1·5	0·8	0·6	0
19	4·2	3·8	3·5	3·3	3·1	2·8	2·6	2·3	2·0	1·5	0·8	0·5	+ 5
20	4·0	3·7	3·5	3·3	3·1	2·9	2·7	2·4	2·1	1·7	1·1	0·1	+10
21	3·9	3·6	3·4	3·2	3·1	2·9	2·7	2·5	2·3	2·0	1·4	0·5	+14
22	3·6	3·5	3·3	3·2	3·1	3·0	2·8	2·7	2·5	2·3	1·9	1·2	+17
23	3·4	3·3	3·2	3·1	3·1	3·0	3·0	2·9	2·8	2·7	2·5	2·1	+19
24	3·1	3·1	3·1	3·1	3·1	3·1	3·1	3·1	3·1	3·1	3·1	3·1	+20

TABLE XI
PHYSICAL CHARACTERISTICS OF THE LARGE PLANETS

Name of planet	True equatorial diameter		Flattening at the pole	Volume		Mass		
	in km	Earth =1		in 10^{12} km³	Earth =1	Sun=1	Earth =1	in 10^{27} g
Mercury	5,140	0·403	0	0·071	0·066	$\frac{1}{8,000,000}$	0·042	0·25
Venus	12,610	0·989	0	1·050	0·970	$\frac{1}{406,400}$	0·818	4·89
Earth	12,757	1·000	$\frac{1}{297}$	1·083	1·000	$\frac{1}{332,300}$	1·000	5·98
Mars	6,860	0·538	$\frac{1}{190}$	0·168	0·155	$\frac{1}{3,088,000}$	0·108	0·64
Jupiter	143,600	11·26	$\frac{1}{16·3}$	1456·9	1344·8	$\frac{1}{1,047·5}$	317·18	1898·3
Saturn	120,600	9·45	$\frac{1}{9·7}$	823·8	760·4	$\frac{1}{3,496}$	94·98	568·2
Uranus	53,400	4·19	$\frac{1}{18}$	75·4	69·6	$\frac{1}{22,580}$	14·72	88·1
Neptune	49,700	3·90	$\frac{1}{50}$	63·0	58·1	$\frac{1}{19,330}$	17·19	102·9

TABLE XII

PHYSICAL CHARACTERISTICS OF THE LARGE PLANETS (cont.)

Name of planet	Mean density		Force of gravity on the equator		Velocity of escape in km/sec	Axial rotation period	Inclination of equator to plane of orbit	Stellar magnitude at mean opposition and at nearest distance
	Earth = 1	g/cm³	Earth = 1	m/sec²				
Mercury	0·633	3·50	0·256	2·51	3·59	87 days 23 hr 15 min 43 sec†	0°	+0·16
Venus	0·843	4·66	0·838	8·20	10·15	30	0°	−4·07
Earth	1·000	5·62	1·000	9·78	10·72	23 56 04	23°27′	–
Mars	0·692	3·82	0·372	3·64	4·76	24 37 23	25 10	−1·85
Jupiter	0·236	1·30	2·322	22·71	46·78	9 50 30	3 06	−2·23
Saturn	0·125	0·69	0·921	9·01	25·21	10 14 24	26 45	+0·89 – −0·18
Uranus	0·212	1·17	0·784	7·67	16·90	10 49	98	+5·74
Neptune	0·296	1·63	1·109	10·85	20·75	15 25	29	+7·65

† *Editor's Note*: Recent work suggests this value is considerably lower.

TABLE XIII

ELEMENTS OF SATELLITE ORBITS

Planet	Satellite	Distance from centre of planet		Sidereal period of rotation	Mean inclination of satellite orbit to the planetary orbit	Eccentricity	Dia. in km
		mean distance in equatorial radii	distance in thous. of km/s				
Earth	Moon	60·267	384·40	27 days 7 hr 43 min 11·51 sec	5°8'·7	0·0549	3476
Mars	Phobos	2·74	9·41	0　7　39　13·85	25　19·6	0·017	15?
	Deimos	6·84	23·47	1　6　17　54·9	24　14·7	0·003	8?
Jupiter	V	2·523	181·2	0　11　57　22·70	3　6·9	0·0028	160?
	I	5·869	421·5	1　18　27　33·51	3　6·7	0·0000	3850
	II	9·339	670·7	3　13　13　42·05	3　5·8	0·0003	3320
	III	14·896	1,069·9	7　3　42　33·35	3　2·3	0·0015	5350
	IV	26·201	1,881·7	16　16　32　11·21	2　42·7	0·0075	5170
	VI	159·5	11,450	250　16　19	28　45	0·155	130?
	VII	163·5	11,740	260　16　1	27　58	0·207	40?
	X	163·6	11,750	260　12　26	28　16	0·132	20?
	XI	314	22,550	692　12	16　37	0·207	20?
	VIII	328	23,500	738　22	148　4	0·378	25?
	IX	334	24,000	745　0	156	0·25	25?
	XII	300?	21,000?	732?	147	0·13	25?

Planet	Satellite			d	h	m	s	Inclination	Eccentricity	Diameter
Saturn	Mimas	3·08	185·5	0	22	37	5·25	26 44·7	0·0190	650 ?
	Enceladus	3·95	238·0	1	8	53	6·82	26 44·7	0·0001	800 ?
	Tethys	4·88	294·5	1	21	18	26·14	26 44·7	0·0000	1300 ?
	Dione	6·26	377·3	2	17	41	9·53	26 44·7	0·0020	1200 ?
	Rhea	8·74	526·8	4	12	25	12·23	26 41·9	0·0009	1750 ?
	Titan	20·26	1,221·5	15	22	41	26·82	26 7·1	0·0289	4360 ?
	Hyperion	24·56	1,480·5	21	6	38	24·0	26 0·0	0·1043	500 ?
	Iapetus	59·03	3,558·8	79	7	56	24·4	16 18·1	0·0284	1800 ?
	Phoebe	214·49	12,932	550	10	34		174 42	0·1659	250 ?
Uranus	Miranda	5·25	130·4	1	9	50	24 ?	?	?	?
	Ariel	7·18	191·7	2	12	29	20·8	97 59	0·007	900 ?
	Umbriel	10·00	267·1	4	3	27	36·7	97 59	0·008	700 ?
	Titania	16·41	438·2	8	16	56	26·7	97 59	0·0023	1700 ?
	Oberon	21·94	585·9	13	11	7	3·5	97 59	0·0010	1500 ?
Neptune	Triton	14·24	353·7	5	21	2	33·1	139 49	0·000	5000
	Nereid	223·1	5,576·3	359	9	36		?	0·76	?

TABLE XIV

SPECTRUM, COLOUR-INDEX (I) AND TEMPERATURE (T) OF STARS

Spectrum	I	T	Spectrum	I	T	Spectrum	I	T
B0	−0·33	23,000°	gG0	0·67	5500°	dG0	0·57	6000°
B5	−0·18	15,000	gG5	0·92	4700	dG5	0·65	5600
A0	0·00	11,200	gK0	1·12	4100	dK0	0·78	5100
A5	0·20	8,600	gK5	1·57	3300	dK5	0·98	4400
F0	0·33	7,400	gM0	1·73	3050	dM0	1·45	3400
F5	0·47	6,500	N	2·6	2200			

d = symbol denoting that the star is a dwarf.
g = symbol denoting that the star is a giant.

TABLE XV

SOME SPECTRAL LINES

Wavelengths in angstrom units	Atom	Wavelengths in angstrom units	Atom
4026	He	4640	N^{++}
4102	$H\delta$	4649	O^+
4200	He^+	4668	Fe
4227	Ca	4686	He^+
4384	Fe	6563	$H\alpha$
4472	He		

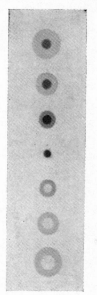

PLATE I. Photographs of stars at various focus settings.

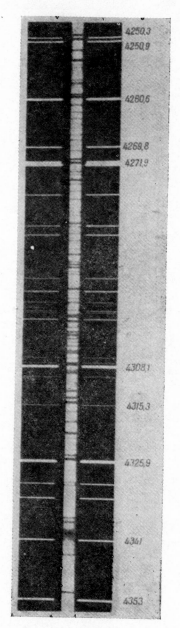

4250,3
4250,9

4260,6

4268,8
4271,9

4308,1

4315,3

4325,9

4341

4353

PLATE II. The spectrum of Procyon.

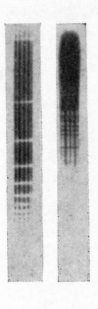

PLATE III. The spectra of a white and of a red star — Sirius — Betelgeuse.

PLATE IV. The spectrum of ζ Tauri.

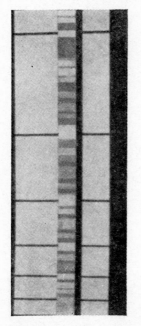

PLATE V. The spectra of Vega, and of a nova in the constellation Hercules.

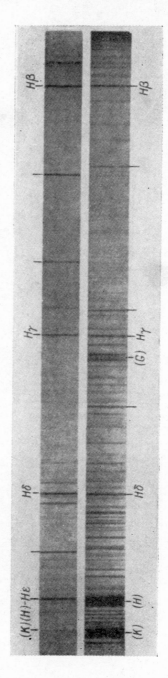

PLATE VI. The spectra of ε Orionis (above) and α Aurigae (below).

PLATE VII. A photograph of part of the surface of the Moon. The crater Theophilus.

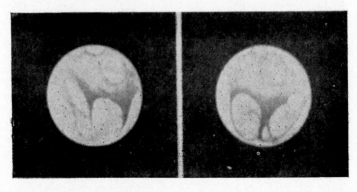

PLATE VIII. Two drawings of Mars. One of them was taken 2 hr after the other.

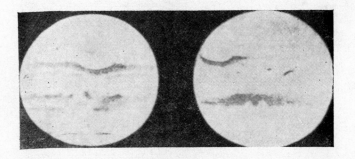

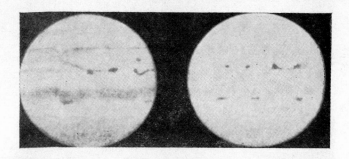

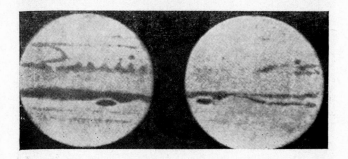

PLATE IX. Photographs of Jupiter

(1) 19th June, 1922 at   8 hr 55 min.
(2) 19th June, 1922, at   10 hr 40 min.
(3) 20th February, 1920, at 7 hr 5 min.
(4) 22nd February, 1920, at 9 hr 0 min.
(5) 27th February, 1920, at 8 hr 50 min.
(6) 27th February, 1920, at 10 hr 35 min.

PLATE X. A drawing of Donati's Comet in 1858.

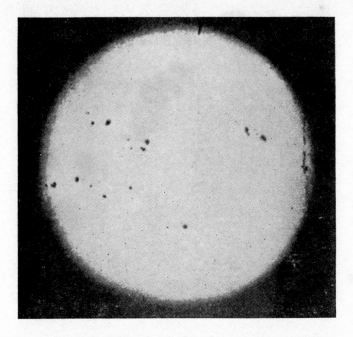

PLATE XI. A photograph of the Sun, showing spots.

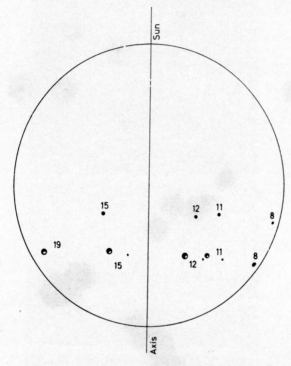

PLATE XII. On this plan of the solar disc are shown the successive positions of two groups of spots during April, 1946:

8th April, at 9 hr 00 min.
11th April, at 10 hr 30 min.
12th April, at 7 hr 10 min.
15th April, at 12 hr 30 min.
19th April, at 9 hr 30 min.

(The isolated spots had disappeared by this date.)

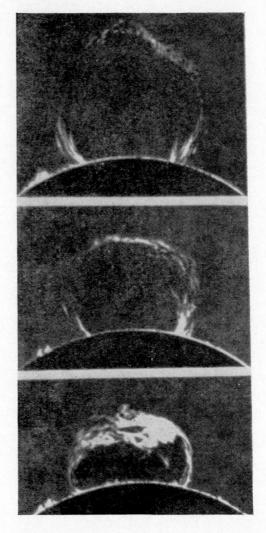

PLATE XIII. A series of photographs of a solar loop prominence.

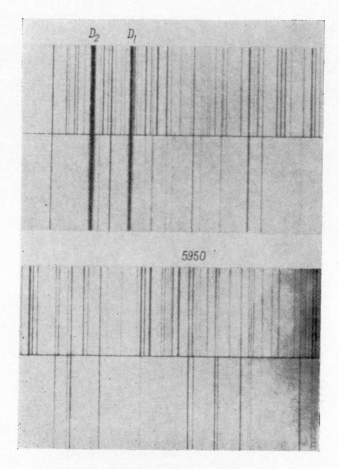

PLATE XIV. Spectrum of the Sun.

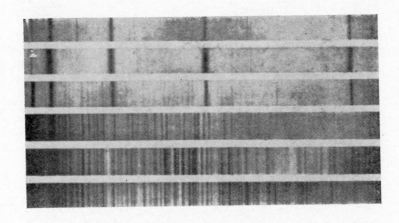

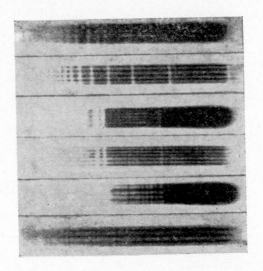

PLATE XV. Stellar spectra: upper images (positives) taken with a slit spectrograph, lower images (negatives) taken with a prism camera.
δ Geminorum, Sirius, Arcturus, Capella, Betelgeuse, ε Orionis,

PLATE XVI. Photographs of the sky in the region of the constellation Centaurus.

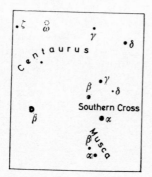

PLATE XVII. Chart of the area shown in Plate XVI.

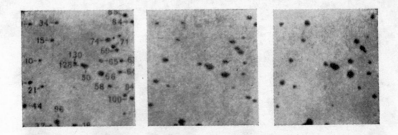

PLATE XVIII. Photographs of the region of the sky in the constellation Perseus.

PLATE XIX. Spiral nebula in the constellation Hunting Dogs.

PRINTED IN HUNGARY